МНОГОЧЛЕНЫ,
ОРТОГОНАЛЬНЫЕ
НА ОКРУЖНОСТИ
И НА ОТРЕЗКЕ

MNOGOCHLENY, ORTOGONAL'NYE NA OKRUZHNOSTI I NA OTREZKE

ORTHOGONAL POLYNOMIALS

ORTHOGONAL POLYNOMIALS

ESTIMATES, ASYMPTOTIC FORMULAS, AND SERIES OF POLYNOMIALS ORTHOGONAL ON THE UNIT CIRCLE AND ON AN INTERVAL

by L. Ya. Geronimus

Authorized translation from the Russian

CONSULTANTS BUREAU

NEW YORK

1961

The Russian text was published by
the State Press for Physicomathematical Literature
in Moscow in 1958 as part of the series
"Modern Problems of Mathematics"
under the direction of the editorial board of
Uspekhi Matematicheskikh Nauk

Library of Congress Catalog Card Number: 60-53450

Printed in the U.S.A.

Noble Offset Printers, Inc.
New York 3, N. Y.

TABLE OF CONTENTS

TABLE OF CONTENTS

INTRODUCTION

The theory of orthogonal polynomials has always been of interest to mathematicians and physicists because, if one excludes the trigonometric functions, polynomials form the simplest orthogonal set.

From the point of view of application, one of the most interesting and important problems of this theory is to find the conditions under which the series expansion of a given function in orthogonal polynomials will converge. To solve this problem one must know the asymptotic properties of orthogonal polynomials, that is to say their behavior when their number increases without bound. Asymptotic formulas for orthogonal polynomials have been found in general by G. Szegö [1, 5] and S. N. Bernshtein [1].*

The first problem we pose in our monograph is to derive the asymptotic formulas under conditions more general than those of previous authors (in particular, under certain given local conditions).

In many cases, however, it is not so much the existence of the asymptotic formulas which is important, but rather the boundedness of the orthogonal set on the entire interval of orthogonality or on some part of it. The problem of finding the conditions for such boundedness was first stated by V. A. Steklov [2]. Its solution is quite important, since many authors formulate their results conditionally, in forms such as "if the orthogonal set is bounded, then . . . ."

The second problem of our monograph is thus to find the conditions under which the set of orthogonal polynomials is bounded on the entire orthogonality interval or on a part of it.

* References are to the bibliography at the back of the book.

But an even more general problem, of primary importance in the study of infinite processes related to orthogonal polynomials, is to find their order of decrease as a function of their number, without assuming in the development that they are bounded; this is the third problem whose solution is discussed in this monograph.

We shall deal with polynomials orthogonal on the unit circle, as well as polynomials orthogonal on a finite interval of the real axis.

In Chapters I and II we investigate some properties of polynomials orthogonal on the unit circle, properties which we will need in the sequel. The discussion does not use the results of our previous related monograph [1], all the propositions being proved anew so that the present work can be read without reference to the earlier one. In the process, we take the opportunity to simplify some of the proofs.

Chapter III is devoted to estimates on the entire circle, and Chapter IV to local estimates. Using the results of these chapters, we find in Chapter V the conditions under which the asymptotic formulas are valid on the entire circle or on some arc.

Chapter VI is devoted to the general theory of series of orthogonal polynomials, which may be thought of as simple generalizations of power series. Some classical properties of power series are generalized to the case of series of orthogonal polynomials.

In Chapter VII we study the sufficient conditions for the convergence of the Fourier-Chebyshev expansion of a given function; in particular we present the equiconvergence theorem relating convergence of the Fourier-Chebyshev series expansion of a given function with the convergence of the Maclaurin series.

In Chapter VIII we study the properties of an orthogonal system in terms of its so-called parameters rather than its measure. We discuss this problem because quite recently M. G. Krein [2] obtained some very interesting results, important for application, which may be thought of as the continuous analogs of the results developed in this chapter.

We go in such great detail into the theory of polynomials orthogonal on the unit circle because a simple formula relates them to polynomials orthogonal on a finite interval of the real axis. With the aid of this formula it is a simple matter to use our results for the circle to arrive at estimates and asymptotic formulas for polynomials orthogonal on the interval [-1, +1]. This is discussed in Chapter IX.

Because many of the results obtained may be difficult to distinguish from each other, we present the principal ones in tabular form at the end of the monograph so that they may be more easily compared. For the reader's convenience we have also presented, in the form of notes at the back of the book, complete statements of all the theorems used in the text.

This monograph is an attempt to develop and apply to the solution of important problems in the theory of orthogonal polynomials the methods and ideas of V. A. Steklov, S. N. Bernshtein, V. I. Smirnov, A. N. Kolmogorov, N. I. Akhiezer, M. G. Krein, and many foreign scientists, especially G. Szegö, P. Erdös, P. Turan, and G. Freud. It is not ours to judge the degree to which the stated problem has been solved; in any case, the author will be extremely appreciative of any remarks or corrections.

The author takes pleasure in acknowledging his debt and expressing his deep gratitude to N. I. Akhiezer for his careful reading of the manuscript and for his many valuable suggestions.

CHAPTER I

SOME PROPERTIES OF POLYNOMIALS ORTHOGONAL ON THE UNIT CIRCLE

Let $\{\varphi_n(z)\}$ be a set of polynomials orthonormal with respect to the measure* $d\sigma(\theta)$ on the unit circle $|z| = 1$, that is, satisfying

$$\frac{1}{2\pi}\int_0^{2\pi} \varphi_n(e^{i\theta})\,\overline{\varphi_m(e^{i\theta})}\,d\sigma(\theta) = \begin{cases} 0, & n \neq m, \\ 1, & n = m, \end{cases} \tag{1.1}$$

$$\varphi_n(z) = \alpha_n z^n + \ldots, \quad \alpha_n > 0, \qquad (n = 0,\ 1,\ 2,\ \ldots),$$

where $\sigma(\theta)$ is a bounded nondecreasing function on the interval $[0, 2\pi]$; it is easily seen that the orthogonality conditions determine the orthonormal set up to a factor, that the normalization requires that this undetermined factor be of modulus one, and finally that the conditions $\alpha_n > 0$ uniquely determine the set. We shall consider $(1/2\pi)\sigma(\theta)$ to be a function characterizing some mass distribution on the interval $[0, 2\pi]$, with the mass on some set $e \subset [0, 2\pi]$, given by $\frac{1}{2\pi}\int_e d\sigma(\theta)$. The derivative $\sigma'(\theta) = p(\theta)$, which exists almost everywhere on $[0, 2\pi]$, will be called the density of the mass distribution; if $\sigma(\theta)$ is absolutely convergent on $[0, 2\pi]$, we shall call $p(\theta)$ the weight. If $\sigma(\theta)$ has a discontinuity at θ_0, we shall call

$$\mu = \frac{1}{2\pi}\{\sigma(\theta_0 + 0) - \sigma(\theta_0 - 0)\}$$

the concentrated mass at that point. We shall assume that $\sigma(\theta)$

* The Russian might be better translated as distribution. Measure is chosen to avoid the rather obvious confusion with modern terminology—Translator.

has a nondenumerable set of points of increase. If this were not so we could not construct the infinite set of polynomials $\{\varphi_n(z)\}$.

The general theory of such polynomials for the case of absolutely continuous $\sigma(\theta)$ has been developed by Szegö [1, 5] and Smirnov [1, 3]. The general case has been treated in the work of Akhiezer and Krein [1], and later by the present author [1, 3], in whose work one will find an explanation of how this theory is related to the trigonometric moment problem, the theory of pseudopositive and bounded functions, etc.

1.1. We shall later have recourse to some algebraic properties of the functions of $\{\varphi_n(z)\}$, to which we now turn.

1) For these functions we have the relations*

$$\left.\begin{aligned} \alpha_n\varphi_{n+1}(z) &= \alpha_{n+1}z\varphi_n(z) + \varphi_{n+1}(0)\,\varphi_n^*(z), \qquad &(1.2)\\ \alpha_n\varphi_{n+1}^*(z) &= \alpha_{n+1}\varphi_n^*(z) + \overline{\varphi_{n+1}(0)}\,z\varphi_n(z) \qquad &(1.2')\\ &(n = 0,\ 1,\ 2,\ \ldots), \end{aligned}\right\}$$

where

$$\varphi_n^*(z) = z^n\bar{\varphi}_n\left(\frac{1}{z}\right), \quad \varphi_n^*(0) = \alpha_n, \quad (n = 0,\ 1,\ 2,\ \ldots). \tag{1.2''}$$

To prove these relations we write

$$\frac{\varphi_n(z) - \alpha_n z^n}{z^{n-1}} = \sum_{k=0}^{n-1} \mu_k^{(n)}\bar{\varphi}_k\left(\frac{1}{z}\right);$$

multiplying on both sides by $\varphi_k(z)$, setting $z = e^{i\theta}$, and integrating, we find that for $k = 0, 1, 2, \ldots, n-1$

$$\frac{1}{2\pi}\int_0^{2\pi} \varphi_n(e^{i\theta})\,\frac{\varphi_k(e^{i\theta})}{e^{i(n-1)\theta}}\,d\sigma(\theta) - \frac{\alpha_n}{2\pi}\int_0^{2\pi} e^{i\theta}\varphi_k(e^{i\theta})\,d\sigma(\theta) = \mu_k^{(n)}.$$

Introducing the notation

$$\frac{1}{2\pi}\int_0^{2\pi} e^{i\theta}\varphi_k(e^{i\theta})\,d\sigma(\theta) = \lambda_k, \qquad (k = 0,\ 1,\ 2,\ \ldots), \tag{1.3}$$

* See G. Szegö [1], Section 11.4; Ya. L. Geronimus [1], Section 3.

we obtain

$$\mu_k^{(n)} = -\alpha_n\lambda_k, \quad \frac{\varphi_n(z)}{\alpha_n} = z^n - z^{n-1}\sum_{k=0}^{n-1}\lambda_k\overline{\varphi_k}\left(\frac{1}{z}\right),$$

from which we have

$$\frac{\varphi_{n+1}(z)}{\alpha_{n+1}} - \frac{z\varphi_n(z)}{\alpha_n} = -\lambda_n\varphi_n^*(z).$$

To find the λ_n, we set $z = 0$, which gives

$$\frac{\varphi_{n+1}(0)}{\alpha_{n+1}} = -\lambda_n\alpha_n, \quad \lambda_n = -\frac{\varphi_{n+1}(0)}{\alpha_n\alpha_{n+1}}, \qquad (1.4)$$

and this leads directly to (1.2). To obtain (1.2') one replaces $\underline{z}$ by $1/z$ and takes the complex conjugates.

2) Our functions satisfy the relations*

$$\alpha_{n+1}^2 - \alpha_n^2 = |\varphi_{n+1}(0)|^2, \qquad (n = 0,\ 1,\ 2,\ \ldots). \quad (1.5)$$

We prove this by multiplying both sides of (1.2) by z^{-n-1}, writing $z = e^{i\theta}$, and integrating, to obtain

$$\frac{\alpha_n}{2\pi}\int_0^{2\pi} e^{-i(n+1)\theta}\varphi_{n+1}(e^{i\theta})\,d\sigma(\theta) = \frac{\alpha_{n+1}}{2\pi}\int_0^{2\pi} e^{-in\theta}\varphi_n(e^{i\theta})\,d\sigma(\theta) +$$

$$+\frac{\varphi_{n+1}(0)}{2\pi}\int_0^{2\pi} e^{-i\theta}\overline{\varphi_n(e^{i\theta})}\,d\sigma(\theta),$$

which, with (1.3) and (1.4), gives

$$\frac{\alpha_n}{\alpha_{n+1}} = \frac{\alpha_{n+1}}{\alpha_n} + \varphi_{n+1}(0)\overline{\lambda}_n = \frac{\alpha_{n+1}}{\alpha_n} - \frac{|\varphi_{n+1}(0)|^2}{\alpha_n\alpha_{n+1}}.$$

3) To the function $\psi_0(\theta) = e^{-i\theta}$ corresponds the formal Fourier-Chebyshev expansion

$$\psi_0(\theta) \sim -\sum_{k=0}^{\infty}\frac{\overline{\varphi_{k+1}(0)}}{\alpha_k\alpha_{k+1}}\varphi_k(e^{i\theta}). \qquad (1.6)$$

---

* See Ya. L. Geronimus [1], Section 4.

Indeed, from (1.3) and (1.4) we have

$$\frac{1}{2\pi}\int_0^{2\pi} e^{-i\theta}\overline{\varphi_k(e^{i\theta})}\, d\sigma(\theta) = \bar{\lambda}_k = -\frac{\overline{\varphi_{k+1}(0)}}{\alpha_k\alpha_{k+1}}, \quad (k = 0, 1, 2, \ldots),$$

and from this together with (1.5) we easily obtain

$$\sum_{k=r}^{p} |\lambda_k|^2 = \sum_{k=r}^{p}\left|\frac{\varphi_{k+1}(0)}{\alpha_k\alpha_{k+1}}\right|^2 = \frac{1}{\alpha_r^2} - \frac{1}{\alpha_{p+1}^2}. \tag{1.6'}$$

4) These functions satisfy the Christoffel-Darboux formula*

$$K_n(x, y) = \sum_{k=0}^{n} \varphi_k(x)\overline{\varphi_k(y)} = \frac{\varphi_n^*(x)\overline{\varphi_n^*(y)} - x\bar{y}\varphi_n(x)\overline{\varphi_n(y)}}{1 - x\bar{y}} =$$

$$= \frac{\varphi_{n+1}^*(x)\overline{\varphi_{n+1}^*(y)} - \varphi_{n+1}(x)\overline{\varphi_{n+1}(y)}}{1 - x\bar{y}}, \quad (n = 0, 1, 2, \ldots). \tag{1.7}$$

To prove this we calculate

$$\frac{\varphi_m^*(x)\overline{\varphi_m^*(y)} - x\bar{y}\varphi_m(x)\overline{\varphi_m(y)}}{1 - x\bar{y}} + \varphi_{m+1}(x)\overline{\varphi_{m+1}(y)}. \tag{1.7'}$$

From (1.2), (1.2'), and (1.5), we obtain

$$\left.\begin{aligned} \alpha_{m+1}x\varphi_m(x) &= \alpha_m\varphi_{m+1}(x) - \varphi_{m+1}(0)\varphi_m^*(x), \\ \alpha_{m+1}\varphi_m^*(x) &= \alpha_m\varphi_{m+1}^*(x) - \overline{\varphi_{m+1}(0)}\,x\varphi_m(x). \end{aligned}\right\} \tag{1.8}$$

Eliminating $\varphi_m^*(x)$ and $x\varphi_m(x)$ by these formulas and using (1.2) and (1.5), we find that (1.7') is equal to

$$\frac{\varphi_{m+1}^*(x)\overline{\varphi_{m+1}^*(y)} - x\bar{y}\varphi_{m+1}(x)\overline{\varphi_{m+1}(y)}}{1 - x\bar{y}}.$$

The second form of (1.7) is obtained by using (1.2), (1.2'), and (1.5).

*See G. Szegö [1], Section 11.4; Ya. L. Geronimus [1], Section 8.

5) The polynomial $\varphi_n^*(z)$ can be represented by†

$$\alpha_n \varphi_n^*(z) = K_n(z, 0) = \sum_{k=0}^{n} \varphi_k(z)\overline{\varphi_k(0)}, \qquad (n = 0, 1, 2, \ldots). \tag{1.9}$$

To prove this, set x = z and y = 0 in (1.7).

6) We obtain the inequality†

$$\frac{1}{2\pi}\int_0^{2\pi} \left|\frac{G_n(e^{i\theta})}{G_n(z_0)}\right|^2 d\sigma(\theta) \geqslant \frac{1}{K_n(z_0, z_0)}, \tag{1.10}$$

where $G_n(z)$ will always denote an arbitrary polynomial of degree no higher than n.

We prove this by writing $G_n(z) = \sum_{k=0}^{n} a_k \varphi_k(z)$ and making use of the Cauchy-Bunyakovskii inequality. Then

$$|G_n(z_0)|^2 = \left|\sum_{k=0}^{n} a_k \varphi_k(z_0)\right|^2 \leqslant \sum_{k=0}^{n} |a_k|^2 \cdot \sum_{k=0}^{n} |\varphi_k(z_0)|^2 =$$

$$= \frac{1}{2\pi}\int_0^{2\pi} |G_n(e^{i\theta})|^2 d\sigma(\theta) \cdot K_n(z_0, z_0).$$

One easily sees that equality is obtained with the polynomial

$$G_n(z) = \varepsilon \frac{K_n(z, z_0)}{K_n(z_0, z_0)}, \qquad |\varepsilon| = 1. \tag{1.10'}$$

7) We obtain the inequality

$$\frac{1}{\alpha_n^2} = \frac{1}{K_n(0, 0)} \leqslant \frac{1}{2\pi}\int_0^{2\pi} \left|1 + \sum_{k=1}^{n} \beta_k e^{ik\theta}\right|^2 d\sigma(\theta), \tag{1.11}$$

for which the extremal polynomial is $(1/\alpha_n)\varphi_n^*(z)$.

To prove this one need only set $z_0 = 0$ in (1.10).

8) All the roots of $\varphi_n(z)$ lie within the region $|z| < 1$. Indeed, from (1.7) we see that if $|z| < 1$,

$$\alpha_0^2 \leqslant K_n(z, z) = \sum_{k=0}^{n} |\varphi_k(z)|^2 = \frac{|\varphi_n^*(z)|^2 - |z\varphi_n(z)|^2}{1 - |z|^2} \leqslant \frac{|\varphi_n^*(z)|^2}{1 - |z|^2}, \tag{1.12}$$

† See G. Szegö [1], Section 11.3.

so that $\varphi_n^*(z) \neq 0$ for $|z| < 1$, since

$$|\varphi_n^*(z)|^2 \geqslant \alpha_0^2(1 - |z|^2), \qquad |z| < 1. \tag{1.12'}$$

The absence of zeros of $\varphi_n(z)$ on the circumference $|z| = 1$ will be demonstrated later.

9) We now introduce polynomials of the second kind defined by

$$\left.\begin{aligned} \psi_n(z) &= \frac{1}{2\pi c_0}\int_0^{2\pi} \frac{e^{i\theta}+z}{e^{i\theta}-z}[\varphi_n(e^{i\theta}) - \varphi_n(z)]\,d\sigma(\theta), \\ c_0 &= \frac{1}{2\pi}\int_0^{2\pi} d\sigma(\theta), \qquad (n = 0, 1, \ldots). \end{aligned}\right\} \tag{1.13}$$

Then the functions $\psi_n^*(z)/\varphi_n^*(z)$ and

$$F(z) = \frac{1}{2\pi c_0}\int_0^{2\pi} \frac{e^{i\theta}+z}{e^{i\theta}-z}\,d\sigma(\theta), \qquad |z| < 1 \tag{1.14}$$

have the same Maclaurin coefficients multiplying the $\{z^k\}_0^n$.

Indeed, we have

$$c_0\psi_n^*(z) = -\frac{1}{2\pi}\int_0^{2\pi} \frac{e^{i\theta}+z}{e^{i\theta}-z}[z^n\overline{\varphi_n(e^{i\theta})} - \varphi_n^*(z)]\,d\sigma(\theta) =$$

$$= c_0 F(z)\varphi_n^*(z) - \frac{z^n}{2\pi}\int_0^{2\pi} \frac{e^{i\theta}+z}{e^{i\theta}-z}\overline{\varphi_n(e^{i\theta})}\,d\sigma(\theta), \tag{1.15}$$

so that

$$c_0[F(z)\varphi_n^*(z) - \psi_n^*(z)] =$$

$$= z^n \cdot \frac{1}{2\pi}\int_0^{2\pi}\left\{1 + 2\sum_{k=1}^{\infty} z^k e^{-ik\theta}\right\}\overline{\varphi_n(e^{i\theta})}\,d\sigma(\theta) =$$

$$= z^n \cdot 2\sum_{k=1}^{\infty} z^k \cdot \frac{1}{2\pi}\int_0^{2\pi} e^{-ik\theta}\overline{\varphi_n(e^{i\theta})}\,d\sigma(\theta) = O(z^{n+1}), \quad |z| < 1. \tag{1.15'}$$

Since $\varphi_n^*(z) \neq 0$, for $|z| < 1$, it follows from (1.15') that

$$F(z) - \frac{\psi_n^*(z)}{\varphi_n^*(z)} = O(z^{n+1}), \qquad |z| < 1. \tag{1.16}$$

Later we shall need the following estimate for $|z| \leq r < 1$, which follows from (1.15) and (1.12'):

$$\left| F(z) - \frac{\psi_n^*(z)}{\varphi_n^*(z)} \right| \leqslant \frac{r^n}{c_0 |\varphi_n^*(z)|} \cdot \frac{1}{2\pi} \int_0^{2\pi} \left| \frac{e^{i\theta} + z}{e^{i\theta} - z} \right| |\varphi_n(e^{i\theta})| \, d\sigma(\theta) \leqslant$$

$$\leqslant \frac{r^n (1+r)}{\sqrt{c_0 \alpha_0} \sqrt{1-r^2} (1-r)} \sqrt{\frac{1}{2\pi} \int_0^{2\pi} |\varphi_n(e^{i\theta})|^2 \, d\sigma(\theta)} \leqslant \frac{\sqrt{2} r^n}{(1-r)^{\frac{3}{2}}}. \tag{1.16'}$$

10) We have the relationship*

$$c_0 \{\psi_n(z) \varphi_n^*(z) + \varphi_n(z) \psi_n^*(z)\} = 2z^n, \quad (n = 0, 1, 2, \ldots); \tag{1.17}$$

in particular

$$c_0 \Re \left\{ \frac{\psi_n^*(e^{i\theta})}{\varphi_n^*(e^{i\theta})} \right\} = \frac{1}{|\varphi_n^*(e^{i\theta})|^2} \qquad (n = 0, 1, 2, \ldots). \tag{1.18}$$

To prove this we use the relations

$$\left.\begin{aligned} c_0 [F(z) \varphi_n^*(z) - \psi_n^*(z)] &= z^n \cdot \frac{1}{2\pi} \int_0^{2\pi} \frac{\zeta + z}{\zeta - z} \overline{\varphi_n(\zeta)} \, d\sigma(\theta), \\ &\qquad \zeta = e^{i\theta}, \\ c_0 [F(z) \varphi_n(z) + \psi_n(z)] &= \frac{1}{2\pi} \int_0^{2\pi} \frac{\zeta + z}{\zeta - z} \varphi_n(\zeta) \, d\sigma(\theta), \end{aligned}\right\} \tag{1.19}$$

which follow from (1.13) and (1.15). We then obtain

$$c_0 [\psi_n(z) \varphi_n^*(z) + \varphi_n(z) \psi_n^*(z)] = \frac{1}{2\pi} \int_0^{2\pi} \frac{\zeta + z}{\zeta - z} \Omega_n(\zeta, z) \, d\sigma(\theta),$$

* It follows from (1.17) that $\varphi_n(z) \neq 0$ for $|z| = 1$.

and from (1.2") and (1.7) we have

$$\Omega_n(\zeta, z) = \varphi_n(\zeta)\varphi_n^*(z) - z^n\varphi_n(\zeta)\varphi_n(z) =$$

$$= \frac{\zeta^n - z^n}{\zeta^n}\varphi_n(\zeta)\varphi_n^*(z) + z^n[\overline{\varphi_n^*(\zeta)}\varphi_n^*(z) - \overline{\varphi_n(\zeta)}\varphi_n(z)] =$$

$$= \frac{\zeta^n - z^n}{\zeta^n}\varphi_n(\zeta)\varphi_n^*(z) + \frac{z^n(\zeta - z)}{\zeta}\sum_{k=0}^{n-1}\overline{\varphi_k(\zeta)}\varphi_k(z).$$

Further,

$$\frac{1}{2\pi}\int_0^{2\pi}\frac{(\zeta^n - z^n)(\zeta + z)}{\zeta^n(\zeta - z)}\varphi_n(\zeta)\,d\sigma(\theta) = \frac{z^n}{\alpha_n}.$$

From (1.3), (1.4), and (1.2') we obtain

$$\frac{1}{2\pi}\int_0^{2\pi}\frac{\zeta + z}{\zeta}\sum_{k=0}^{n-1}\overline{\varphi_k(\zeta)}\varphi_k(z)\,d\sigma(\theta) =$$

$$= 1 + z\sum_{k=0}^{n-1}\varphi_k(z)\frac{1}{2\pi}\int_0^{2\pi}\frac{1}{\zeta}\overline{\varphi_k(\zeta)}\,d\sigma(\theta) = 1 - z\sum_{k=0}^{n-1}\varphi_k(z)\frac{\overline{\varphi_{k+1}(0)}}{\alpha_k\alpha_{k+1}} =$$

$$= 1 - \sum_{k=0}^{n-1}\left\{\frac{\varphi_{k+1}^*(z)}{\alpha_{k+1}} - \frac{\varphi_k^*(z)}{\alpha_k}\right\} = 2 - \frac{\varphi_n^*(z)}{\alpha_n},$$

which leads to (1.17).

11) For k = 0, 1, . . . , n we have

$$\frac{1}{2\pi}\int_0^{2\pi}\frac{e^{-ik\theta}\,d\theta}{|\varphi_n^*(e^{i\theta})|^2} = \frac{1}{2\pi}\int_0^{2\pi}e^{-ik\theta}\,d\sigma(\theta) = c_k. \tag{1.20}$$

From proposition 9) above, it follows that

$$\frac{c_0}{2}\cdot\frac{\psi_n^*(z)}{\varphi_n^*(z)} = \frac{c_0}{2} + c_1z + \ldots + c_nz^n + \sum_{k=n+1}^{\infty}c_k^{(n)}z^k,$$

and this series converges if $|z| \leq 1$. Setting $c_{-k} = \bar{c}_k$, therefore, we have

$$c_0\Re\left\{\frac{\psi_n^*(e^{i\theta})}{\varphi_n^*(e^{i\theta})}\right\} = \frac{1}{|\varphi_n^*(e^{i\theta})|^2} = \sum_{k=-n}^{n}c_ke^{ik\theta} + \sum_{|k|>n}c_k^{(n)}e^{ik\theta},$$

which leads to (1.20).

If, therefore, $\sigma(\theta)$ is replaced by $\int_0^\theta \frac{d\theta}{|\varphi_n^*(e^{i\theta})|^2}$, we find that none of the moments $\{c_k\}_0^n$, and therefore also none of the polynomials $\{\varphi_k(z)\}_0^n$ are changed.

12) Within the circle $|z| < 1$ the function defined in (1.14) has a positive real part; almost everywhere on the circle $z = e^{i\theta}, 0 \leq \theta \leq 2\pi$, the real radial boundary values

$$\lim_{r \to 1-0} F(re^{i\theta}) = F(e^{i\theta}), \qquad \lim_{r \to 1-0} \Re F(re^{i\theta}) = \frac{1}{c_0} p(\theta) \quad (1.21)$$

exist. More specifically, at all points θ_0, at which the generalized symmetric first derivative

$$\sigma_{(1)}(\theta_0) = \lim_{h \to 0} \frac{\sigma(\theta_0 + h) - \sigma(\theta_0 - h)}{2h}$$

exists, we have

$$\lim_{r \to 1-0} \Re F(re^{i\theta_0}) = \frac{1}{c_0} \sigma_{(1)}(\theta_0). \quad (1.21')$$

To prove this we note that the real part of $F(re^{i\theta})$ is given by the the Poisson-Stieltjes integral

$$c_0 \Re F(re^{i\theta_0}) = \frac{1}{2\pi} \int_0^{2\pi} \frac{1 - r^2}{1 - 2r\cos(\theta_0 - \theta) + r^2} d\sigma(\theta), \quad r < 1 \quad (1.22)$$

with a nondecreasing function $\sigma(\theta)$, and is therefore positive for $r < 1$. It follows therefore from Smirnov's* theorem that $F(z)$ belongs to the class H_δ, $\delta < 1$, and hence has radial boundary values almost everywhere on $|z| = 1$.†

Assertion (1.21') follows from well-known results of the summation of Fourier-Stieltjes series by Abel's (or Poisson's) method.‡

1.2. Let us now study some relations which obtain in the limit as $n \to \infty$.

* See V. I. Smirnov [3]; see also I. I. Privalov [1], Chapter II, 4.5.

† See I. I. Privalov [1], Chapter II, 1.1, 2.1.

‡ See A. Zygmund [1], Sections 2.14, 3.44.

We introduce the space $L_r^\sigma(0, 2\pi)$ of complex-valued periodic functions $f(\theta)$ with the usual definition of the norm

$$\|f\|_r^\sigma = \sqrt[r]{\frac{1}{2\pi}\int_0^{2\pi} |f(\theta)|^r \, d\sigma(\theta)} < \infty \qquad (r > 0), \quad (1.23)$$

and when $d\sigma(\theta) = d\theta$, we will suppress the index σ for simplicity.

13) The infinite or finite limit

$$\lim_{n\to\infty} \alpha_n = \alpha \leqslant \infty \qquad (1.24)$$

exists. To prove this it is sufficient to note that according to (1.5) $0 < \alpha_n \le \alpha_{n+1}$.

14) For the function $\psi_0(\theta) = e^{-i\theta}$ we have

$$\sum_{k=0}^{\infty} |\lambda_k|^2 = \sum_{k=0}^{\infty} \left| \frac{\varphi_{k+1}(0)}{\alpha_k \alpha_{k+1}} \right|^2 = \frac{1}{\alpha_0^2} - \frac{1}{\alpha^2} =$$

$$= \frac{1}{2\pi}\int_0^{2\pi} |\psi_0(\theta)|^2 \, d\sigma(\theta) - \frac{1}{\alpha^2}, \quad (1.25)$$

where

$$\lim_{n\to\infty} \min_{G_n} \|\psi_0(\theta) - G_n(e^{i\theta})\|_2^\sigma = \frac{1}{\alpha} \geqslant 0. \qquad (1.25')$$

15) The following statements are all equivalent:

a) the function $\ln \sigma'(\theta)$ is integrable; this is to say

$$\int_0^{2\pi} \ln \sigma'(\theta) \, d\sigma > -\infty; \qquad (1.26)$$

b) the set $U = \{\varphi_n(e^{i\theta})\}_0^\infty$ of polynomials, i.e., the set of powers $\{e^{in\theta}\}_0^\infty$, is not closed in L_2^σ;

c) the function $\psi_0(\theta) = e^{-i\theta}$ cannot be approximated by polynomials to arbitrary accuracy with the metric L_2^σ;

d) the finite limit

$$\lim_{n\to\infty} \alpha_n = \alpha \qquad (1.27)$$

exists;

e) the series $\sum_{k=0}^{\infty} |\varphi_k(z)|^2$ converges at least at one point in the region $|z| < 1$;

f) there exists a subsequence $\{\varphi^*_{n_\nu}(z)\}$ bounded at least at one point in the region $|z| < 1$.*

Let us assume that U is not closed, and therefore not complete in L_2^σ; then there exists a function $\varphi(\theta) \in L_2^\sigma$ inequivalent to zero and orthogonal to all functions of U, i.e., satisfying the conditions

$$\frac{1}{2\pi}\int_0^{2\pi} \overline{\varphi(\theta)}\, e^{ik\theta}\, d\sigma(\theta) = 0, \qquad (k = 0,\ 1,\ 2,\ \ldots). \tag{1.28}$$

Multiplying each of these integrals by z^{-k-1}, $|z| > 1$ and summing over k, we obtain

$$\frac{1}{2\pi}\int_0^{2\pi} \frac{\overline{\varphi(\theta)}\, d\sigma(\theta)}{e^{i\theta} - z} = 0, \qquad |z| > 1. \tag{1.28'}$$

We introduce the notation

$$\lambda(z) = \frac{1}{2\pi}\int_0^{2\pi} \frac{e^{i\theta}\, d\tau(\theta)}{e^{i\theta} - z}, \qquad d\tau(\theta) = e^{-i\theta}\overline{\varphi(\theta)}\, d\sigma(\theta) \tag{1.29}$$

Since

$$\frac{1}{2\pi}\int_0^{2\pi} |d\tau(\theta)| = \frac{1}{2\pi}\int_0^{2\pi} |\varphi(\theta)|\, d\sigma(\theta) \leqslant \|\varphi\|_2^\sigma \cdot \sqrt{c_0} < \infty,$$

$\tau(\theta)$ is a function of bounded variation.

The function $\lambda(z)$ in (1.29) is an analytic function, regular for $|z| < 1$; since (1.29) is a representation of this function in the form of

---

* The equivalence of a) and b) has been shown by A.N. Kolmogorov [1, 2] and M. G. Krein [1]. The condition under which a set of polynomials is not closed in L_r^σ for $r \geq 1$ was found by N. I. Akhiezer [1] for the case of orthogonality on the unit circle; for the general case of orthogonality on a rectifiable Jordan curve, this condition was found by the author [2] for $r \geq 1$, and by G. Ts. Tumarkin [1] for $r > 0$.

an integral of the Cauchy-Stieltjes type, and since $\lambda(z) \equiv 0$ for $z > 1$, Eq. (1.29) is indeed a Cauchy-Stieltjes integral. Thus $\lambda(z) \in H_1$, $|z| < 1$ and the boundary values

$$\lambda(e^{i\theta}) = \lim_{r \to 1-0} \lambda(re^{i\theta}) = \tau'(\theta) = e^{-i\theta}\overline{\varphi(\theta)}\,\sigma'(\theta) \qquad (1.30)$$

exist almost everywhere in $[0, 2\pi]$, with the boundary-value function $\lambda(e^{i\theta})$ satisfying*

$$\int_0^{2\pi} \ln|\lambda(e^{i\theta})|\,d\theta > -\infty, \qquad \int_0^{2\pi} |\lambda(e^{i\theta})|\,d\theta < \infty. \qquad (1.31)$$

Using (1.30) we find that $\ln\{|\varphi(\theta)|\sigma'(\theta)\} \in L_1$, whence

$$-\infty < \int_0^{2\pi} \ln^+ \sigma'(\theta)\,d\theta + \int_0^{2\pi} \ln^+\{|\varphi(\theta)|^2\sigma'(\theta)\}\,d\theta +$$

$$+ \int_0^{2\pi} \ln^- \sigma'(\theta)\,d\theta + \int_0^{2\pi} \ln^-\{|\varphi(\theta)|^2\sigma'(\theta)\}\,d\theta < +\infty\,†.$$

On the other hand, the conditions $\sigma'(\theta) \in L_1$, $\varphi(\theta) \in L_2^\sigma$ imply that

$$\left.\begin{aligned} &\int_0^{2\pi} \ln^+ \sigma'(\theta)\,d\theta < \int_0^{2\pi} \sigma'(\theta)\,d\theta < +\infty, \\ &\int_0^{2\pi} \ln^+\{|\varphi(\theta)|^2\sigma'(\theta)\}\,d\theta < \int_0^{2\pi} |\varphi(\theta)|^2\sigma'(\theta)\,d\theta < \\ &\qquad < \int_0^{2\pi} |\varphi(\theta)|^2\,d\sigma(\theta) < +\infty, \end{aligned}\right\} \qquad (1.32)$$

and therefore

$$-\infty < \int_0^{2\pi} \ln^- \sigma'(\theta)\,d\theta + \int_0^{2\pi} \ln^-\{|\varphi(\theta)|^2\sigma'(\theta)\,d\theta.$$

* See I. I. Privalov [1], Chapter II, Section 5.

† We use the notation $\ln^+ a = \begin{cases} \ln a, & a \geqslant 1, \\ 0, & 0 < a < 1, \end{cases}$ $\quad \ln^- a = \ln a - \ln^+ a.$

Since both terms are negative, we arrive at

$$-\infty < \int_0^{2\pi} \ln^- \sigma'(\theta)\, d\theta, \qquad -\infty < \int_0^{2\pi} \ln \sigma'(\theta)\, d\theta < +\infty.$$

Assume now that (1.26) is given. From (1.11) we have

$$\frac{1}{\alpha_n^2} = \frac{1}{2\pi}\int_0^{2\pi} \left|\frac{\varphi_n^*(e^{i\theta})}{\alpha_n}\right|^2 d\sigma(\theta) \geqslant \frac{1}{2\pi}\int_0^{2\pi} \left|\frac{\varphi_n^*(e^{i\theta})}{\alpha_n}\right|^2 \cdot \sigma'(\theta)\, d\theta,$$

and using the fact that the geometric mean of a function is no greater than its arithmetic mean, we obtain

$$\frac{1}{\alpha_n^2} \geqslant \exp\left\{\frac{2}{2\pi}\int_0^{2\pi} \ln\left|\frac{\varphi_n^*(e^{i\theta})}{\alpha_n}\right| d\theta\right\} \exp\left\{\frac{1}{2\pi}\int_0^{2\pi} \ln \sigma'(\theta)\, d\theta\right\} =$$

$$= \exp\left\{\frac{1}{2\pi}\int_0^{2\pi} \ln \sigma'(\theta)\, d\theta\right\}, \qquad (1.33)$$

where we have used the fact that $\varphi_n^*(0) = \alpha_n$. According to (1.26), therefore,

$$\frac{1}{\alpha^2} = \lim_{n\to\infty} \frac{1}{\alpha_n^2} \geqslant \exp\left\{\frac{1}{2\pi}\int_0^{2\pi} \ln \sigma'(\theta)\, d\theta\right\} > 0, \qquad (1.34)$$

which then implies d).

The equivalence of c) and d) follows from (1.25'), and c) in turn implies b).

Equation (1.12') implies that for $|z| \leq r < 1$ the sequence $\{\varphi_n^*(z)\}$ is uniformly bounded from below. A theorem due to P. Montel* states that there exists a subsequence of polynomials $\{\varphi_{n_\nu}^*(z)\}$ such that we have uniformly

$$\lim_{\nu\to\infty} \varphi_{n_\nu}^*(z) = \pi(z), \qquad |z| \leqslant r < 1, \qquad (1.35)$$

* See P. Montel [1], Section 17.

where $\pi(z)$ is an analytic function which may, however, be infinite identically; since $\varphi_n^*(z) \neq 0$ for $|z| \leq 1$, it follows from Hurwitz's theorem that $\pi(z) \neq 0$ for $|z| < 1$.

Because $\varphi_{n_\nu}^*(0) = \alpha_{n_\nu}$ it follows that condition a) is equivalent to the condition that $\pi(z) \not\equiv \infty$, which means that the subsequence of (1.35) converges to a function $\pi(z)$ which is not identically infinite.

From (1.12) and (1.9) we obtain the inequalities

$$K_n(z_0, z_0) \leqslant \frac{|\varphi_n^*(z_0)|^2}{1 - |z|^2}, \tag{1.36}$$

$$|\alpha_n \varphi_n^*(z_0) - \alpha_m \varphi_m^*(z_0)|^2 \leqslant \sum_{k=m+1}^{n} |\varphi_k(z_0)|^2 \cdot \sum_{k=m+1}^{n} |\varphi_k(0)|^2,$$
$$m < n, \quad |z_0| < 1, \tag{1.36'}$$

and we are assured in all cases of the existence of the limit

$$\lim_{n\to\infty} K_n(z_0, z_0) = \sum_{k=0}^{\infty} |\varphi_k(z_0)|^2 \leqslant \infty, \qquad |z_0| < 1. \tag{1.37}$$

The boundedness of the subsequence $\{\varphi_{n_\nu}^*(z_0)\}$ at a single point $|z| < 1$ implies that this subsequence converges for all $|z| < 1$ to the function $\pi(z) \not\equiv \infty$, and then (1.36) implies in turn that the series in (1.37) converges throughout the region $|z| < 1$. This together with (1.36') then leads to the convergence of the entire sequence $\{\varphi_n(z)\}$ throughout the region $|z| < 1$; thus assertions a), e), and f) are equivalent.

CHAPTER II

THE PROPERTIES OF THE FUNCTION $\pi(z)$

Let us consider in more detail the case in which the integral of (1.26) exists. This case was first investigated (on the assumption that $\sigma(\theta)$ is absolutely continuous) by Szegö, who also introduced the function $\pi(z)$, defining it not as the limit of the sequence $\{\varphi_n^*(z)\}$, but directly in terms of the weight $p(\theta)$; in the sequel we will show the equivalence of these two definitions.

It follows from the above considerations that condition (1.26) is necessary and sufficient for the validity of the limit relation *

$$\lim_{n\to\infty} \varphi_n^*(z) = \frac{1}{\alpha}\sum_{k=0}^{\infty} \overline{\varphi_k(0)}\,\varphi_k(z) = \pi(z), \qquad |z| < 1, \quad (2.1)$$

and in a closed region $|z| \leq r < 1$ the convergence is uniform. We will show that the limit function $\pi(z)$, regular for $|z| < 1$ according to Weierstrass' theorem, possesses the following important properties:

a) $\dfrac{1}{\pi(z)} \in H_2$, from which it follows that the radial boundary values

$$\frac{1}{\pi(e^{i\theta})} = \lim_{r\to 1-0} \frac{1}{\pi(re^{i\theta})} \qquad (2.2)$$

exist almost everywhere in $[0, 2\pi]$ and fulfill the inequalities

$$\int_0^{2\pi} \frac{d\theta}{|\pi(e^{i\theta})|^2} < \infty, \quad \int_0^{2\pi} \ln \frac{1}{|\pi(e^{i\theta})|^2}\, d\theta > -\infty. \quad (2.3)$$

---

*G. Szegö ([1], Section 12.1) has shown the sufficiency of this condition for absolutely continuous $\sigma(\theta)$.

b) Almost everywhere in $[0, 2\pi]$ we have

$$\frac{1}{|\pi(e^{i\theta})|^2} = p(\theta) = \sigma'(\theta). \tag{2.4}$$

c) The function $\pi(z)$ can be represented by the formula

$$\pi(z) = \exp\left\{-\frac{1}{4\pi}\int_0^{2\pi} \frac{e^{i\theta}+z}{e^{i\theta}-z} \ln p(\theta)\, d\theta\right\}, \qquad |z| < 1, \tag{2.5}$$

almost everywhere in $[0, 2\pi]$, and its radial boundary values are given by

$$\left.\begin{aligned} \pi(e^{i\varphi}) &= \lim_{r\to 1-0} \pi(re^{i\varphi}) = \frac{1}{\sqrt{p(\varphi)}}\, e^{i\gamma(\varphi)}, \\ \gamma(\varphi) &= \arg \pi(e^{i\varphi}) = \frac{1}{4\pi}\int_0^{2\pi} \operatorname{ctg}\frac{\theta-\varphi}{2} \ln p(\theta)\, d\theta \end{aligned}\right\} \tag{2.6}$$

(the integral is understood in the sense of the Cauchy principal value, and exists almost everywhere in $[0, 2\pi]$, since $\ln p(\theta) \in L_1$) .

d) If $p(\theta) \geq m > 0$ almost everywhere in $[0, 2\pi]$, then $|\pi(z)| \leq 1/\sqrt{m}$ throughout the region $|z| < 1$.

e) if $E \subset [0, 2\pi]$ is a set of points on which the derivative $\sigma'(\theta) = p(\theta)$ exists and is finite and positive,* and if one writes

$$\pi_0(\theta) = \pi(e^{i\theta})\,\gamma_E(\theta), \quad \gamma_E(\theta) = \begin{cases} 1, & \theta \in E, \\ 0, & \theta \,\bar{\in}\, E, \end{cases} \tag{2.7}$$

where $\gamma_E(\theta)$ is the characteristic function of the set E, one obtains the formal Fourier-Chebyshev expansion

$$\left.\begin{aligned} \pi_0(\theta) &\sim \frac{1}{\alpha}\sum_{k=0}^{\infty} \overline{\varphi_k(0)}\, \varphi_k(e^{i\theta}), \\ \alpha &= \pi(0) = \lim_{n\to\infty} \alpha_n = \lim_{n\to\infty} \varphi_n^*(0), \end{aligned}\right\} \tag{2.7'}$$

---

* Obviously mes $E = 2\pi$.

which implies that

$$\delta_n = \min_{G_n} \| \pi_0(\theta) - G_n(e^{i\theta}) \|_2^\sigma = \left\| \pi_0(\theta) - \frac{\alpha_n}{\alpha} \varphi_n^*(e^{i\theta}) \right\|_2^\sigma =$$

$$= \frac{\sqrt{\alpha^2 - \alpha_n^2}}{\alpha} = \frac{1}{\alpha} \sqrt{\sum_{k=n+1}^{\infty} |\varphi_k(0)|^2} . \quad (2.8)$$

f) The function $\pi_0(\theta) \in L_2^\sigma$ satisfies the condition of closure*

$$\lim_{n\to\infty} \delta_n = \lim_{n\to\infty} \min_{G_n} \| \pi_0(\theta) - G_n(e^{i\theta}) \|_2^\sigma = 0. \quad (2.9)$$

g) We obtain the limit relations

$$\frac{1}{\alpha^2} = \lim_{n\to\infty} \frac{1}{\alpha_n^2} = \exp\left\{ \frac{1}{2\pi} \int_0^{2\pi} \ln p(\theta)\, d\theta \right\}, \quad (2.10)$$

which go further than (1.34).†

To prove property a) we recall that (2.1) tells us that in the closed region $|z| \le r < 1$ we have uniform convergence of

$$\lim_{n\to\infty} \frac{1}{|\varphi_n^*(z)|^2} = \frac{1}{|\pi(z)|^2};$$

on the other hand, according to (1.20)

$$\frac{1}{2\pi} \int_0^{2\pi} \frac{d\theta}{|\varphi_n^*(re^{i\theta})|^2} \leqslant \frac{1}{2\pi} \int_0^{2\pi} \frac{d\theta}{|\varphi_n^*(e^{i\theta})|^2} = c_0,$$

since the integral on the left side is a nondecreasing function‡ of r.

---

* For absolutely continuous $\sigma(\theta)$ this result was obtained by V. I. Smirnov [3], Section 10.

† Equation (2.10) holds also when the integral in (1.26) does not exist if we agree to consider the right side of (2.10) zero for this case. This result was first obtained by S. Verblunsky [1]; for the case of absolutely continuous $\sigma(\theta)$, it was obtained by G. Szegö [1], Section 12.3, N. I. Akhiezer [1], and others.

‡ See, for instance, I. I. Privalov's monograph [1], p. 41.

In view of the fact that the sequence of functions $\left\{ \frac{1}{|\varphi_n^*(z)|^2} \right\}$, continuous for $|z| \leq r < 1$, converges uniformly to a function which is therefore also continuous in this region, we have

$$\lim_{n\to\infty} \frac{1}{2\pi} \int_0^{2\pi} \frac{d\theta}{|\varphi_n^*(re^{i\theta})|^2} = \frac{1}{2\pi} \int_0^{2\pi} \frac{d\theta}{|\pi(re^{i\theta})|^2} \leqslant c_0, \qquad r < 1.$$

Now this inequality holds for all values of $r < 1$, so that $\frac{1}{\pi(z)} \in H_2$ (by definition of the class H_2); then the existence of the radial boundary values of (2.2) with the properties given by (2.3) follows from the known properties of class H_δ functions.

To prove property b) consider the harmonic function $c_0 \Re \left\{ \frac{\psi_n^*(re^{i\theta})}{\varphi_n^*(re^{i\theta})} \right\}$, which according to (1.18) takes on the value $\frac{1}{|\varphi_n^*(e^{i\theta})|^2}$ on the circumference $z = e^{i\theta}$, and the harmonic function $\ln \frac{1}{|\varphi_n^*(re^{i\theta})|^2}$, which takes on the value $\ln \frac{1}{|\varphi_n^*(e^{i\theta})|^2}$ on the same circumference. We express both these functions in terms of their boundary values by means of Poisson's integral

$$c_0 \Re \left\{ \frac{\psi_n^*(re^{i\theta})}{\varphi_n^*(re^{i\theta})} \right\} = \frac{1}{2\pi} \int_0^{2\pi} P(r, \theta - \varphi) \frac{d\varphi}{|\varphi_n^*(e^{i\varphi})|^2},$$

$$\frac{1}{|\varphi_n^*(re^{i\theta})|^2} = \exp\left\{ \frac{1}{2\pi} \int_0^{2\pi} P(r, \theta - \varphi) \ln \frac{1}{|\varphi_n^*(e^{i\varphi})|^2} d\varphi \right\},$$

where $P(r,\theta-\varphi)$ is the Poisson kernel

$$P(r, \theta - \varphi) = \frac{1 - r^2}{1 - 2r\cos(\theta - \varphi) + r^2}, \quad r < 1,$$

which has the well-known property

$$\frac{1}{2\pi}\int_0^{2\pi} P(r,\ \theta-\varphi)\,d\varphi = 1.$$

We now use the fact that the weighted geometric mean of a function is no greater than its weighted arithmetic mean, obtaining

$$\frac{1}{|\varphi_n^*(re^{i\theta})|^2} \leqslant c_0\Re\left\{\frac{\psi_n^*(re^{i\theta})}{\varphi_n^*(re^{i\theta})}\right\}, \quad r<1, \quad 0\leqslant\theta\leqslant 2\pi.$$

We now fix $r < 1$, go to the limit as $n \to \infty$, and make use of (2.1) and (1.16'), obtaining

$$\frac{1}{|\pi(re^{i\theta})|^2} \leqslant c_0\Re\{F(re^{i\theta})\}, \quad 0\leqslant\theta\leqslant 2\pi, \quad r<1. \tag{2.11}$$

Now both functions

$$\frac{1}{\pi(re^{i\theta})}, \qquad F(re^{i\theta})$$

have radial boundary values in the limit $r \to 1-0$ almost everywhere on the circle $z = e^{i\theta}$, $0 \leq \theta \leq 2\pi$. Let E' be the set of points on which this is true. We then see that both these functions are continuous for $e^{i\theta} \in E'$ for all values $0 \leq r \leq 1$, and therefore going to the limit $r \to 1-0$, in (2.11), we obtain, using (2.2) and (1.21),

$$\frac{1}{|\pi(e^{i\theta})|^2} \leqslant p(\theta) \tag{2.12}$$

for $e^{i\theta} \in E'$, or almost everywhere on $[0,\ 2\pi]$.

Let us assume that the strict inequality in (2.12) holds on some set of positive measure; we apply Gauss' theorem to the harmonic function $\ln\frac{1}{|\pi(z)|^2}$, whose boundary values on the circle $z = e^{i\theta}$ give a summable function. This then gives

$$\exp\left\{\frac{1}{2\pi}\int_0^{2\pi}\ln p(\theta)\,d\theta\right\} > \exp\left\{\frac{1}{2\pi}\int_0^{2\pi}\ln\frac{1}{|\pi(e^{i\theta})|^2}\,d\theta\right\} =$$

$$= \exp\left\{\ln\frac{1}{|\pi(0)|^2}\right\} = \frac{1}{\alpha^2},$$

which contradicts (1.34), so that (2.4) is valid almost everywhere on $[0, 2\pi]$.

To prove property c) we note that according to a) and b) and the parametric representation of class H_2 functions,* we have

$$\frac{1}{\pi(z)} = e^{i\lambda} b(z) \exp\left\{\frac{1}{4\pi}\int_0^{2\pi} \frac{e^{i\theta}+z}{e^{i\theta}-z} \ln p(\theta)\, d\theta\right\} \times$$

$$\times \exp\left\{\frac{1}{2\pi}\int_0^{2\pi} \frac{e^{i\theta}+z}{e^{i\theta}-z} d\psi(\theta)\right\}, \quad |z| < 1, \quad (2.13)$$

where $b(z)$ is the Blaschke product for this function, λ is a positive number, and $\psi(\theta)$ is a nonincreasing function whose derivative vanishes almost everywhere.

Since $\pi(z)$ is regular for $|z| < 1$, it follows that $1/\pi(z)$ has no zeros in this region, and therefore $b(z) \equiv 1$. Setting $z = 0$ in (2.13), we obtain

$$\frac{1}{\pi(0)} = \frac{1}{\alpha} = e^{i\lambda} \cdot \exp\left\{\frac{1}{4\pi}\int_0^{2\pi} \ln p(\theta)\, d\theta\right\} \cdot \exp\left\{\frac{1}{2\pi}\int_0^{2\pi} d\psi(\theta)\right\}, \quad (2.14)$$

and since α is a real number it follows that $\lambda = 0$. Furthermore, we have

$$\int_0^{2\pi} d\psi(\theta) \leqslant 0, \quad (2.15)$$

since $\psi(\theta)$ is a nonincreasing function, and we therefore obtain

$$\frac{1}{\alpha} \leqslant \exp\left\{\frac{1}{4\pi}\int_0^{2\pi} \ln p(\theta)\, d\theta\right\},$$

which, together with (1.34), implies that $\int_0^{2\pi} d\psi(\theta) = 0$ and therefore that $\psi(\theta) \equiv$ const. We thus arrive at (2.5), which in turn gives (2.10) when we set $z = 0$.

---

* See V. I Smirnov [2] and I. I. Privalov [1], Chapter II.

Consider the analytic function

$$\ln \pi(z) = \ln |\pi(z)| + i \arg \pi(z) =$$

$$= -\frac{1}{4\pi}\int_0^{2\pi} \frac{e^{i\theta}+z}{e^{i\theta}-z} \ln p(\theta)\, d\theta, \quad |z| < 1, \quad (2.16)$$

regular in the region $|z| < 1$. Properties a) and b) and (1.26) imply that this function has radial boundary values almost everywhere on the circumference $|z| = 1$. Its real part is given by the Poisson integral

$$\ln |\pi(re^{i\varphi})| =$$

$$= \frac{1}{2\pi}\int_0^{2\pi} \frac{1-r^2}{1-2r\cos(\varphi-\theta)+r^2} \ln \frac{1}{\sqrt{p(\theta)}}\, d\theta, \quad r < 1 \quad (2.16')$$

and therefore has a radial boundary value at every point at which $p(\theta)$ is the derivative of its indefinite integral. The imaginary part, according to the theory of summation of conjugate trigonometric series by Abel's (or Poisson's) method, has a radial boundary value at every point φ at which the integral

$$\frac{1}{4\pi}\int_0^{2\pi} \operatorname{ctg}\frac{\theta-\varphi}{2} \ln p(\theta)\, d\theta = \arg \pi(e^{i\varphi}) = \lim_{r\to 1-0} \arg \pi(re^{i\varphi}) \quad (2.17)$$

exists in the sense of the Cauchy principal value.*

Property d) is obvious: if it were true that $|\pi(z_0)| > 1/\sqrt{m}$, $|z_0| < 1$, the harmonic function $\ln|\pi(z)|$ would attain its maximum at some internal point of the interval $|z| < 1$, and this is impossible.

---

* See A. Zygmund [1], Sections 3.321, 3.45, 7.1; see also G. Szegö [1], Section 10.3.

To prove (2.7) and therefore (2.8) we calculate the Fourier-Chebyshev coefficients of $\pi_0(\theta)$:

$$a_n = \frac{1}{2\pi}\int_0^{2\pi} \pi_0(\theta)\,\overline{\varphi_n(e^{i\theta})}\,d\sigma(\theta) = \frac{1}{2\pi}\int_0^{2\pi} \pi(e^{i\theta})\,\overline{\varphi_n(e^{i\theta})}\,p(\theta)\,d\theta =$$

$$= \frac{1}{2\pi}\int_0^{2\pi} \frac{\overline{\varphi_n(e^{i\theta})}}{\overline{\pi(e^{i\theta})}}\,d\theta, \qquad (n = 0,\ 1,\ 2,\ \ldots).$$

For n = 0, 1, 2, . . . , we have

$$\overline{a}_n = \frac{1}{2\pi}\int_0^{2\pi} \frac{\varphi_n(e^{i\theta})}{\pi(e^{i\theta})}\,d\theta = \frac{1}{2\pi i}\int_{|z|=1} \frac{\varphi_n(z)\,dz}{z\pi(z)} = \frac{\varphi_n(0)}{\pi(0)},$$

and this leads directly to (2.7) and (2.8).

Equation (2.9) is a consequence of (1.5), (1.9), and (2.7), according to which

$$\alpha^2 - \alpha_n^2 = \sum_{k=n+1}^{\infty} |\varphi_k(0)|^2, \qquad \lim_{n\to\infty} \alpha_n = \alpha,$$
$$\alpha_n \varphi_n^*(z) = \sum_{k=0}^{n} \overline{\varphi_k(0)}\,\varphi_k(z). \tag{2.18}$$

We note in conclusion that from (2.8) and from the inequalities

$$\alpha_0 \leqslant \alpha_n \leqslant \alpha, \qquad (n = 0,\ 1,\ 2,\ \ldots), \tag{2.19}$$

we are led to

$$\sqrt{\frac{\alpha_0+\alpha}{\alpha^2}}\cdot\sqrt{\alpha-\alpha_n} \leqslant \delta_n =$$
$$= \frac{1}{\alpha}\sqrt{\sum_{k=n+1}^{\infty} |\varphi_k(0)|^2} \leqslant \sqrt{\frac{2}{\alpha}}\cdot\sqrt{\alpha-\alpha_n}, \tag{2.20}$$

inequalities which show that as $n \to \infty$, the decreasing quantities δ_n and $\sqrt{\alpha - \alpha_n}$ are of the same order.

Remark 2.1. For future use we prove the following proposition.

Let integral (1.26) exist and $\varphi(\theta) \in L_2^\sigma$ be a function all of whose Fourier-Chebyshev coefficients vanish, i.e., such that

$$c_n = \frac{1}{2\pi} \int_0^{2\pi} \varphi(\theta) \overline{\varphi_n(e^{i\theta})}\, d\sigma(\theta) = 0, \quad (n = 0, 1, 2, \ldots). \tag{2.21}$$

Then this function may in general be represented in the form

$$\varphi(\theta) = e^{-i\theta} \pi_0(\theta) \overline{\mu(e^{i\theta})}, \tag{2.22}$$

where $\mu(e^{i\theta})$ is the boundary value of an arbitrary function $\mu(z) \in H_2$.

Indeed, from (1.28) and (1.29) we have

$$\int_0^{2\pi} e^{ik\theta}\, d\tau(\theta) = 0, \qquad (k = 1, 2, 3, \ldots),$$

from which, according to a well-known theorem of F. and M. Riesz it follows that $\tau(\theta)$ is absolutely continuous.* Then according to (1.29) we should have $\varphi(\theta) = 0,\ \theta \bar{\in} E$, and thus (1.30) implies that

$$\varphi(\theta) = e^{-i\theta} |\pi(e^{i\theta})|^2 \overline{\lambda(e^{i\theta})}\, \gamma_E(\theta).$$

Since $\lambda(z) \in H_1$ and $\frac{1}{\pi(z)} \in H_2$, it follows obviously that $\ln|\lambda(e^{i\theta})|$, $\ln|\pi(e^{i\theta})| \in L_1$ and hence that $\ln|\pi(e^{i\theta})\lambda(e^{i\theta})| \in L_1$. In view of the fact that $\varphi(\theta) \in L_2^\sigma$, we have

$$\int_0^{2\pi} |\varphi(\theta)|^2\, d\sigma(\theta) = \int_0^{2\pi} |\lambda(e^{i\theta})\pi(e^{i\theta})|^2\, d\theta < \infty,$$

and if we set $\mu(z) = \lambda(z)\pi(z)$, we find that $\mu(z) \in H_2$, so that (2.22) holds. The converse is also easily demonstrated, namely, that given any function $\varphi(\theta)$ satisfying (2.22) (i.e., with an arbitrary function $\mu(z) \in H_2$), all of its Fourier-Chebyshev coefficients vanish.

* See, for instance, I. I. Privalov [1], Chapter II, Section 5.6.

Assume that $\frac{1}{p(\theta)} \in L_1$. Then we have the following example, due to Szegö [5] (Section 15):

$$\varphi(\theta) = \frac{\pi(e^{i\theta})\,[\overline{\pi(\alpha)} - \overline{\pi(e^{i\theta})}]}{1 - \bar{\alpha}e^{i\theta}}, \qquad |\alpha| < 1.$$

The Fourier-Chebyshev coefficients of this function all vanish; for this particular case

$$\mu(z) = \frac{\pi(z) - \pi(\alpha)}{z - \alpha}.$$

In a previous note [9] the present author has given the simpler example $\varphi(\theta) = e^{-i\theta}\pi_0(\theta)$, to which corresponds the extremely simple function $\mu(z) \equiv 1$.

Remark 2.2. We make an observation about the properties of orthogonal polynomials which we shall find important in the sequel.

If the integral (1.26) exists and if one writes

$$d\sigma(\theta) = p(\theta)\,d\theta + d\sigma_1(\theta),$$

where $\sigma_1(\theta)$ is the sum of a step function and the singular component of $\sigma(\theta)$, one obtains

$$\| \varphi_n(e^{i\theta}) \|_2^{\sigma_1} < \sqrt{\frac{2\alpha}{\alpha + \alpha_0}}\,\delta_n \qquad (n = 0, 1, 2, \ldots). \quad (2.23)$$

We prove this by considering the inequality

$$0 < \frac{1}{2\pi}\int_0^{2\pi} \left| \frac{\varphi_n^*(e^{i\theta})}{\pi(e^{i\theta})} - 1 \right|^2 d\theta = \frac{1}{2\pi}\int_0^{2\pi} \left| \frac{\varphi_n^*(e^{i\theta})}{\pi(e^{i\theta})} \right|^2 d\theta -$$

$$- 2\Re\left\{ \frac{1}{2\pi}\int_0^{2\pi} \frac{\varphi_n^*(e^{i\theta})}{\pi(e^{i\theta})}\,d\theta \right\} + 1 = \frac{1}{2\pi}\int_0^{2\pi} p(\theta)\,|\varphi_n(e^{i\theta})|^2\,d\theta -$$

$$- 2\Re\left\{ \frac{1}{2\pi i}\int_{|z|=1} \frac{\varphi_n^*(z)}{\pi(z)} \cdot \frac{dz}{z} \right\} + 1 =$$

$$= 2 - 2\cdot\frac{\alpha_n}{\alpha} - \frac{1}{2\pi}\int_0^{2\pi} |\varphi_n(e^{i\theta})|^2\,d\sigma_1(\theta),$$

which, together with (2.20), gives (2.23).

CHAPTER III

ESTIMATES ON THE ENTIRE UNIT CIRCLE

3.1. Consider a complex-valued function $f(\theta)\in L_1$, of period 2π, and construct for it the Jackson sum (or polynomial)*

$$u_\nu(\theta)=\frac{3}{2\pi\nu(2\nu^2+1)}\int_0^{2\pi}\left\{\frac{\sin\frac{\nu}{2}(t-\theta)}{\sin\frac{1}{2}(t-\theta)}\right\}^4 f(t)\,dt. \quad (3.1)$$

Since

$$\left\{\frac{\sin\frac{\nu}{2}(t-\theta)}{\sin\frac{1}{2}(t-\theta)}\right\}^4=\sum_{k=0}^{2\nu-2} l_k(\cos k\theta\cos kt+\sin k\theta\sin kt),$$

$u_\nu(\theta)$ is a trigonometric sum of order $2\nu-2$, i.e.,

$$u_\nu(\theta)=\sum_{k=0}^{2\nu-2}(a_k\cos k\theta+b_k\sin k\theta),$$

with

$$a_k+ib_k=\frac{3l_k}{2\pi\nu(2\nu^2+1)}\int_0^{2\pi} f(t)\,e^{ikt}\,dt \quad (k=0,\ 1,\ 2,\ \ldots,\ 2\nu-2).$$

If almost everywhere on $[0,\ 2\pi]$ the function $f(t)$ coincides with the boundary value of some analytic function of class H_1 on the circle $z=e^{it}$, then as is well known† we must have

$$\int_0^{2\pi} f(t)\,e^{ikt}\,dt=a_k+ib_k=0 \qquad (k=1,\ 2,\ \ldots).$$

---

* See, for instance, I. P. Natanson [1], p. 114.

† See I. I. Privalov [1], Chapter II.

We then have

$$a_k \cos k\theta + b_k \sin k\theta = \frac{e^{ik\theta}(a_k - ib_k) + e^{-ik\theta}(a_k + ib_k)}{2} = \frac{a_k - ib_k}{2} e^{ik\theta},$$

which means that $u_\nu(\theta)$ is a polynomial of degree $2\nu - 2$ in $e^{i\theta}$.

We now define for a function $f(\theta) \in L_r^\sigma$ its weighted integral modulus of continuity

$$\omega_r^\sigma(\delta; f) = \sup_{|h| \leqslant \delta} \|f(\theta + h) - f(\theta)\|_r^\sigma ; \tag{3.2}$$

when $d\sigma(\theta) = d\theta$, we will drop the index σ.*

The function $\omega_r^\sigma(\delta; f)$ has the following properties:

1) It is a nondecreasing function of δ. Indeed, if $\delta_1 > \delta_2 > 0$, then $|h| \leq \delta_2$ implies $|h| \leq \delta_1$. Therefore the upper bound for $|h| \leq \delta_1$ is no less than the upper bound for $|h| \leq \delta_2$.

2) For any positive integer <u>m</u> we have

$$\omega_r^\sigma(m\delta; f) \leqslant m\omega_r^\sigma(\delta; f). \tag{3.3}$$

To prove this it is sufficient to note that

$$f(\theta + mh) - f(\theta) = \sum_{k=1}^{m} \{f(\theta + kh) - f[\theta + (k-1)h]\},$$

whence

$$\|f(\theta + mh) - f(\theta)\|_r^\sigma \leqslant \sum_{k=1}^{m} \|f(\theta + kh) - f[\theta + (k-1)h]\|_r^\sigma.$$

Setting, now, $|h| \leq \delta$ and taking the upper bound, we obtain (3.3).

3) If $\lambda > 0$, then

$$\omega_r^\sigma(\lambda\delta; f) \leqslant (\lambda + 1)\, \omega_r^\sigma(\delta; f). \tag{3.4}$$

Indeed, let $0 < m \leq \lambda < m + 1$, where <u>m</u> is an integer. We then have

$$\omega_r^\sigma(\lambda\delta; f) \leqslant \omega_r^\sigma[(m+1)\delta; f] \leqslant (m+1)\, \omega_r^\sigma(\delta; f) \leqslant$$
$$\leqslant (\lambda + 1)\, \omega_r^\sigma(\delta; f).$$

---

* If $\omega_r(\delta; f) \leq M\delta^\alpha$, $0 < \alpha \leq 1$, we will write $f(\theta) \in \mathrm{Lip}(\alpha, r)$.

4) If $d\sigma(\theta) = d\theta$, then*

$$\lim_{\delta \to 0} \omega_r(\delta; f) = 0. \tag{3.5}$$

3.2. Lemma 3.1. Let $f(\theta) \in L_r^\sigma$ and $f(\theta) \in L_1$; then

$$\| f(\theta) - u_\nu(\theta) \|_r^\sigma \leqslant 6\omega_r^\sigma\left(\frac{1}{\nu}; f\right), \qquad (\nu = 1, 2, \ldots). \tag{3.6}$$

From (3.1) we find that†

$$\left.\begin{aligned} u_\nu(\theta) - f(\theta) &= \frac{3}{\pi\nu(2\nu^2+1)} \int_0^{\frac{\pi}{2}} \left(\frac{\sin \nu t}{\sin t}\right)^4 A(t, \theta)\, dt, \\ A(t, \theta) &= f(\theta + 2t) + f(\theta - 2t) - 2f(\theta). \end{aligned}\right\} \tag{3.7}$$

Since the norm of the sum is never greater than the sum of the norms, we obtain

$$\| u_\nu(\theta) - f(\theta) \|_r^\sigma \leqslant \frac{3}{\pi\nu(2\nu^2+1)} \int_0^{\frac{\pi}{2}} \left(\frac{\sin \nu t}{\sin t}\right)^4 \| A(t, \theta) \|_r^\sigma\, dt.$$

Using (3.3), we arrive at

$$\begin{aligned} \| A(t, \theta) \|_r^\sigma &\leqslant \| f(\theta + 2t) - f(\theta) \|_r^\sigma + \| f(\theta) - f(\theta - 2t) \|_r^\sigma \leqslant \\ &\leqslant 2\omega_r^\sigma(2|t|; f) \leqslant 2(2\nu|t| + 1)\, \omega_r^\sigma\left(\frac{1}{\nu}; f\right), \end{aligned}$$

if, following de la Vallée Poussin, we write $\lambda = 2\nu\,|t|$, $\delta = 1/\nu$. This then gives us‡

$$\begin{aligned} \| u_\nu(\theta) - f(\theta) \|_r^\sigma &\leqslant \omega_r^\sigma\left(\frac{1}{\nu}; f\right) \times \\ &\times \frac{6}{\pi\nu(2\nu^2+1)} \int_0^{\frac{\pi}{2}} \left(\frac{\sin \nu t}{\sin t}\right)^4 (2\nu t + 1)\, dt \leqslant 6\omega_r^\sigma\left(\frac{1}{\nu}; f\right). \end{aligned}$$

* See, for instance, N. I. Akhiezer [2], Section 80.
† See, for instance, I. P. Natanson [1], p. 116.
‡ I. P. Natanson [1], pp. 116-117.

Let us apply the above considerations to the function $f(\theta) = \pi_0(\theta)$ [see (2.7)]; since for this case we have

$$\|\pi_0(\theta)\|_2^\sigma = 1, \qquad \|\pi_0(\theta)\|_1 = \left\| \frac{1}{\sqrt{p(\theta)}} \right\|_1,$$

we will assume that $\frac{1}{\sqrt{p(\theta)}} \in L_1$.

We introduce the notation

$$\delta_n' = \sup_{|h| \leqslant \frac{1}{n}} \left\| \frac{\pi_0(\theta+h) - \pi_0(\theta)}{\pi_0(\theta)} \right\|_2 = \sup_{|h| \leqslant \frac{1}{n}} \left\| \frac{\pi(e^{i(\theta+h)}) - \pi(e^{i\theta})}{\pi(e^{i\theta})} \right\|_2 =$$

$$= \omega_2^{\sigma_0}\left(\frac{1}{n};\, \pi_0\right), \qquad d\sigma_0 = p(\theta)\, d\theta. \quad (3.8)$$

Since in our case $\pi(z) \in H_1$, it follows that $u_\nu(\theta)$ is a polynomial of degree $2\nu - 2$ in $e^{i\theta}$; denoting by $2\nu' - 2$ the largest positive integer $\leq n$, the above lemma shows that

$$\delta_n = \left\| \pi_0(\theta) - \frac{a_n}{a} \varphi_n^*(e^{i\theta}) \right\|_2^\sigma \leqslant \left\| \pi_0(\theta) - \frac{a_{2\nu-2}}{a} \varphi_{2\nu-2}^*(e^{i\theta}) \right\|_2^\sigma \leqslant$$

$$\leqslant \|\pi_0(\theta) - u_\nu(\theta)\|_2^\sigma \leqslant 6\omega_2^\sigma\left(\frac{1}{\nu};\, \pi_0\right).$$

Since

$$2\nu - 2 \geqslant n - 1,\ \frac{1}{n} \leqslant \frac{2}{n+1} < \frac{2}{n},\ \omega_2^\sigma\left(\frac{1}{\nu};\, \pi_0\right) \leqslant 2\omega_2^\sigma\left(\frac{1}{n};\, \pi_0\right),$$

$$\|\pi_0(\theta+h) - \pi_0(\theta)\|_2^\sigma \leqslant \|\pi_0(\theta+h) - \pi_0(\theta)\|_2^{\sigma_1} +$$

$$+ \left\| \frac{\pi_0(\theta) + h) - \pi_0(\theta)}{\pi_0(\theta)} \right\|_2,$$

we arrive at

$$\delta_n \leqslant 6\omega_2^\sigma\left(\frac{1}{\nu};\, \pi_0\right) \leqslant 12\omega_2^\sigma\left(\frac{1}{n};\, \pi_0\right) \leqslant$$

$$\leqslant 12 \sup_{|h| \leqslant \frac{1}{n}} \|\pi_0(\theta+h)\|_2^{\sigma_1} + 12\delta_n'. \quad (3.9)$$

Consider the expression

$$\|\pi_0(\theta+h)\|_2^{\sigma_1} = \sqrt{\frac{1}{2\pi} \int_0^{2\pi} \frac{d\sigma_1(\theta)}{p_0(\theta+h)}},$$

where, in agreement with (2.7), we have written

$$\frac{1}{p_0(\theta)} = |\pi_0(\theta)|^2 = \frac{1}{p(\theta)} \gamma_E(\theta).$$

Let E_h be the set obtained by displacing the set CE, the complement of E, a distance h, where $|h| \le h_0$; then if $\theta \overline{\in} E$ we have $\theta + h \in E_h$. If $\frac{1}{p_0(\theta)} \leqslant M$ on E_h, then for $\theta \overline{\in} E$ it follows that $\frac{1}{p_0(\theta + h)} \leqslant M$, so that

$$\|\pi_0(\theta + h)\|_2^{\sigma_1} \leqslant \sqrt{M} \cdot \sqrt{\frac{1}{2\pi} \int_0^{2\pi} d\sigma_1(\theta)} \leqslant \sqrt{c_0 M}. \quad (3.9')$$

If, however, $1/p_0(\theta)$ is uniformly continuous on E_h with modulus of continuity $\omega'(\delta; 1/p_0)$, we obtain

$$\leqslant \sqrt{\sup_{|h| \leqslant \delta} \frac{1}{2\pi} \int_0^{2\pi} \left| \frac{1}{p_0(\theta + h)} - \frac{1}{p_0(\theta)} \right| d\sigma_1(\theta)} \leqslant$$

$$\leqslant \sqrt{c_0 \omega'\left(\delta; \frac{1}{p_0}\right)},$$

so that for this case we arrive at

$$\delta_n \leqslant 12 \left[\sqrt{c_0} \cdot \sqrt{\omega'\left(\frac{1}{n}; \frac{1}{p_0}\right)} + \delta'_n \right]. \quad (3.9'')$$

Let us obtain some estimates for the δ'_n.

Theorem 3.1. Assume that for h of sufficiently small modulus the integral

$$\int_0^{2\pi} \frac{p(\theta + h)}{p(\theta)} d\theta \quad (3.10)$$

exists. Then

$$\delta_n' \leqslant \sqrt{I\left(\frac{1}{n}\right)}, \quad I(\delta) = \sup_{|h| \leqslant \delta} \left\| \frac{p(\theta+h) - p(\theta)}{p(\theta)} \right\|_1^{*}; \quad (3.11)$$

$$\delta_n' \leqslant \sup_{|\delta| \leqslant \frac{1}{n}} \left\| \frac{\sqrt{p(\theta)} - \sqrt{p(\theta-\delta)}}{\sqrt{p(\theta)}} \right\|_2 + C\omega_4\left(\frac{1}{n};\ \ln p\right)^{\dagger}. \quad (3.12)$$

We have

$$\frac{1}{2\pi i} \int\limits_{|z|=1} \left| \frac{\pi(ze^{i\delta})}{\pi(z)} - 1 \right|^2 \frac{dz}{z} =$$

$$= \frac{1}{2\pi i} \int\limits_{|z|=1} \left| \frac{\pi(ze^{i\delta})}{\pi(z)} \right|^2 \frac{dz}{z} - 2\Re\left\{ \frac{1}{2\pi i} \int\limits_{|z|=1} \frac{\pi(ze^{i\delta})}{\pi(z)} \cdot \frac{dz}{z} \right\} + 1.$$

Since $\ln \left| \frac{\pi(e^{i(\theta+\delta)})}{\pi(e^{i\theta})} \right| = \frac{1}{2} \ln \frac{p(\theta)}{p(\theta+\delta)} \in L_1$, it follows from (3.10) that $\frac{\pi(ze^{i\delta})}{\pi(z)} \in H_2$; and therefore

$$\frac{1}{2\pi i} \int\limits_{|z|=1} \frac{\pi(ze^{i\delta})}{\pi(z)} \cdot \frac{dz}{z} = 1,$$

$$\left\| \frac{\pi(e^{i(\theta+\delta)}) - \pi(e^{i\theta})}{\pi(e^{i\theta})} \right\|_2 = \sqrt{\frac{1}{2\pi} \int_0^{2\pi} \frac{p(\theta)}{p(\theta+\delta)}\, d\theta - 1},$$

which implies (3.11).

To prove (3.12) we note that according to (2.6)

$$\frac{\pi(e^{i(\theta+\delta)})}{\pi(e^{i\theta})} - 1 = \sqrt{\frac{p(\theta)}{p(\theta+\delta)}}\, e^{i\gamma} - 1,$$

$$\gamma = \arg \pi(e^{i(\theta+\delta)}) - \arg \pi(e^{i\theta}).$$

We thus obtain

$$\left| \frac{\pi(e^{i(\theta+\delta)})}{\pi(e^{i\theta})} - 1 \right|^2 = \left(\sqrt{\frac{p(\theta)}{p(\theta+\delta)}} - 1 \right)^2 + 2\sqrt{\frac{p(\theta)}{p(\theta+\delta)}} \times$$

$$\times (1 - \cos\gamma) \leqslant \left(\sqrt{\frac{p(\theta)}{p(\theta+\delta)}} - 1 \right)^2 + \sqrt{\frac{p(\theta)}{p(\theta+\delta)}} \cdot \gamma^2. \quad (3.13)$$

* This characterization was first introduced by G. Freud [1].

† Here C and in the sequel $C_1, C_2, \ldots$ are independent of n.

and it therefore follows from the Bunyakovskii-Schwarz inequality that

$$\left\|\frac{\pi(e^{i(\theta+\delta)})-\pi(e^{i\theta})}{\pi(e^{i\theta})}\right\|_2 \leqslant \left\|\frac{\sqrt{p(\theta-\delta)}-\sqrt{p(\theta)}}{\sqrt{p(\theta)}}\right\|_2 + \\ + \|\gamma\|_4 \cdot \left\|\sqrt[4]{\frac{p(\theta-\delta)}{p(\theta)}}\right\|_4. \quad (3.13')$$

According to (2.6), the function

$$\gamma = \arg \pi(e^{i(\theta+\delta)}) - \arg \pi(e^{i\theta})$$

is a harmonic function conjugate to

$$\ln \frac{1}{\sqrt{p(\theta+\delta)}} - \ln \frac{1}{\sqrt{p(\theta)}}.$$

Therefore from the theorem of M. Riesz [1] it follows that for any $r > 1$ we have

$$\|\gamma\|_r \leqslant C\|\ln p(\theta+\delta) - \ln p(\theta)\|_r; \quad (3.14)$$

setting $r = 4$ and making use of the existence of the integral in (3.10) we arrive at (3.12).

3.3. We now turn our attention to some cases for which we can establish simple sufficient conditions for the existence of the integral in (3.10) and can evaluate the δ_n' *in terms of the integral moduli of continuity*; these conditions are all tabulated in Table I at the back of the book.

Condition I is the most restrictive; the estimate corresponding to it is obtained from (3.13)

$$\left|\frac{\pi(e^{i(\theta+\delta)})-\pi(e^{i\theta})}{\pi(e^{i\theta})}\right| \leqslant \frac{|p(\theta+\delta)-p(\theta)|}{\sqrt{p(\theta+\delta)}\{\sqrt{p(\theta+\delta)}+\sqrt{p(\theta)}\}} + \\ + \sqrt[4]{\frac{M}{m}}|\gamma| \leqslant \frac{1}{2m}|p(\theta+\delta)-p(\theta)| + \sqrt[4]{\frac{M}{m}}\cdot\gamma,$$

as well as from (3.14) with $r = 2$ and from the inequality

$$\frac{1}{k}|\ln p(\theta+\delta) - \ln p(\theta)| \leqslant \\ \leqslant \frac{1}{\sqrt[k]{m}}\left|\sqrt[k]{p(\theta+\delta)} - \sqrt[k]{p(\theta)}\right|, \quad p(\theta) \geqslant m. \quad (3.15)$$

When condition II is fulfilled, the existence of the integral (3.10) is obvious; then from (3.11) and (3.12) we obtain

$$\delta_n' \leqslant C_1 \sqrt{\omega_1\left(\frac{1}{n};\ p\right)},$$

$$\delta_n' \leqslant C_2\omega_2\left(\frac{1}{n};\ \sqrt{p}\right) + C_3\omega_4\left(\frac{1}{n};\ \ln p\right).$$

Under condition III, the existence of the integral (3.10) follows from Hölder's inequality; in the same way as above we obtain our estimate from (3.13').

To derive condition IV, note that $I(\delta)$ [see (3.11)] remains unchanged if $p(\theta)$ is replaced by $1/p(\theta)$, so that condition IV follows from II. Condition V is obvious.

3.4. In what follows we shall need an estimate for the sums

$$K_n(z,\ z) = \sum_{k=0}^{n} |\varphi_k(z)|^2, \qquad |z| = 1. \tag{3.16}$$

Theorem 3.3. 1) If $\sigma(\theta)$ satisfies the condition

$$\sigma(\theta_2) - \sigma(\theta_1) \geqslant m(\theta_2 - \theta_1), \quad 0 \leqslant \theta_1 < \theta_2 \leqslant 2\pi, \quad m > 0, \tag{3.17}$$

then

$$K_n(e^{i\theta},\ e^{i\theta}) \leqslant \frac{n+1}{m}, \qquad 0 \leqslant \theta \leqslant 2\pi. \tag{3.18}$$

2) If $\sigma(\theta)$ is absolutely continuous on $[0,\ 2\pi]$, and if $p(\theta) \leq M$ almost everywhere in $[0,\ 2\pi]$, then

$$K_n(e^{i\theta},\ e^{i\theta}) \geqslant \frac{n+1}{M}, \qquad 0 \leqslant \theta \leqslant 2\pi. \tag{3.19}$$

According to (1.10),

$$\frac{1}{K_n(e^{i\theta_0},\ e^{i\theta_0})} = \min_{G_n} \frac{1}{2\pi} \int_0^{2\pi} \left| \frac{G_n(e^{i\theta})}{G_n(e^{i\theta_0})} \right|^2 d\sigma(\theta). \tag{3.20}$$

If we have two measures $d\sigma^{(1)}(\theta)$ and $d\sigma^{(2)}(\theta)$ such that

$$\left.\begin{aligned} \sigma^{(1)}(\theta_2) - \sigma^{(1)}(\theta_1) \leqslant \sigma(\theta_2) - \sigma(\theta_1) \leqslant \sigma^{(2)}(\theta_2) - \sigma^{(2)}(\theta_1), \\ 0 \leqslant \theta_1 < \theta_2 \leqslant 2\pi, \end{aligned}\right\} \tag{3.21}$$

then obviously

$$\sum_{k=0}^{n} |\varphi_k^{(2)}(e^{i\theta_0})|^2 = K_n^{(2)}(e^{i\theta_0}, e^{i\theta_0}) \leqslant K_n(e^{i\theta_0}, e^{i\theta_0}) \leqslant$$
$$\leqslant K_n^{(1)}(e^{i\theta_0}, e^{i\theta_0}) = \sum_{k=0}^{n} |\varphi_k^{(1)}(e^{i\theta_0})|^2, \quad (3.22)$$

where the polynomials $\{\varphi_k^{(1)}(z)\}$ and $\{\varphi_k^{(2)}(z)\}$ are orthonormal with respect to the measures $d\sigma^{(1)}(\theta)$ and $d\sigma^{(2)}(\theta)$, respectively.

Now (3.21) follows from (3.17) if we set $d\sigma^{(1)}(\theta) = m\, d(\theta)$; then, as is easily seen, $\varphi_k^{(1)}(z) = z^k/\sqrt{m}$, and therefore $K_n^{(1)}(e^{i\theta_0}, e^{i\theta_0}) = =(n+1)/m$.

For condition 2), we set $d\sigma^{(2)}(\theta) = M\, d\theta$, obtaining

$$\sigma(\theta_2) - \sigma(\theta_1) = \int_{\theta_1}^{\theta_2} p(\theta)\, d\theta \leqslant M(\theta_2 - \theta_1) = [\sigma^{(2)}(\theta_2) - \sigma^{(2)}(\theta_1)],$$

whence we arrive at

$$K_n(e^{i\theta_0}, e^{i\theta_0}) \geqslant K_n^{(2)}(e^{i\theta_0}, e^{i\theta_0}) = \frac{n+1}{M}.$$

Remark 3.1. The estimate of (3.18) was obtained by using (3.17). A method due to Freud [1] can be used to show that

$$K_n(e^{i\theta}, e^{i\theta}) \leqslant C(n+1) \qquad (n = 0, 1, 2, \ldots) \quad (3.23)$$

almost everywhere in $[0, 2\pi]$, under the following conditions: $\sigma(\theta)$ is absolutely continuous on $[0, 2\pi]$, for sufficiently small h

$$\frac{p(\theta+h) - p(\theta)}{p(\theta)} \in L_1 \quad (3.24)$$

and, finally,

$$I(\delta) \leqslant C\left(\ln\frac{1}{\delta}\right)^{-\alpha}, \qquad \alpha > 1. \quad (3.25)$$

In particular, if

$$p(\theta) \in L_r, \qquad \frac{1}{p(\theta)} \in L_{r'}, \qquad \frac{1}{r} + \frac{1}{r'} = 1, \quad (3.26)$$

it is easily seen that Freud's condition (3.25) is fulfilled if

$$\omega_r(\delta;\ p) \leqslant C\left(\ln\frac{1}{\delta}\right)^{-\alpha}, \qquad \alpha > 1. \tag{3.27}$$

3.5. Theorem 3.4. If

$$\int_0^{2\pi} \ln \sigma'(\theta)\, d\theta > -\infty, \tag{3.28}$$

then the series

$$\sum_{n=0}^{\infty} \left| \frac{\varphi_n(e^{i\theta})}{\sqrt{K_n(e^{i\theta}, e^{i\theta})}} \right|^4 < \infty, \qquad 0 \leqslant \theta \leqslant 2\pi \tag{3.29}$$

converges.

To prove this, consider a new measure $d\sigma^{(1)}(\theta)$, which differs from $d\sigma(\theta)$ by the addition of a point mass equal to μ at a point θ_0, and let

$$\varphi_n^{(1)}(z) = \alpha_n^{(1)} z^n + \ldots \qquad (n = 0, 1, 2, \ldots)$$

denote polynomials orthonormal with respect to $d\sigma^{(1)}(\theta)$. We will show that

$$\frac{\alpha_n}{\alpha_n^{(1)}} \varphi_n^{(1)}(z) = \varphi_n(z) - \frac{\mu \varphi_n(z_0) K_{n-1}(z, z_0)}{1 + \mu K_{n-1}(z_0, z_0)}, \qquad z_0 = e^{i\theta_0}. \tag{3.30}$$

Indeed, from this expression we obtain

$$\frac{\alpha_n}{\alpha_n^{(1)}} \cdot \frac{1}{2\pi} \int_0^{2\pi} \varphi_n^{(1)}(e^{i\theta}) \overline{\varphi_k(e^{i\theta})}\, d\sigma^{(1)}(\theta) =$$

$$= \frac{1}{2\pi} \int_0^{2\pi} \varphi_n(e^{i\theta}) \overline{\varphi_k(e^{i\theta})}\, d\sigma^{(1)}(\theta) -$$

$$- \frac{\mu \varphi_n(z_0)}{1 + \mu K_{n-1}(z_0, z_0)} \cdot \frac{1}{2\pi} \int^{2\pi} K_{n-1}(e^{i\theta}, z_0) \overline{\varphi_k(e^{i\theta})}\, d\sigma^{(1)}(\theta),$$

which leads in a simple way to

$$\frac{\alpha_n}{\alpha_n^{(1)}} \cdot \frac{1}{2\pi} \int_0^{2\pi} \varphi_n^{(1)}(e^{i\theta}) \overline{\varphi_k(e^{i\theta})}\, d\sigma^{(1)}(\theta) =$$

$$= \frac{1}{2\pi} \int_0^{2\pi} \varphi_n(e^{i\theta}) \overline{\varphi_k(e^{i\theta})}\, d\sigma(\theta) + \mu\varphi_n(z_0)\overline{\varphi_k(z_0)} -$$

$$- \frac{\mu\varphi_n(z_0)}{1+\mu K_{n-1}(z_0, z_0)} \cdot \left\{ \frac{1}{2\pi} \int_0^{2\pi} K_{n-1}(e^{i\theta}, z_0) \overline{\varphi_k(e^{i\theta})}\, d\sigma(\theta) + \right.$$

$$\left. + \mu K_{n-1}(z_0, z_0) \overline{\varphi_k(z_0)} \right\}.$$

Thus for k = 0, 1, . . . , n - 1, we have

$$\frac{1}{2\pi} \int_0^{2\pi} \varphi_n^{(1)}(e^{i\theta}) \overline{\varphi_k(e^{i\theta})}\, d\sigma^{(1)}(\theta) = 0.$$

Setting z = 0 in (3.30) and using (1.9), we arrive at

$$\frac{\mu\varphi_n(z_0)\varphi_{n-1}^{*}(z_0)}{1+\mu K_{n-1}(z_0, z_0)} = \frac{\varphi_n(0)}{\alpha_{n-1}} - \frac{\alpha_n\varphi_n^{(1)}(0)}{\alpha_n^{(1)}\alpha_{n-1}}.$$

From (1.2') we obtain

$$\left| \frac{\alpha_{n-1}\varphi_n^{*}(z_0)}{\alpha_n\varphi_{n-1}^{*}(z_0)} \right| = \left| 1 + \frac{z_0\overline{\varphi_n(0)}\varphi_{n-1}(z_0)}{\alpha_n\varphi_{n-1}^{*}(z_0)} \right| \leqslant$$

$$\leqslant 1 + \frac{|\varphi_n(0)|}{\alpha_n} \leqslant 1 + \alpha_{n-1}\sqrt{c_0},$$

since according to (1.4) and (1.3), $|\varphi_n(0)| \leq \alpha_n\alpha_{n-1}\sqrt{c_0}$. Therefore

$$\frac{\mu\alpha_0 |\varphi_n^{*}(z_0)|^2}{(1+\alpha\sqrt{c_0})[1+\mu K_{n-1}(z_0, z_0)]} \leqslant$$

$$\leqslant \frac{\mu\alpha_{n-1}|\varphi_n^{*}(z_0)|^2}{\alpha_n(1+\alpha_{n-1}\sqrt{c_0})[1+\mu K_{n-1}(z_0, z_0)]} \leqslant \frac{\mu|\varphi_n(z_0)\varphi_{n-1}^{*}(z_0)|}{1+\mu K_{n-1}(z_0, z_0)} \leqslant$$

$$\leqslant \frac{|\varphi_n(0)|}{\alpha_0} + \frac{\alpha|\varphi_n^{(1)}(0)|}{\alpha_0\alpha_0^{(1)}}.$$

and setting $\mu > 1/\alpha_0^2$, we obtain $1+\mu K_{n-1}(z_0, z_0) < 2\mu K_n(z_0, z_0)$ and thus arrive at

$$\frac{|\overset{*}{\varphi}_n(z_0)|^2}{K_n(z_0, z_0)} \leqslant \frac{2\alpha(1+\alpha\sqrt{c_0})}{\alpha_0^2}\left\{\frac{|\varphi_n(0)|}{\alpha}+\frac{|\varphi_n^{(1)}(0)|}{\alpha_0^{(1)}}\right\}.$$

Since the integral of (3.28) exists by assumption, the two series

$$\sum_{n=0}^{\infty}|\varphi_n(0)|^2, \quad \sum_{n=0}^{\infty}|\varphi_n^{(1)}(0)|^2$$

converge, and then (3.29) follows.

From the theorem just proved we obtain the estimate

$$|\overset{*}{\varphi}_n(e^{i\theta})| = o\left\{\sqrt{K_n(e^{i\theta}, e^{i\theta})}\right\}, \quad 0 \leqslant \theta \leqslant 2\pi. \tag{3.31}$$

Theorems (3.3) and (3.4) lead to an estimate for the orthonormal polynomials.

Theorem 3.5. If $\sigma(\theta)$ satisfies the condition

$$\sigma(\theta_2)-\sigma(\theta_1) \geqslant m(\theta_2-\theta_1), \quad 0 \leqslant \theta_1 < \theta_2 \leqslant 2\pi, \quad m > 0, \tag{3.32}$$

then

$$|\varphi_n(e^{i\theta})| = o\left(\sqrt{n}\right), \qquad 0 \leqslant \theta \leqslant 2\pi. \tag{3.33}$$

Indeed, from (3.29) and (3.18) we have

$$|\varphi_n(e^{i\theta})| = o\left\{\sqrt{K_n(e^{i\theta}, e^{i\theta})}\right\} = o(\sqrt{n}).$$

3.6. We now present some more accurate estimates of orthonormal polynomials on the entire circumference $|z| = 1$.

Theorem 3.6. If the integral of (3.28) exists, then in the closed circle $|z| \leq 1$ we have

$$|\overset{*}{\varphi}_n(z)| \leqslant \max_{0\leqslant\theta\leqslant 2\pi}|\pi(re^{i\theta})| \cdot \left\{C_1+C_2\sqrt{n}\,\delta_n\right\}, \quad r = 1-\frac{1}{2n}. \tag{3.34}$$

If $1/p_0(\theta)$ is continuous on the set E_h with modulus of continuity $\omega'(\delta; 1/p_0)$, then for $|z| \leq 1$ we have

$$|\varphi_n^*(z)| \leqslant \max_{0 \leqslant \theta \leqslant 2\pi} |\pi(re^{i\theta})| \cdot \left\{ C_1 + C_3 \sqrt{n} \left[\sqrt{\omega'\left(\frac{1}{n}; \frac{1}{p_0}\right)} + \delta_n' \right] \right\}, \quad r = 1 - \frac{1}{2n}, \quad (3.35)$$

with the estimates given in Table I for the δ_n'.*

Recalling (1.9) and (2.1), we have

$$|\alpha\pi(re^{i\theta}) - \alpha_n\varphi_n^*(re^{i\theta})| = \left| \sum_{k=n+1}^{\infty} \varphi_k(re^{i\theta}) \overline{\varphi_k(0)} \right| \leqslant$$

$$\leqslant \sqrt{\sum_{k=n+1}^{\infty} |\varphi_k(re^{i\theta})|^2 \cdot \sum_{k=n+1}^{\infty} |\varphi_k(0)|^2}; \quad (3.36)$$

then from (1.7) and (2.1) we find that

$$\sum_{k=n+1}^{\infty} |\varphi_k(re^{i\theta})|^2 \leqslant \sum_{k=0}^{\infty} |\varphi_k(re^{i\theta})|^2 = \frac{|\pi(re^{i\theta})|^2}{1-r^2}, \quad r < 1.$$

Using (2.8), Eq. (3.36) leads to

$$|\alpha\pi(re^{i\theta}) - \alpha_n\varphi_n^*(re^{i\theta})| \leqslant \frac{|\pi(re^{i\theta})| a\delta_n}{\sqrt{1-r}}. \quad (3.37)$$

From this, setting $r = 1 - 1/2n$, we arrive at

$$|\varphi_n^*(re^{i\theta})| \leqslant \frac{\alpha}{\alpha_n} |\pi(re^{i\theta})| (1 + \sqrt{2n}\,\delta_n) \leqslant$$

$$\leqslant \frac{\alpha}{\alpha_0} |\pi(re^{i\theta})| (1 + \sqrt{2n}\,\delta_n). (3.38)$$

Let

$$M_n = |\varphi_n^*(e^{i\theta_0})| = \max |\varphi_n^*(e^{i\theta})|, \quad 0 \leqslant \theta \leqslant 2\pi, \quad (3.39)$$

so that

$$\varphi_n^*(e^{i\theta_0}) - \varphi_n^*(re^{i\theta_c}) = \int_{rz_0}^{z_0} \frac{d\varphi_n^*(z)}{dz}\, dz, \quad z_0 = e^{i\theta_0},$$

---

* Here C, C_1, C_2, . . . , are constants independent of $\underline{n}$.

from which it is a simple matter to arrive at

$$|\varphi_n^*(e^{i\theta_0}) - \varphi_n^*(re^{i\theta})| \leqslant (1-r) \max_{|z|\leqslant 1} \left|\frac{d\varphi_n^*(z)}{dz}\right|. \quad (3.40)$$

It is well known that if

$$|\varphi_n^*(z)| \leqslant M_n, \quad |z| \leqslant 1, \quad (3.41)$$

then*

$$\left|\frac{d\varphi_n^*(z)}{dz}\right| \leqslant nM_n, \quad |z| \leqslant 1, \quad (3.42)$$

so that if we set $r = 1 - 1/2n$, we arrive at

$$|\varphi_n^*(e^{i\theta_0}) - \varphi_n^*(re^{i\theta_0})| \leqslant (1-r)\, nM_n = \frac{M_n}{2}. \quad (3.42')$$

This in turn leads to†

$$|\varphi_n^*(re^{i\theta_0})| \geqslant \frac{M_n}{2}, \quad r = 1 - \frac{1}{2n}. \quad (3.43)$$

Setting $\theta = \theta_0$, in the (3.38), we arrive at

$$\frac{M_n}{2} \leqslant |\varphi_n^*(re^{i\theta_0})| \leqslant \frac{\alpha}{\alpha_0} |\pi(re^{i\theta_0})| (1 + \sqrt{2n}\,\delta_n),$$

from which (3.34) is obtained.

3.7. Some rather simple estimates obtain from Theorem 3.6.

Theorem 3.7. If $\sigma(\theta)$ is such that

$$\sigma(\theta_2) - \sigma(\theta_1) \geqslant m(\theta_2 - \theta_1), \quad 0 \leqslant \theta_1 < \theta_2 \leqslant 2\pi, \quad m > 0, \quad (3.44)$$

then in the closed circle $|z| \leq 1$,

$$|\varphi_n^*(z)| \leqslant \frac{1}{\sqrt{m}} (C_1 + C_2 \sqrt{n}\,\delta_n) \leqslant$$

$$\leqslant \frac{1}{\sqrt{m}} \left\{ C_1 + C_3 \sqrt{n} \left(\sqrt{\omega'\left(\frac{1}{n}; \frac{1}{p_0}\right)} + \delta'_n \right) \right\}. \quad (3.45)$$

* See O. Szasz, [1]; this inequality, however, follows from S. N. Bernshtein's well-known inequality for the derivative of a trigonometric polynomial.

† The method used here for obtaining (3.43) is due to D. Jackson [1], Chapter III, Section 3.

By using Table I, we easily obtain conditions IV-VII of Table II. We will say that the function $\sigma(\theta) \in A$ if it is absolutely continuous throughout $[0, 2\pi]$ and if almost everywhere on this interval it satisfies the inequalities

$$0 < m \leqslant p(\theta) \leqslant M. \tag{3.46}$$

Then if $\sigma(\theta) \in A$, condition I of Table I gives

$$|\varphi_n^*(z)| \leqslant C_1 + C_2 \sqrt{n} \left\{ \omega_r \left(\frac{1}{n}; p \right) \right\}^{\frac{r}{2}}, |z| \leqslant 1, r = 1 \text{ or } 2. \tag{3.47}$$

From this we easily obtain the condition that the orthonormal system be uniformly bounded in the closed circle $|z| \leq 1$.

Theorem 3.8. Let $\sigma(\theta) \in A$ and $p(\theta) \in \text{Lip}\left(\frac{1}{2}, 2\right)$. Then in the closed circle $|z| \leq 1$ we have

$$|\varphi_n^*(z)| \leqslant C, \tag{3.48}$$

where C is independent of both z and n.

To prove this it is sufficient to study condition I of Table I, for which in the present case we have $\omega_2(\delta; p) \leq C_1 \sqrt{\delta}$.

Remark 3.2. We may replace the requirement that $p(\theta) \in \text{Lip}\left(\frac{1}{2}, 2\right)$ by another sufficient condition, namely that the Fourier coefficients of $p(\theta)$ be $O(1/n)$. In fact it has been shown by Hardy and Littlewood that this condition implies that

$$p(\theta) \in \text{Lip}\left(\frac{1}{2}, 2\right).$$

Theorem 3.8 may be stated in yet another way.

Theorem 3.8'. If $\sigma(\theta)$ is absolutely continuous in $[0, 2\pi]$, and if $p(\theta)$ has bounded variation in $[0, 2\pi]$ and satisfies

$$0 < m \leqslant p(\theta) \tag{3.49}$$

almost everywhere in $[0, 2\pi]$, then (3.48) holds.

Indeed, Hardy and Littlewood [1] have shown that the bounded variation of $p(\theta)$ is equivalent to the condition that $p(\theta) \in \text{Lip}(1,1)$;

they have shown also that from this second condition it follows that

$p(\theta) \in \mathrm{Lip}\left(\frac{1}{r}, r\right), r > 1$, and therefore that

$$p(\theta) \in \mathrm{Lip}\left(\frac{1}{2}, 2\right).$$

3.8. Let us now turn our attention to some necessary conditions for uniform boundedness.

Theorem 3.9. If there exists a subsequence of orthonormal polynomials $\{\varphi_{n_\nu}(z)\}$ uniformly bounded on the entire circumference $|z| = 1$, then

$$\int_0^{2\pi} \ln \sigma'(\theta)\, d\theta > -\infty. \tag{3.50}$$

Indeed, as a result of the compactness principle,

$$|\overset{*}{\varphi}_{n_\nu}(z)| \leqslant a, \quad |z| = 1 \quad (\nu = 1, 2, \ldots) \tag{3.51}$$

implies the uniform convergence

$$\lim_{k\to\infty} \overset{*}{\varphi}_{n_k}(z) = \varphi(z), \quad |z| \leqslant r < 1, \tag{3.52}$$

of some subsequence, where $\varphi(z)$ is an analytic function regular for $|z| < 1$. This then implies (3.50) as a result of the equivalence of f) and a) of proposition 15, Chapter I. Thus the uniform convergence of the subsequence $\{\varphi_{n_\nu}(z)\}$ on the circumference $|z| = 1$ implies that the orthogonal set is not closed in L_2^σ.

We now show that if the conditions of the above theorem are satisfied, one can obtain a more exact result than (3.50).

Theorem 3.10. If there exists a subsequence $\{\varphi_{n_\nu}(z)\}$ uniformly bounded on the entire circumference $|z| = 1$, i.e., if

$$|\varphi_{n_\nu}(z)| \leqslant a \quad (\nu = 1, 2, \ldots), \tag{3.53}$$

then for any two points $\theta_1, \theta_2 \in [0, 2\pi]$ at which $\sigma(\theta)$ is continuous, we have

$$\sigma(\theta_2) - \sigma(\theta_1) \geqslant \frac{\theta_2 - \theta_1}{a^2}. \tag{3.54}$$

To prove this we use (1.20), which we restate in the form

$$\frac{1}{2\pi}\int_0^{2\pi} \psi_{n_\nu}(\theta)\, e^{ik\theta}\, d\theta = \frac{1}{2\pi}\int_0^{2\pi} e^{ik\theta}\, d\sigma(\theta)$$

$$(k = 0, \pm 1, \ldots, \pm n_\nu), \tag{3.55}$$

$$\psi_r(\theta) = \frac{1}{|\varphi_r(e^{i\theta})|^2}.$$

Now the nondecreasing functions

$$\mu_{n_\nu}(\theta) = \int_0^\theta \psi_{n_\nu}(\theta)\, d\theta, \quad 0 \leqslant \theta \leqslant 2\pi \tag{3.56}$$

are uniformly bounded, so that according to Helly's known theorem

there exists a subsequence $\mu_{n_s}(\theta)$ which converges to some nondecreasing function $\mu(\theta)$.

$$\lim_{s\to\infty} \mu_{n_s}(\theta) = \mu(\theta) \tag{3.57}$$

at all of its points of continuity; from Helly's second theorem we obtain

$$\lim_{s\to\infty} \frac{1}{2\pi}\int_0^{2\pi} e^{ik\theta}\, d\mu_{n_s}(\theta) = \lim_{s\to\infty} \frac{1}{2\pi}\int_0^{2\pi} e^{ik\theta}\psi_{n_s}(\theta)\, d\theta =$$

$$= \frac{1}{2\pi}\int_0^{2\pi} e^{ik\theta}\, d\mu(\theta) = \frac{1}{2\pi}\int_0^{2\pi} e^{ik\theta}\, d\sigma(\theta) \quad (k = 0, \pm 1, \pm 2, \ldots),$$

from which it follows that $\mu(\theta) = \sigma(\theta) + C$, since the trigonometric moment problem has a unique solution. Hence

$$\lim_{s\to\infty} \frac{1}{2\pi}\int_0^{\theta} \frac{d\theta}{|\varphi_{n_s}(e^{i\theta})|^2} = \frac{\sigma(\theta)}{2\pi} + C.$$

If θ_1, θ_2 are points of continuity of $\sigma(\theta)$, we obtain

$$\lim_{s\to\infty} \frac{1}{2\pi}\int_{\theta_1}^{\theta_2} \frac{d\theta}{|\varphi_{n_s}(e^{i\theta})|^2} = \frac{\sigma(\theta_2) - \sigma(\theta_1)}{2\pi}.$$

But (3.53) implies

$$\frac{1}{2\pi}\int_{\theta_1}^{\theta_2}\frac{d\theta}{|\varphi_{n_s}(e^{i\theta})|^2}\geqslant\frac{1}{a^2}\cdot\frac{1}{2\pi}\int_{\theta_1}^{\theta_2}d\theta=\frac{\theta_2-\theta_1}{2\pi a^2},$$

and this in turn implies (3.54).

Remark 3.3. We have thus shown that (3.44), or the condition $p(\theta) \geq m > 0$, $0 \leq \theta \leq 2\pi$ following from it, as has been conjectured by Steklov [2], is a condition for uniform boundedness of the orthonormal set on the interval $[0, 2\pi]$; we have proven, however, only the necessity of this condition, for in the sufficient conditions we have formulated above we were forced to subject $p(\theta)$ to additional requirements, e.g., that its variation be bounded on $[0, 2\pi]$.

Table II presents a summary of the estimates of which the author is aware. Condition II was treated by Freud [1], and the estimate given is valid almost everywhere in $[0, 2\pi]$. Condition III was dealt with by Szegö [1], Chapter VII, and Shohat [1], and condition IX by Korous [1]. Condition IX has as consequences cases VII and VIII, which, however, are more general than IX, since they do not require the continuity of $p(\theta)$. If, however, this function is assumed continuous, IX can be replaced by the much less restrictive condition X, as has been shown by both Bernshtein [1] and Szegö [1]. From it one obtains the asymptotic expression $\lim_{n\to\infty}\overset{*}{\varphi}_n(e^{i\theta}) = \pi(e^{i\theta})$, valid uniformly on $[0,2\pi]$, and therefore also the uniform boundedness of the orthonormal set on $[0,2\pi]$. Conditions IV-VI give more accurate estimates than that obtained with condition I, a consequence of Theorem 3.5. If XI is fulfilled, then $\pi(z)\in H_{2r'}$, which implies* that $|\pi(re^{i\theta})| \leqslant C(1-r)^{-\frac{1}{2r'}}$, and then from (3.34) we obtain the estimate $o\left(n^{\frac{1}{2}+\frac{1}{2r'}}\right)$ which we have listed.

Conditions XII and XIII are easily obtained from III and IV of Table I. Finally, condition XIV is obtained by methods which are entirely different from those that led to any of the previous ones; this will be discussed in Chapter VIII.

* See I. I. Privalov [1], Chapter II, Section 3.

CHAPTER IV

LOCAL ESTIMATES

4.1. To obtain local estimates on some arc

$$[e^{i\alpha}, e^{i\beta}], \qquad [\alpha, \beta] \subset [0, 2\pi]$$

let us first find local estimates for the sums $K_n(e^{i\theta}, e^{i\theta})$.

Theorem 4.1. Consider two measures $d\sigma(\theta)$ and $d\sigma_0(\theta)$ related by

$$d\sigma(\theta) = \prod_{k=1}^{s} |e^{i\theta} - e^{i\theta_k}|^{\nu_k} d\sigma_0(\theta), \qquad \nu_k > -1. \quad (4.1)$$

Then on any interval with a finite separation from each of the points $\{\theta_k\}_1^s$, we obtain

$$K_n(e^{i\theta}, e^{i\theta}) \leqslant CK_p^{(0)}(e^{i\theta}, e^{i\theta}) = C \sum_{k=0}^{p} |\varphi_k^{(0)}(e^{i\theta})|^2, \quad (4.2)$$

where the polynomials $\{\varphi_k^{(0)}(z)\}$ are orthonormal with respect to the measure $d\sigma_0(\theta)$; here $p = n + \sum_{k=1}^{s} r_k$, where $2r_k$ is the smallest even number no less than ν_k $(k = 1, 2, \ldots, s)$.*

To prove this we first introduce the new measure

$$d\sigma_1(\theta) = \prod_{k=1}^{s} |e^{i\theta} - e^{i\theta_k}|^{2r_k} d\sigma_0(\theta). \quad (4.3)$$

* This theorem has been proved by Szegö [1], Section 12.6, for the case in which $\nu_k > 0$, $(k = 1, 2, \ldots, s)$ and for absolutely continuous $\sigma(\theta)$. Here C is independent of n.

Since

$$\frac{\prod_{k=1}^{s}|e^{i\theta}-e^{i\theta_k}|^{\nu_k}}{\prod_{k=1}^{s}|e^{i\theta}-e^{i\theta_k}|^{2r_k}}=\prod_{k=1}^{s}|e^{i\theta}-e^{i\theta_k}|^{\nu_k-2r_k}\geqslant C_0>0$$

is bounded from below for $0 \leq \theta \leq 2\pi$, we have

$$\sigma(\theta_2)-\sigma(\theta_1)\geqslant C_0[\sigma_1(\theta_2)-\sigma_1(\theta_1)], \quad 0\leqslant\theta_1<\theta_2\leqslant 2\pi, \tag{4.4}$$

and therefore

$$\frac{1}{2\pi}\int_0^{2\pi}\left|\frac{G_n(e^{i\theta})}{G_n(z_0)}\right|^2 d\sigma(\theta)\geqslant\frac{C_0}{2\pi}\int_0^{2\pi}\left|\frac{G_n(e^{i\theta})}{G_n(z_0)}\right|^2 d\sigma_1(\theta),$$

where $G_n(z)$ is an arbitrary polynomial of degree $\leq n$. We introduce the notation

$$G_p(z)=G_n(z)\prod_{k=1}^{s}(z-z_k)^{r_k},\quad p=n+\sum_{k=1}^{s}r_k,\quad z_k=e^{i\theta_k}, \tag{4.5}$$

in terms of which

$$\frac{1}{2\pi}\int_0^{2\pi}\left|\frac{G_n(e^{i\theta})}{G_n(z_0)}\right|^2 d\sigma(\theta)\geqslant$$

$$\geqslant C_0\prod_{k=1}^{s}|z_0-e^{i\theta_k}|^{2r_k}\cdot\frac{1}{2\pi}\int_0^{2\pi}\left|\frac{G_p(e^{i\theta})}{G_p(z_0)}\right|^2 d\sigma_0(\theta),$$

so that

$$\min_{G_n}\left\{\frac{1}{2\pi}\int_0^{2\pi}\left|\frac{G_n(e^{i\theta})}{G_n(z_0)}\right|^2 d\sigma(\theta)\right\}\geqslant$$

$$\geqslant C_0\prod_{k=1}^{s}|z_0-e^{i\theta_k}|^{2r_k}\min_{G_p}\left\{\frac{1}{2\pi}\int_0^{2\pi}\left|\frac{G_p(e^{i\theta})}{G_p(z_0)}\right|^2 d\sigma_0(\theta)\right\}.$$

Using (1.10), we arrive at

$$\frac{1}{\sum_{k=0}^{n}|\varphi_k(z_0)|^2}\geqslant C_0\prod_{k=1}^{s}|z_0-e^{i\theta_k}|^{2r_k}\frac{1}{\sum_{\nu=0}^{p}|\varphi_\nu^{(0)}(z_0)|^2}. \tag{4.6}$$

If $z_0 = e^{i\theta_0}$ and $|\theta_0 - \theta_k| \geq \epsilon$, this last inequality implies (4.2). From the theorem just proved we obtain the following

Theorem 4.2. If on some interval $[\alpha, \beta] \subset [0, 2\pi]$

$$\sigma(\theta_2) - \sigma(\theta_1) \geqslant m(\theta_2 - \theta_1), \quad \alpha \leqslant \theta_1 < \theta_2 \leqslant \beta, \quad m > 0, \tag{4.7}$$

then

$$K_n(e^{i\theta}, e^{i\theta}) < C(n+1), \quad \alpha + \varepsilon \leqslant \theta \leqslant \beta - \varepsilon, \quad \varepsilon > 0, \tag{4.8}$$

where C is independent of n.

To prove this let us assume that $\beta = 2\pi - \alpha$, $(\alpha < \pi)$, which involves no loss of generality since to go over to the general case we need only perform the substitution of variables $z_1 = z e^{i\gamma}$.

Consider two absolutely continuous functions $\sigma^{(1)}(\theta)$ and $\sigma^{(2)}(\theta)$, constant outside of $[\alpha, \beta]$ and given on $[\alpha, \beta]$ by

$$\left.\begin{aligned} &\sigma^{(1)}(\theta) = \int p^{(1)}(\theta)\, d\theta, \qquad && \sigma^{(2)}(\theta) = \int p^{(2)}(\theta)\, d\theta, \\ &p^{(1)}(\theta) = m, && p^{(2)}(\theta) = \sqrt{\frac{\sin\frac{\theta+\alpha}{2}}{\sin\frac{\theta-\alpha}{2}}}. \end{aligned}\right\} \tag{4.9}$$

Let $\{\varphi_k^{(1)}(z)\}$, and $\{\varphi_k^{(2)}(z)\}$ denote the corresponding sets of orthonormal polynomials.

First, then, we have

$$\sigma(\theta_2) - \sigma(\theta_1) \geqslant \sigma^{(1)}(\theta_2) - \sigma^{(1)}(\theta_1), \qquad 0 \leqslant \theta_1 < \theta_2 \leqslant 2\pi, \tag{4.10}$$

whence

$$K_n(e^{i\theta}, e^{i\theta}) \leqslant K_n^{(1)}(e^{i\theta}, e^{i\theta}), \qquad 0 \leqslant \theta \leqslant 2\pi. \tag{4.11}$$

On the other hand,

$$d\sigma^{(1)}(\theta) = m\, |e^{i\theta} - e^{i\alpha}|^{\frac{1}{2}}\, |e^{i\theta} - e^{-i\alpha}|^{-\frac{1}{2}}\, d\sigma^{(2)}(\theta).$$

Let us set $\nu_1 = 1/2$, $\nu_2 = -1/2$, in the preceding theorem, so that $r_1 = 1$, $r_2 = 0$. This gives

$$K_n^{(1)}(e^{i\theta}, e^{i\theta}) \leqslant C K_{n+1}^{(2)}(e^{i\theta}, e^{i\theta}), \qquad \alpha + \varepsilon \leqslant \theta \leqslant \beta - \varepsilon. \tag{4.12}$$

From (4.11) and (4.12) we find that for $\alpha+\epsilon \leq \theta \leq \beta-\epsilon$

$$K_n\left(e^{i\theta},\ e^{i\theta}\right) \leqslant C K_{n+1}^{(2)}\left(e^{i\theta},\ e^{i\theta}\right). \tag{4.13}$$

The $\{\varphi_n^{(2)}(z)\}$ polynomials may be written down explicitly: setting

$$\cos\lambda = \frac{\cos\frac{\theta}{2}}{\cos\frac{\alpha}{2}}, \qquad \alpha \leqslant \theta \leqslant 2\pi-\alpha,\ 0 \leqslant \lambda \leqslant \pi, \tag{4.14}$$

we have*

$$\varphi_n^{(2)}(e^{i\theta}) = \alpha_0 \left\{ e^{\frac{i\theta}{2}} \frac{\sin(n+1)\lambda}{\sin\lambda} - e^{\frac{i\alpha}{2}} \frac{\sin n\lambda}{\sin\lambda} \right\} e^{i\frac{n-1}{2}\theta} \tag{4.14'}$$

$$(n = 0,\ 1,\ \ldots).$$

Now if $\epsilon_1 \leq \lambda \leq \pi - \epsilon_1$, i.e., if $\alpha+\epsilon \leq \theta \leq \beta-\epsilon$, the expressions $\left|\frac{\sin n\lambda}{\sin\lambda}\right|$ are uniformly bounded for all n, as can be seen from the fact that

$$\left|\frac{\sin n\lambda}{\sin\lambda}\right| \leqslant \frac{1}{\sin\lambda} \leqslant \frac{1}{\sin\varepsilon_1}.$$

Hence

$$K_{n+1}^{(2)}\left(e^{\theta},\ e^{i\theta}\right) \leqslant C_1(n+1), \qquad \alpha+\varepsilon \leqslant \theta \leqslant \beta-\varepsilon,$$

where C_1 is independent of n; this implies (4.8).

A lower estimate for the sum $K_n(e^{i\theta},\ e^{i\theta})$ leads us to the following

Theorem 4.3. Assume that on the interval $[\alpha, \beta]$ the function $\sigma(\theta)$ is absolutely continuous, and that $p(\theta) \leq M$. We then have

$$K_n(e^{i\theta},\ e^{i\theta}) \geqslant C(n+1), \qquad \alpha+\varepsilon \leqslant \theta \leqslant \beta-\varepsilon, \tag{4.15}$$

where C is independent of n.

* These polynomials were first discussed by Akhiezer [4] with relation to some aerodynamic problems. Their explicit form was found by the present author [3], Sections 4-6; the derivation of (4.14') is indicated in 8.1.

To prove this we make use of (1.10), writing*

$$\left.\begin{aligned} &\left|\frac{G_n(e^{i\theta})}{G_n(e^{i\theta_0})}\right|^2 = S_\nu(\theta-\theta_0), \quad \nu = \left[\frac{n+1}{2}\right], \\ &G_n(z) = \frac{z^{2\nu}-z_0^{2\nu}}{z-z_0}, \\ &S_\nu(\varphi) = \frac{1}{4\nu^2}\left(\frac{\sin\nu\varphi}{\sin\frac{1}{2}\varphi}\right)^2 = \\ &= \frac{1}{4\nu^2}\{2\nu + 2[(2\nu-1)\cos\varphi + \ldots + \cos(2\nu-1)\varphi]\}. \end{aligned}\right\} \quad (4.16)$$

We are then led to

$$\frac{1}{K_n(e^{i\theta_0}, e^{i\theta_0})} \leqslant \frac{1}{2\pi}\int_0^{2\pi} S_\nu(\theta-\theta_0)\, d\sigma(\theta) =$$

$$= \frac{1}{2\pi}\int_0^{2\pi} S_\nu(\theta-\theta_0)\, p(\theta)\, d\theta + \frac{1}{2\pi}\int_0^{2\pi} S_\nu(\theta-\theta_0)\, d\sigma_1(\theta), \quad (4.17)$$

where $\sigma_1(\theta)$ is the sum of the singular component and the step function in $\sigma(\theta)$, and in particular $\sigma_1(\theta) \equiv$ const for $\alpha \leq \theta \leq \beta$.

For $\alpha + \varepsilon \leqslant \theta_0 \leqslant \beta - \varepsilon$, $\theta \overline{\in} [\alpha, \beta]$ we have $|\theta - \theta_0| \geq \epsilon$. which leads to the following estimate for the second integral:

$$\frac{1}{2\pi}\int_0^{2\pi} S_\nu(\theta-\theta_0)\, d\sigma_1(\theta) = \frac{1}{8\pi\nu^2}\int_0^{2\pi}\left\{\frac{\sin\nu(\theta-\theta_0)}{\sin\frac{1}{2}(\theta-\theta_0)}\right\}^2 d\sigma_1(\theta) \leqslant$$

$$\leqslant \frac{1}{8\pi\nu^2\sin^2\frac{\varepsilon}{2}}\int_0^{2\pi} d\sigma_1(\theta) \leqslant \frac{C}{n^2}. \quad (4.18)$$

For the first integral we have the estimate

$$\frac{1}{2\pi}\int_0^{2\pi} S_\nu(\theta-\theta_0)\, p(\theta)\, d\theta = \frac{1}{2\nu}\sigma_\nu(\theta_0) \leqslant \frac{\sigma_\nu(\theta_0)}{n}, \quad (4.19)$$

where $\sigma_\nu(\theta)$ is the Fejèr sum of order $2\nu - 1$ for the function $p(\theta)$.

* See N. I. Akhiezer [3].

If $\alpha + \epsilon \leq \theta_0 \leq \beta - \epsilon$, therefore

$$\frac{n+1}{K_n(e^{i\theta_0}, e^{i\theta_0})} \leqslant \left[\sigma_\nu(\theta_0) + \frac{C}{n}\right]\frac{n+1}{n} =$$

$$= \sigma_\nu(\theta_0) + \frac{1}{n}\sigma_n(\theta_0) + \frac{C}{n}\left(1 + \frac{1}{n}\right). \quad (4.20)$$

Recall the following property of Fejèr sums:* if $p(\theta_0) \leq M$ for $\alpha \leq \theta_0 \leq \beta$, then for every $\epsilon > 0$ there exists an integer $\nu_0 = \nu_0(\epsilon)$ such that for $\alpha + \epsilon \leq \theta_0 \leq \beta - \epsilon$, $\nu > \nu_0$ we have $\sigma_\nu(\theta_0) \leq M + \epsilon$. If $\nu > \nu_0$, therefore, we obtain

$$\frac{K_n(e^{i\theta}, e^{i\theta_0})}{n+1} \geqslant \frac{1}{\sigma_\nu(\theta_0) + \varepsilon_n} \geqslant \frac{1}{M + \varepsilon + \varepsilon_n} \geqslant C',$$
$$\alpha + \varepsilon \leqslant \theta_0 \leqslant \beta - \varepsilon,$$

where C' is independent of n since the ϵ_n tend uniformly to zero with 1/ n.

With this appraisal for $K_n(e^{i\theta}, e^{i\theta})$, we easily obtain a local estimate for the orthonormal polynomials.

Theorem 4.4. If the integral of (3.28) exists and if on the interval $[\alpha, \beta]$

$$\sigma(\theta_2) - \sigma(\theta_1) \geqslant m(\theta_2 - \theta_1), \quad \alpha \leqslant \theta_1 < \theta_2 \leqslant \beta, \quad m > 0, \quad (4.21)$$

then at every point in the interior of the arc $[e^{i\alpha}, e^{i\beta}]$

$$|\varphi_n(e^{i\theta})| = o(\sqrt{n}). \quad (4.22)$$

Indeed, using Theorems 3.4 and 4.2 we find easily that

$$|\varphi_n(e^{i\theta})| = o\left\{\sqrt{K_n(e^{i\theta}, e^{i\theta})}\right\} = o(\sqrt{n}).$$

Remark 4.1. If on some interval $[\alpha, \beta]$ condition (4.7) is fulfilled, as is the case of Theorem 4.2, then at every internal point θ_0 of $[\alpha, \beta]$ there exists a subsequence of indices $\{n_\nu\}$ such that

* See A. Zygmund [1], Section 3.22.

$$|\varphi_{n_\nu}(e^{i\theta_0})| \leqslant B^* \qquad (\nu = 1, 2, \ldots).$$

Indeed, according to (4.8) if $\alpha + \epsilon \leq \theta_0 \leq \beta - \epsilon$, then

$$\frac{1}{n+1}\sum_{k=0}^{n} |\varphi_k(e^{i\theta_0})|^2 \leqslant C, \quad \overline{\lim_{n\to\infty}} \left\{ \frac{\sum_{k=0}^{n} |\varphi_k(e^{i\theta_0})|^2}{n+1} \right\} \leqslant C.$$

If we were to assume that

$$\underline{\lim_{n\to\infty}} |\varphi_n(e^{i\theta_0})| = \infty,$$

then the limit $\lim_{n\to\infty} |\varphi_n(e^{i\theta_0})| = \infty$ would exist, and therefore we would obtain the same limit for the arithmetic mean

$$\lim_{n\to\infty} \left\{ \frac{1}{n+1} \sum_{k=0}^{n} |\varphi_k(e^{i\theta_0})|^2 \right\} = \infty,$$

which, as has been pointed out before, contradicts (4.8). Hence

$$\underline{\lim_{n\to\infty}} |\varphi_n(e^{i\theta_0})| = B < \infty,$$

which means that at every point $\alpha - \epsilon \leq \theta_0 \leq \beta + \epsilon$ there exists an infinite bounded subsequence $\{\varphi_{n_\nu}(e^{i\theta_0})\}$.

4.2. We now turn to some simple theorems giving local estimates for the orthonormal set. We start from simple sufficient conditions for uniform boundedness.

Theorem 4.5. Let $\frac{1}{p(\theta)} \in L_1$ and assume that on the interval $[\alpha, \beta]$ the function $\sigma(\theta)$ is absolutely continuous, while $p(\theta)$ is bounded from below, i.e., $0 < m \leq p(\theta)$, and satisfies one of the following two conditions on $[\alpha, \beta]$:

1) it is continuous and satisfied the Dini-Lipschitz condition

$$\omega(\delta; p) \leqslant C\left(\ln\frac{1}{\delta}\right)^{-\gamma}, \qquad \gamma > 1; \tag{4.23}$$

2) its total variation is bounded. Then the orthonormal set is uniformly bounded in $[\alpha, \beta]$; that is to say

---

* Here B and C, C_1, C_2, . . . are independent of n.

$$|\varphi_n(e^{i\theta})| \leqslant C_1, \qquad \alpha+\varepsilon \leqslant \theta \leqslant \beta-\varepsilon,$$

where C_1 is independent of $\underline{n}$.

To prove this we introduce the weight $p_1(\theta)$, defined in the following way: on $[\alpha, \beta]$ let $p_1 \equiv p(\theta)$, and outside this interval let $p_1(\theta)$ vary linearly and continuously; then

$$p_1(+0) = p_1(2\pi - 0), \quad p_1(\alpha) = p(\alpha - 0), \quad p_1(\beta) = p(\beta + 0).$$

Let $\{\gamma_n(z)\}$ denote the set of orthonormal polynomials corresponding to this weight $p_1(\theta)$. It is easily seen that these are uniformly bounded on the entire interval $[0, 2\pi]$, i.e. that

$$|\gamma_n(e^{i\theta})| \leqslant B, \quad 0 \leqslant \theta \leqslant 2\pi \qquad (n=0, 1, 2, \ldots). \quad (4.24)$$

Indeed, from the fact that outside of $[\alpha, \beta]$ the weight function $p_1(\theta)$ is Lip 1, it follows that if condition 2) is fulfilled, it is of bounded variation not only on $[\alpha, \beta]$, but throughout $[0, 2\pi]$, and our assertion is then a consequence of condition VIII of Table II. If condition 1) is fulfilled, $p_1(\theta)$ satisfies the Dini-Lipschitz condition not only on $[\alpha, \beta]$, but throughout $[0, 2\pi]$, and in this case our assertion follows from condition X of Table II.

We now expand $\varphi_n(z)$ in the polynominals $\{\gamma_k(z)\}_0^n$, obtaining

$$\varphi_n(e^{i\theta}) = \sum_{k=0}^{n} c_k \gamma_k(e^{i\theta_0}), \quad c_k = \frac{1}{2\pi}\int_0^{2\pi} \varphi_n(e^{i\theta})\overline{\gamma_k(e^{i\theta})}\, p_1(\theta)\, d\theta,$$
$$(k=0, 1, \ldots, n).$$

Using (1.7), we find that

$$\varphi_n(e^{i\theta}) = \frac{\alpha_n}{\alpha'_n}\gamma_n(e^{i\theta}) + \frac{1}{2\pi}\int_0^{2\pi} p_1(\theta) K'_{n-1}\left(e^{i\theta_0}, e^{i\theta}\right)\varphi_n\left(e^{i\theta}\right) d\theta, \quad (4.24')$$

$$K'_{n-1}(z_0, z) = \frac{\overset{*}{\gamma}_n(z_0)\overline{\overset{*}{\gamma}_n(z)} - \gamma_n(z_0)\overline{\gamma_n(z)}}{1 - z_0\cdot\bar{z}}, \quad \gamma_n(z) = \alpha'_n z^n + \ldots$$

Since

$$\frac{1}{2\pi}\int_0^{2\pi} K'_{n-1}(e^{i\theta_0}, e^{i\theta})\,\varphi_n(e^{i\theta})\,d\sigma(\theta) =$$

$$= \frac{1}{2\pi}\int_0^{2\pi} K'_{n-1}(e^{i\theta_0}, e^{i\theta})\,\varphi_n(e^{i\theta})\,p(\theta)\,d\theta + d_n = 0,$$

where

$$d_n = \frac{1}{2\pi}\int_0^{2\pi} K'_{n-1}(e^{i\theta_0}, e^{i\theta})\,\varphi_n(e^{i\theta})\,d\sigma_1(\theta),$$

we arrive finally at

$$\varphi_n(e^{i\theta_0}) = \frac{\alpha_n}{\alpha'_n}\gamma_n(e^{i\theta_0}) + \frac{1}{2\pi}\int_0^{2\pi}\frac{p_1(\theta)-p(\theta)}{\sqrt{p(\theta)}}\times$$

$$\times\sqrt{p(\theta)}\,\varphi_n(e^{i\theta})\,K'_{n-1}(e^{i\theta_0}, e^{i\theta})\,d\theta - d_n. \qquad (4.25)$$

Let us first evaluate $|K'_{n-1}(e^{i\theta_0}, e^{i\theta})|$. If $|\theta-\theta_0| \geq \epsilon$, we have

$$|K'_{n-1}(e^{i\theta_0}, e^{i\theta})| \leqslant \frac{2B^2}{2\left|\sin\frac{\theta-\theta_0}{2}\right|} < \frac{B^2}{\sin\frac{\varepsilon}{2}} < \frac{\pi B^2}{\varepsilon},$$

in which case if $\alpha + \epsilon \leq \theta_0 \leq \beta - \epsilon$, we may use the fact that $\sigma_1(\theta) \equiv$ const for $\theta \in [\alpha, \beta]$, and then according to (2.23) obtain

$$|d_n| < \frac{\pi B^2}{\varepsilon}\|\varphi_n(e^{i\theta})\|_1^{\sigma_1} \leqslant \frac{\sqrt{c_0}\,\pi B^2}{\varepsilon}\|\varphi_n(e^{i\theta})\|_2^{\sigma_1} \leqslant$$

$$\leqslant \frac{\pi B^2}{\varepsilon}\sqrt{\frac{2\alpha c_0}{\alpha+\alpha_0}}\,\delta_n = C\,\delta_n.$$

To evaluate the integral entering into (4.25), we remark that $p_1(\theta) \equiv p(\theta)$ for $\theta \in [\alpha, \beta]$. This means that $|\theta - \theta_0| \geq \epsilon$ in the integrand, and then setting $d\sigma_0(\theta) = p(\theta)\,d\theta$, we again have

$$\frac{1}{2\pi}\int_0^{2\pi}\frac{|p_1(\theta)-p(\theta)|}{\sqrt{p(\theta)}}\sqrt{p(\theta)}\,|\varphi_n(e^{i\theta})|\cdot|K'_{n-1}(e^{i\theta_0}, e^{i\theta})|\,d\theta \leqslant$$

$$\leqslant \frac{\pi B^2}{\varepsilon}\|\varphi_n(e^{i\theta})\|_2^{\sigma_0}\times$$

$$\times\sqrt{\frac{1}{2\pi}\int_0^{2\pi}\frac{p_1^2(\theta)}{p(\theta)}\,d\theta - \frac{1}{\pi}\int_0^{2\pi}p_1(\theta)\,d\theta + \frac{1}{2\pi}\int_0^{2\pi}p(\theta)\,d\theta} = C_1,$$

from which we obtain the inequality

$$|\varphi_n(e^{i\theta_0})| \leqslant \frac{\alpha}{\alpha_0'} B + C_1 + C\delta_n \leqslant C_2, \quad \alpha + \varepsilon \leqslant \theta_0 \leqslant \beta - \varepsilon.$$

Having proved this theorem, let us use it to obtain local estimates for the orthonormal set.

Theorem 4.6. Let $\frac{1}{p(\theta)} \in L_1$, and assume that on $[\alpha, \beta]$ the function $\sigma(\theta)$ is absolutely continuous; assume also that

$$p(\theta) \leqslant M, \quad \theta \in [\alpha, \alpha + 2\varepsilon], \quad \theta \in [\beta - 2\varepsilon, \beta];$$
$$0 < m \leqslant p(\theta), \quad \theta \in [\alpha, \beta].$$

Then for $\alpha + 2\epsilon \leq \theta_0 \leq \beta - 2\epsilon$ we are led to the inequalities*

$$|\varphi_n(e^{i\theta_0})| \leqslant C_1 + C_2\delta_n^{(1)}\sqrt{n} \quad (n = 0, 1, 2, \ldots), \tag{4.26}$$

where the $\delta_n^{(1)}$ defined by (3.8) are constructed here for the weight function $p_1(\theta)$, and $p_1(\theta)$ coincides with $p(\theta)$ on $[\alpha + \epsilon, \beta - \epsilon]$, varying linearly and continuously outside this interval.

Let us try to apply the preceding theorem to the $\{\gamma_n(z)\}$ polynomials. We see that for $\theta \in e$, where $e = [0, 2\pi] - [\alpha + \epsilon, \beta - \epsilon]$, the weight $p_1(\theta)$ satisfies both conditions 1) and 2), so that the $\{\gamma_n(e^{i\theta})\}$ are uniformly bounded in the interior of e; in other words

$$|\gamma_n(e^{i\theta_0})| \leqslant B, \quad \theta \in e', \quad e' = [0, 2\pi] - [\alpha, \beta]$$
$$(n = 0, 1, 2, \ldots).$$

We introduce the notation

$$\mu_n' = \max |\gamma_n(e^{i\theta_0})|, \quad \alpha + 2\varepsilon \leqslant \theta_0 \leqslant \beta - 2\varepsilon, \tag{4.27}$$

in terms of which

$$|K_{n-1}'(e^{i\theta_0}, e^{i\theta})| \leqslant \frac{\pi B\mu_n'}{2\varepsilon}, \quad \alpha + 2\varepsilon \leqslant \theta_0 \leqslant \beta - 2\varepsilon, \quad \theta \in e',$$

which means that for d_n we obtain the estimate

$$|d_n| \leqslant C'\mu_n'\delta_n$$

* Here $C, C', C_1, C_2, \ldots$ are independent of n.

and that for the integral over e' in (4.25) we obtain

$$\left| \frac{1}{2\pi} \int_{e'} \right| \leqslant C_1 \mu_n'.$$

For the integral over $[\alpha, \alpha + \epsilon]$, the conditions of the theorem provide us with the estimate

$$\left| \frac{1}{2\pi} \int_{\alpha}^{\alpha+\varepsilon} \right| \leqslant \frac{\mu_n'}{2\pi \sin \frac{\varepsilon}{2}} \int_{\alpha}^{\alpha+\varepsilon} \frac{|p_1(\theta) - p(\theta)|}{\sqrt{p(\theta) p_1(\theta)}} \times$$

$$\times \sqrt{p(\theta)} \, |\varphi_n(e^{i\theta})| \sqrt{p_1(\theta)} \, |\gamma_n(e^{i\theta})| \, d\theta \leqslant \max_{\alpha \leqslant \theta \leqslant \alpha+\varepsilon} \frac{p_1(\theta) + p(\theta)}{\sqrt{p(\theta) p_1(\theta)}} \times$$

$$\times \sqrt{\frac{1}{2\pi} \int_0^{2\pi} p(\theta) |\varphi_n(e^{i\theta})|^2 d\theta \, \frac{1}{2\pi} \int_0^{2\pi} p_1(\theta) |\gamma_n(e^{i\theta})|^2 d\theta} \times$$

$$\times C_2 \mu_n' = C_3 \mu_n',$$

and a similar estimate for the integral over $[\beta - \epsilon, \beta]$.

We thus arrive at

$$|\varphi_n(e^{i\theta_0})| \leqslant C \mu_n', \quad \alpha + 2\varepsilon \leqslant \theta_0 \leqslant \beta - 2\varepsilon.$$

Since $p_1(\theta)$ is bounded from below throughout $[0, 2\pi]$, it follows from property d) of Chapter II and from (3.34) that

$$\mu_n' \leqslant C_5 + C_4 \sqrt{n} \, \delta_n^{(1)},$$

where $\delta_n^{(1)}$ is associated with the weight function $p_1(\theta)$.

We now make use of (3.8) and (3.9). The estimates for the δ_n' (Table I) involve the integral moduli of continuity of $p_1(\theta)$, taken over the entire interval $[0, 2\pi]$. By using the definition of $p_1(\theta)$, we can replace these by analogous moduli of continuity for $p(\theta)$ but taken over the interval $[\alpha, \beta]$.

Consider the integral

$$I = \frac{1}{2\pi} \int_0^{2\pi} |p_1(\theta + h) - p_1(\theta)|^r \, d\theta, \quad r \geqslant 1.$$

On the intervals $[0, \alpha + \epsilon - |h|]$, and $[\beta - \epsilon + |h|, 2\pi]$, such that $|h| \le \epsilon$, we have

$$|p_1(\theta+h) - p_1(\theta)| \leqslant C|h|,$$

so that the integrals over these intervals have a bound given by

$$\left|\int\limits_0^{\alpha+\varepsilon-|h|}\right|, \quad \left|\int\limits_{\beta-\varepsilon+|h|}^{2\pi}\right| \leqslant C_1|h|^r.$$

Further, one easily obtains

$$\left|\int\limits_{\alpha+\varepsilon-|h|}^{\alpha+\varepsilon+|h|}\right|, \quad \left|\int\limits_{\beta-\varepsilon-|h|}^{\beta-\varepsilon+|h|}\right| \leqslant C_2|h|,$$

by using the boundedness of the integrand. Hence

$$I \leqslant C_3|h| + C_4|h|^r + \frac{1}{2\pi}\int\limits_{\alpha+|h|+\varepsilon}^{\beta-|h|-\varepsilon} |p_1(\theta+h) - p_1(\theta)|^r\, d\theta \leqslant$$

$$\leqslant C_5|h| + \frac{1}{2\pi}\int\limits_{\alpha+|h|+\varepsilon}^{\beta-|h|-\varepsilon} |p_1(\theta+h) - p_1(\theta)|^r\, d\theta$$

and finally

$$\omega_r(\delta;\ p_1) \leqslant C\delta^{\frac{1}{r}} + C_1\omega_r'(\delta;\ p),$$

where we have written

$$\omega_r'(\delta;\ p) = \sup_{|h| \leqslant \delta < \varepsilon} \left\{\frac{1}{2\pi}\int\limits_{\alpha+\varepsilon}^{\beta-\varepsilon} |p(\theta+h) - p(\theta)|^r\, d\theta\right\}^{\frac{1}{r}}. \tag{4.28}$$

In deriving this result we have used the fact that on our interval $[\alpha + \epsilon + |h|, \beta - \epsilon - |h|]$ the two weights are defined so that $p_1(\theta + h) \equiv p(\theta + h)$ if $|h| \le \epsilon$, as well as the fact that $r \ge 1$. In this way we are led to the inequality

$$\omega_r\left(\frac{1}{n};\ p_1\right) \leqslant Cn^{-\frac{1}{r}} + C'\omega_r'\left(\frac{1}{n};\ p\right), \tag{4.29}$$

which in turn leads to entries VIII and IX of Table III.

4.3. To obtain further local estimates we will need the following theorem, which may be considered a local analogy of a well-known theorem of Privalov.

Theorem 4.7. Let $u(\theta) \in L_1$ be a real function with period 2π, such that on the interval $[\alpha, \beta] \subset [0, 2\pi]$ it is continuous with modulus of continuity $\omega(\delta; u)$, and such that the integral

$$\int_0^a \frac{\omega\left(x \ln \frac{1}{x}; u\right)}{x} dx$$

exists. Then in the interior of $[\alpha, \beta]$ the conjugate function $v(\theta)$ satisfies the inequality*

$$|v(\theta + h) - v(\theta)| \leqslant C\lambda(h), \quad \lambda(\delta) = \int_0^\delta \frac{\omega\left(x \ln \frac{1}{x}; u\right)}{x} dx. \quad (4.30)$$

Assume in particular that

$$\omega(\delta; u) \leqslant C_1 \delta^\lambda \left(\ln \frac{1}{\delta}\right)^{-\gamma}; \quad \gamma \geqslant \lambda, \quad 0 \leqslant \lambda < 1. \quad (4.30')$$

In this case we have

$$\lambda(\delta) \leqslant C_1 \int_0^\delta \frac{\left(x \ln \frac{1}{x}\right)^\lambda dx}{x\left[\ln\left(\frac{1}{x \ln \frac{1}{x}}\right)\right]^\gamma}.$$

Now since $y > 1$ implies that $\ln y < y$, it follows that $\ln(1/x) < 2\sqrt{1/x}$, and $x < 1$ thus that $\frac{1}{x \ln \frac{1}{x}} > \frac{1}{2}\sqrt{\frac{1}{x}}$. Then if $x < 1/16$, we have

* See Ya. L. Geronimus [4], Section 6. From the proof of the theorem one may conclude that if $u(\theta) \in \text{Lip}\,\gamma$, then $\lambda(\delta) \leq C\delta^\gamma$, for $\gamma < 1$, while $\lambda(\delta) \leq C\delta \ln(1/\delta)$ for $\gamma = 1$. In this special case the theorem is a local analog of Privalov's theorem. If the formulas are required for $x \geq 1$, one introduces $\ln(b/x)$, $b > \pi$. Here C and in what follows C_1, C_2, A are constants.

$$\ln\left(\frac{1}{x\ln\frac{1}{x}}\right) > \frac{1}{2}\ln\frac{1}{x} + \ln\frac{1}{2}, \qquad \frac{1}{\left[\ln\left(\frac{1}{x\ln\frac{1}{x}}\right)\right]^{\gamma}} < \frac{A}{\left(\ln\frac{1}{x}\right)^{\gamma}}$$

and therefore

$$\lambda(\delta) \leqslant C_2 \int_0^{\delta} x^{\lambda-1}\left(\ln\frac{1}{x}\right)^{\lambda-\gamma} dx.$$

Since $\left(\ln\frac{1}{x}\right)^{\lambda-\gamma}$ is an increasing function, we arrive finally, referring to (4.30), at the inequality for the conjugate function in the interior of $[\alpha, \beta]$

$$\lambda(\delta) \leqslant \frac{C\delta^{\lambda}}{\left(\ln\frac{1}{\delta}\right)^{\gamma-\lambda}}, \quad \lambda \neq 0; \quad \lambda(\delta) \leqslant \frac{C_1}{\left(\ln\frac{1}{\delta}\right)^{\gamma-1}}, \quad \lambda = 0. \tag{4.31}$$

4.4. Later we shall make use of the following

Lemma 4.1. Assume that the integral of (3.28) exists, and let $f_0(\theta)$ be a complex-valued function such that

$$\frac{1}{2\pi}\int_0^{2\pi} \frac{f_0(\theta)\, e^{i\theta}}{\pi(e^{i\theta})}\, d\theta = 0. \tag{4.32}$$

Write

$$\left.\begin{aligned} a_n &= \frac{1}{2\pi}\int_0^{2\pi} f_0(\theta)\, e^{i\theta}\,\overline{\overset{*}{\varphi}_n(e^{i\theta})}\, d\sigma(\theta), \\ b_n &= \frac{1}{2\pi}\int_0^{2\pi} f_0(\theta)\,\overline{\varphi_n(e^{i\theta})}\, d\sigma(\theta). \\ &(n = 0, 1, 2, \dots) \end{aligned}\right\} \tag{4.33}$$

Then a sufficient condition for the existence of the limits

$$\lim_{n\to\infty} a_n = \lim_{n\to\infty} b_n = 0 \tag{4.33'}$$

is either of the following:*

1) $f_0(\theta) \in L_2^\sigma$;

2) the function $\sigma(\theta)$ satisfies condition VII of Table II, and $f_0(\theta) \in L_1$.

First we note that according to (2.7),

$$a_n\alpha_n = \frac{1}{2\pi}\int_0^{2\pi} f_0(\theta)\{a_n\overline{\overset{*}{\varphi}_n(e^{i\theta})} - \alpha\overline{\pi_0(\theta)}\}\, e^{i\theta}\, d\sigma(\theta) + \\ + \frac{\alpha}{2\pi}\int_0^{2\pi} \frac{f_0(\theta)\, e^{i\theta}\, d\theta}{\pi(e^{i\theta})}, \tag{4.34}$$

and the second integral vanishes by assumption.

Let us start by considering case 1). As the b_n are Fourier-Chebyshev coefficients of $f_0(\theta) \in L_2^\sigma$, Bessel's inequality

$$\sum_{k=0}^{\infty} |b_n|^2 < \infty$$

tells us that $\lim_{n\to\infty} b_n = 0$. Further, applying the Bunyakovskii-Schwarz inequality to (4.34) and making use of the closure condition for $\pi_0(\theta)$, we find that $\lim_{n\to\infty} a_n = 0$.

We turn now to condition 2). Since L_2 is dense in L_1, given an $\epsilon > 0$, no matter how small, one can always find a function $f_1(\theta) \in L_2$ such that

$$\int_0^{2\pi} |f_0(\theta) - f_1(\theta)|\, d\theta < \varepsilon.$$

Let us write

$$f_0(\theta) = f_1(\theta) + f_2(\theta), \quad a_n = a_n^{(1)} + a_n^{(2)}, \quad b_n = b_n^{(1)} + b_n^{(2)}.$$

We recall now that $\sigma'(\theta)$ is a bounded and measurable function, and that $\sigma(\theta)$ is absolutely continuous, so that

---

* Each of these conditions alone insures the existence of the integrals in (4.33).

$$\frac{1}{2\pi}\int_0^{2\pi}|f_1(\theta)|^2\sigma'(\theta)\,d\theta=\frac{1}{2\pi}\int_0^{2\pi}|f_1(\theta)|^2\,d\sigma(\theta)<\infty.$$

Then using case 1) we have

$$\lim_{n\to\infty} a_n^{(1)}=\lim_{n\to\infty} b_n^{(1)}=0.$$

To evaluate the $a_n^{(2)}$ and $b_n^{(2)}$, we use the fact that under condition 2) the orthonormal set is uniformly bounded, i.e. that $\{|\varphi_n(e^{i\theta})|\}_0^\infty\leqslant C$. We then obtain the inequalities

$$|b_n^{(2)}|\leqslant\frac{MC}{2\pi}\int_0^{2\pi}|f_0(\theta)-f_1(\theta)|\,d\theta\leqslant\frac{MC\varepsilon}{2\pi},$$

$$|a_n^{(2)}|\leqslant\frac{1}{2\pi}\left(C+\frac{\alpha}{\alpha_0}\cdot\frac{1}{\sqrt{m}}\right)\int_0^{2\pi}|f_0(\theta)-f_1(\theta)|\,d\theta\leqslant$$

$$\leqslant\frac{1}{2\pi}\left(C+\frac{\alpha}{\alpha_0\sqrt{m}}\right)\varepsilon$$

and thus arrive at*

$$\lim_{n\to\infty} a_n^{(2)}=\lim_{n\to\infty} b_n^{(2)}=0,\quad \lim_{n\to\infty} a_n=\lim_{n\to\infty} b_n=0.$$

Using the lemma just proved, we have the following

Theorem 4.8. Let

$$\int_0^{2\pi}\ln\sigma'(\theta)\,d\theta>-\infty. \tag{4.35}$$

Assume that on some interval $[\alpha, \beta]\subset[0, 2\pi]$, the function $\sigma(\theta)$ is absolutely continuous, and that $p(\theta)$ is continuous, and let**

$$\omega(\delta;\ p)\leqslant\frac{C\sqrt{\delta}}{\left(\ln\frac{1}{\delta}\right)^\gamma},\qquad \gamma>1, \tag{4.36}$$

* Later, in Section 7.8, we shall examine a more general situation in which the limit (4.33') exists.

** Here C and in what follows $C_1, C_2, \ldots$ are constants.

and $p(\theta)$ be bounded from below almost everywhere:

$$0 < m \leqslant p(\theta). \tag{4.37}$$

Then at every internal point θ_0 of $[\alpha, \beta]$, we have

$$\overline{\lim_{n \to \infty}} \left| \varphi_n^*\left(e^{i\theta_0}\right) \right| < \infty. \tag{4.38}$$

To prove this, let us set $u(\theta) = \ln \frac{1}{p(\theta)}$ in Theorem 4.7. Since on $[\alpha, \beta]$ the function $p(\theta)$ is bounded both from above and from below, the modulus of continuity of $\ln p(\theta)$ is of the same order as is $p(\theta)$, and therefore $\omega\left\{\delta; \ln \frac{1}{p(\theta)}\right\}$ approaches zero more rapidly than does $\left(\ln \frac{1}{\delta}\right)^{-1-\lambda}$ for $\lambda > 0$. Therefore, according to a well- known theorem, the Fourier series of $\ln \frac{1}{p(\theta)}$ and the conjugate series both converge uniformly within $[\alpha, \beta]$. This implies that the Maclaurin series of $\ln \pi(z)$ converges uniformly in the arc $e^{i\theta}$, $\theta \in [\alpha, \beta]$, and therefore within this arc both $\ln \pi(z)$ and $\pi(z)$ have boundary values, and the boundary value $\pi(e^{i\theta})$ is a continuous function.

Equation (4.31) implies that $\arg \pi(e^{i\theta})$, the function conjugate to $\frac{1}{2} \ln \frac{1}{p(\theta)}$, satisfies the inequality

$$|\gamma| = |\arg \pi(e^{i(\theta+\delta)}) - \arg \pi(e^{i\theta})| \leqslant \frac{C_1 \sqrt{\delta}}{\left(\ln \frac{1}{\delta}\right)^{\gamma - \frac{1}{2}}}. \tag{4.39}$$

It follows from (2.6) and (3.13) that in the interior of $[\alpha, \beta]$, that is, for $\alpha + \epsilon \leq \theta \leq \beta - \epsilon$, $\epsilon > 0$, we have

$$|\pi(e^{i(\theta+\delta)}) - \pi(e^{i\theta})|^2 \leqslant \left\{\frac{1}{\sqrt{p(\theta+\delta)}} - \frac{1}{\sqrt{p(\theta)}}\right\}^2 + $$
$$+ \frac{\gamma^2}{\sqrt{p(\theta)\, p(\theta+\delta)}} \leqslant C_2 |p(\theta+\delta) - p(\theta)|^2 +$$
$$+ C_3 |\arg \pi(e^{i(\theta+\delta)}) - \arg \pi(e^{i\theta})|^2,$$

and from this we obtain

$$|\pi(e^{i(\theta+\delta)})-\pi(e^{i\theta})|\leqslant\frac{C_4\sqrt{\delta}}{\left(\ln\frac{1}{\delta}\right)^{\gamma-\frac{1}{2}}},\qquad \theta,\ \theta+\delta\in[\alpha,\ \beta]. \quad (4.40)$$

From (1.9) and (1.7) we obtain

$$\varphi_n^*(e^{i\theta_0})\,\varphi_n^*(0)=\frac{\alpha}{2\pi}\int_0^{2\pi}\pi_0(\theta)\,K_n(e^{i\theta_0},\ e^{i\theta})\,d\sigma(\theta);$$

$$K_n(e^{i\theta_0},\ e^{i\theta})=\frac{e^{i\theta}\varphi_n^*(e^{i\theta_0})\,\overline{\varphi_n^*(e^{i\theta})}-e^{i\theta_0}\varphi_n(e^{i\theta_0})\,\overline{\varphi_n(e^{i\theta})}}{e^{i\theta}-e^{i\theta_0}}. \quad (4.41)$$

Since

$$\frac{1}{2\pi}\int_0^{2\pi}K_n(e^{i\theta_0},\ e^{i\theta})\,d\sigma(\theta)=1, \quad (4.42)$$

we have

$$\alpha_n\varphi_n^*(e^{i\theta_0})-\alpha\pi_0(\theta_0)=\frac{\alpha}{2\pi}\int_0^{2\pi}\frac{\pi_0(\theta)-\pi_0(\theta_0)}{e^{i\theta}-e^{i\theta_0}}\{e^{i\theta_0}\varphi_n^*(e^{i\theta_0})\,\overline{\varphi_n^*(e^{i\theta})}-$$

$$-e^{i\theta_0}\varphi_n(e^{i\theta_0})\,\overline{\varphi_n(e^{i\theta})}\}\,d\sigma(\theta). \quad (4.43)$$

Let $\alpha+2\epsilon\leq\theta_0\leq\beta+2\epsilon$, and introduce the new function

$$f_0(\theta)=\frac{\pi_0(\theta)-\pi_0(\theta_0)}{e^{i\theta}-e^{i\theta_0}}. \quad (4.44)$$

Then in the notation of (4.33) we may write our equation in the form

$$\frac{\alpha_n}{\alpha}\varphi_n^*(e^{i\theta_0})-\pi(e^{i\theta_0})=a_n\varphi_n^*(e^{i\theta_0})-e^{i\theta}b_n\varphi_n(e^{i\theta_0}). \quad (4.45)$$

From this expression and the equation obtained from it by taking the complex conjugate, we arrive at

$$\left(\frac{\alpha_n}{\alpha}-a_n\right)\varphi_n^*(e^{i\theta_0})+b_ne^{i\theta_0}\varphi_n(e^{i\theta_0})=\pi(e^{i\theta_0}),$$

$$\bar{b}_ne^{-i\theta_0}\varphi_n^*(e^{i\theta_0})+\left(\frac{\alpha_n}{\alpha}-\bar{a}_n\right)\varphi_n(e^{i\theta_0})=e^{in\theta_0}\overline{\pi(e^{i\theta_0})},$$

whence

$$\varphi_n^*(e^{i\theta_0}) = \frac{\left(\frac{\alpha_n}{\alpha} - a_n\right)\pi(e^{i\theta_0}) - b_n e^{i(n+1)\theta_0}\overline{\pi(e^{i\theta_0})}}{\left|\frac{\alpha_n}{\alpha} - a_n\right|^2 - |b_n|^2}. \quad (4.46)$$

It is easily shown that $f_0(\theta) \in L_2^\sigma$, and what is more, that on the interval $\alpha + 2\epsilon \leq \theta_0 \leq \beta - 2\epsilon$ we have

$$\|f_0(\theta)\|_2^\sigma \leqslant A, \quad (4.47)$$

independent of θ_0.

We prove this as follows. The function $p(\theta)$ is continuous on $[\alpha, \beta]$, so that, assuming that $p(\theta) \leq M$ for $\theta \in [\alpha, \beta]$, according to (4.40).

$$\int_{\alpha+\varepsilon}^{-\varepsilon} |f_0(\theta)|^2 d\sigma(\theta) \leqslant \frac{M}{4} \int_{\alpha+\varepsilon}^{\beta-\varepsilon} \left| \frac{\pi_0(\theta) - \pi_0(\theta_0)}{\sin\frac{\theta-\theta_0}{2}} \right|^2 d\theta \leqslant$$

$$\leqslant \frac{M\pi^2}{4} \int_{\alpha+\varepsilon}^{\beta-\varepsilon} \left| \frac{\pi_0(\theta) - \pi_0(\theta_0)}{\theta - \theta_0} \right|^2 d\theta \leqslant$$

$$\leqslant \frac{MC^2\pi^2}{4} \int_{\alpha+\varepsilon}^{\beta-\varepsilon} \frac{d\theta}{|\theta-\theta_0|} \left| \ln \frac{1}{|\theta-\theta_0|} \right|^{1-2\gamma}. \quad (4.48)$$

This implies that

$$\int_{\alpha+\varepsilon}^{\beta-\varepsilon} |f_0(\theta)|^2 d\sigma(\theta) \leqslant \frac{MC^2\pi^2}{8(\gamma-1)} \left\{ \left[\ln \frac{1}{\beta-\varepsilon-\theta_0}\right]^{2-2\gamma} + \right.$$

$$\left. + \left[\ln \frac{1}{\theta_0 - \alpha - \varepsilon}\right]^{2-2\gamma} \right\} \leqslant C_1 \left[\ln \frac{1}{\beta - \alpha - 3\varepsilon}\right]^{2-2\gamma}, \quad (4.49)$$

independent of θ_0. For $\theta \in e$, where

$$e = [0, 2\pi] - [\alpha + \varepsilon, \beta - \varepsilon],$$

we have

$$|\theta - \theta_0| \geqslant \varepsilon, \quad |e^{i\theta} - e^{i\theta_0}| = 2\left|\sin\frac{\theta-\theta_0}{2}\right| \geqslant \frac{2}{\pi}|\theta - \theta_0| \geqslant \frac{2\varepsilon}{\pi}, \quad (4.50)$$

and this leads to the inequality

$$\left|\frac{1}{2\pi}\int_{e}\right| \leqslant \left(\frac{\pi}{2\varepsilon}\right)^2 \{\|\pi_0(\theta) - \pi_0(\theta_0)\|_2^{\sigma}\}^2 \leqslant$$

$$\leqslant \left(\frac{\pi}{2\varepsilon}\right)^2 \{\|\pi_0(\theta_0)\|_2^{\sigma} + \sqrt{c_0}\,|\pi(\theta_0)|\}^2, \qquad (4.51)$$

which is also independent of θ_0, since $|\pi(\theta_0)| = \frac{1}{\sqrt{p(\theta_0)}} \leqslant \frac{1}{\sqrt{m}}$.
This proves the assertion and (4.47).

According to (4.44) we have

$$\frac{1}{2\pi}\int_0^{2\pi} \frac{e^{i\theta} f_0(\theta)\,d\theta}{\pi(e^{i\theta})} = \frac{1}{2\pi i}\int_{|z|=1} \frac{\pi(z) - \pi(z_0)}{(z - z_0)\,\pi(z)}\,dz =$$

$$= -\frac{\pi(z_0)}{2\pi i}\int_{|z|=1} \frac{\frac{1}{\pi(z)} - \frac{1}{\pi(z_0)}}{z - z_0}\,dz = 0, \quad z = e^{i\theta}, \quad z_0 = e^{i\theta_0}, \qquad (4.51')$$

since $\frac{1}{\pi(z)} \in H_2$, and therefore $f_0(\theta)$ satisfies all the conditions of case 1), Lemma 4.1. Hence if $\alpha + 2\epsilon \leq \theta_0 \leq \beta - 2\epsilon$, we have

$$\lim_{n\to\infty} a_n = \lim_{n\to\infty} b_n = 0. \qquad (4.52)$$

These conditions and (1.27) imply that at each point of the interval $[\alpha + 2\epsilon, \beta - 2\epsilon]$ expression (4.46) has the limit

$$\lim_{n\to\infty} \varphi_n^*(e^{i\theta_0}) = \pi(e^{i\theta_0}), \qquad (4.53)$$

from which one obtains (4.38).

4.5. Since both the a_n and b_n coefficients of (4.33) are functions of θ_0, namely,

$$a_n = a_n(\theta_0), \quad b_n = b_n(\theta_0)$$

(as follows from the fact that $f_0(\theta)$ in (4.44) depends on θ_0), we are not assured that the $a_n(\theta_0)$, $b_n(\theta_0)$ converge uniformly to zero or, hence, that the orthonormal set is uniformly bounded in the interior of $[e^{i\alpha}, e^{i\beta}]$. There is another method, however, by which we can prove the following

Theorem 4.9. Under the conditions of Theorem 4.8, we have uniformly

$$|\varphi_n^*(e^{i\theta_0})| \leqslant C, \quad (n=0,\ 1,\ \ldots),\ \alpha+2\varepsilon \leqslant \theta_0 \leqslant \beta-2\varepsilon. \quad (4.54)$$

Writing $z = e^{i\theta}$, $z_0 = e^{i\theta_0}$, we find from (4.33) and (4.44) that

$$b_n(\theta_0) = \frac{1}{2\pi}\int_0^{2\pi} \frac{\pi_0(\theta)-\pi_0(\theta_0)}{z-z_0}\,\overline{\varphi_n(z)}\,d\sigma(\theta) =$$

$$= \frac{1}{2\pi}\int_{|z|=1} \frac{\overline{\varphi_n(z)}\,d\theta}{\pi(z)(z-z_0)} - \pi(z_0)\cdot\frac{1}{2\pi}\int_{|z|=1}\frac{\overline{\varphi_n(z)}\,d\sigma(\theta)}{z-z_0}\,^{*)},$$

$$\alpha+2\varepsilon \leqslant \theta_0 \leqslant \beta-2\varepsilon.$$

Setting $\zeta = rz_0$, we have

$$\frac{1}{2\pi i}\int_{|z|=1}\frac{\varphi_n(z)\,dz}{\pi(z)(z-\zeta)} = \begin{cases} 0, & r>1,\\ \dfrac{\varphi_n(\zeta)}{\pi(\zeta)}, & r<1,\end{cases}$$

which leads simply to

$$\frac{1}{2\pi i}\int_{|z|=1}\frac{\varphi_n(z)\,dz}{\pi(z)(z-z_0)} = \frac{\varphi_n(z_0)}{2\pi(z_0)}. \quad (4.55)$$

The first integral, therefore is

$$\frac{1}{2\pi}\int_{|z|=1}\frac{\overline{\varphi_n(z)}\,d\theta}{\overline{\pi(z)}\,(z-z_0)} = -\frac{\overline{\varphi_n(z_0)}}{2z_0\overline{\pi(z_0)}}. \quad (4.56)$$

To calculate the second integral, we use the identity

$$\frac{z+z_0}{z-z_0} = 1+\frac{2z_0}{z-z_0} = -1+\frac{2z}{z-z_0} \quad (4.57)$$

to obtain

$$\frac{1}{2\pi}\int_{|z|=1}\frac{\overline{\varphi_n(z)}\,d\sigma(\theta)}{z-z_0} = \frac{1}{2\pi z_0}\int\frac{z\overline{\varphi_n(z)}\,d\sigma(\theta)}{z-z_0}.$$

Let

$$\overline{\varphi_n(e^{i\theta})}\,d\sigma(\theta) = d\mu_n(\theta),$$

---

* Both of these integrals are understood in the sense of the Cauchy principal value.

so that

$$\frac{1}{2\pi}\int_0^{2\pi} |d\mu_n(\theta)| = \frac{1}{2\pi}\int_0^{2\pi} |\varphi_n(e^{i\theta})|\, d\sigma(\theta) \leqslant \sqrt{c_0}\|\varphi_n\|_2^\sigma = \sqrt{c_0},$$

and this implies that $\mu_n(\theta)$ is a function of bounded variation.

Using a theorem due to Privalov on the boundary values of an integral of the Cauchy-Stieltjes type,* we have

$$\frac{1}{2\pi}\int_{|z|=1} \frac{\overline{\varphi_n(z)}\, d\sigma(\theta)}{z-z_0} = \frac{1}{2\pi z_0}\int_{|z|=1} \frac{z\, d\mu_n(\theta)}{z-z_0} =$$

$$= \frac{1}{z_0}\lim_{\zeta\to z_0} \frac{1}{2\pi}\int_{|z|=1} \frac{z\, d\mu_n(\theta)}{z-\zeta} - \frac{\mu_n'(\theta_0)}{2z_0}, \quad |\zeta|<1,$$

from which, again using (4.57), we obtain

$$\frac{1}{2\pi}\int_{|z|=1} \frac{\overline{\varphi_n(z)}\, d\sigma(\theta)}{z-z_0} = \frac{1}{2z_0}\lim_{\zeta\to z_0}\frac{1}{2\pi}\int_0^{2\pi}\frac{z+\zeta}{z-\zeta}\overline{\varphi_n(z)}\, d\sigma(\theta) - \frac{\overline{\varphi_n(z_0)}\, p(\theta_0)}{2z_0}. \tag{4.58}$$

From (1.19) with $\zeta = rz_0$, $r<1$, we have

$$\frac{1}{2\pi}\int_0^{2\pi}\frac{z+\zeta}{z-\zeta}\overline{\varphi_n(z)}\, d\sigma(\theta) = c_0\zeta^{-n}\left[F(\zeta)\varphi_n^*(\zeta) - \psi_n^*(\zeta)\right], \quad z=e^{i\theta},$$

whence we obtain

$$\lim_{\zeta\to z_0}\frac{1}{2\pi}\int_0^{2\pi}\frac{z+\zeta}{z-\zeta}\overline{\varphi_n(z)}\, d\sigma(\theta) = c_0 z_0^{-n}\left[F(z_0)\varphi_n^*(z_0) - \psi_n^*(z_0)\right], \tag{4.59}$$

where

$$F(z_0) = \lim_{r\to 1-0} F(re^{i\theta_0}). \tag{4.60}$$

According to (1.21),

$$\Re F(z_0) = \frac{p(\theta_0)}{c_0} = \frac{1}{c_0|\pi(z_0)|^2}. \tag{4.60'}$$

---

* See I. I. Privalov, [1], Chapter III, Section 2.

Using (4.55), (4.56), (4.58), and (4.59), it is easily seen that

$$b_n(\theta_0) = -\frac{\overline{\varphi_n(z_0)}}{2z_0\overline{\pi(z_0)}} - \frac{\pi(z_0)}{2z_0}\Big\{ c_0 z_0^{-n}\left[F(z_0)\varphi_n^*(z_0) - \psi_n^*(z_0)\right] -$$

$$- \frac{\overline{\varphi_n(z_0)}}{|\pi(z_0)|^2}\Big\} = -\frac{c_0\pi(z_0)\varphi_n^*(z_0)}{2z_0^{n+1}}\left\{F(z_0) - \frac{\psi_n^*(z_0)}{\varphi_n^*(z_0)}\right\}. \quad (4.61)$$

This, with (1.21) and (1.18), leads to

$$\frac{c_0|\pi(z_0)\varphi_n^*(z_0)|}{2}\cdot\left|\Re\left\{F(z_0) - \frac{\psi_n^*(z_0)}{\varphi_n^*(z_0)}\right\}\right| =$$

$$= \frac{c_0}{2}|\pi(z_0)\varphi_n^*(z_0)|\cdot\left|\frac{p(\theta_0)}{c_0} - \frac{1}{c_0|\varphi_n^*(z_0)|^2}\right| =$$

$$= \frac{1}{2}|\pi(z_0)\varphi_n^*(z_0)|\cdot\left|\frac{1}{|\pi(z_0)|^2} - \frac{1}{|\varphi_n^*(z_0)|^2}\right| \leqslant |b_n(\theta_0)|. \quad (4.62)$$

Finally, we arrive at the inequality

$$\left|\left|\frac{\varphi_n^*(z_0)}{\pi(z_0)}\right| - \left|\frac{\pi(z_0)}{\varphi_n^*(z_0)}\right|\right| \leqslant 2|b_n(\theta_0)|, \qquad (n = 1, 2, \ldots). \quad (4.63)$$

It is easily shown that the $|b_n(\theta_0)|$ are uniformly bounded on the interval $\alpha + 2\epsilon \leq \theta_0 \leq \beta - 2\epsilon$. Indeed, we have

$$\begin{aligned} |b_n(\theta_0)| &\leqslant \frac{1}{2\pi}\int_0^{2\pi} |f_0(\theta)||\varphi_n(e^{i\theta})|\,d\sigma(\theta) \leqslant \\ &\leqslant \|f_0(\theta)\|_2^\sigma \cdot \|\varphi_n(e^{i\theta})\|_2^\sigma \leqslant A, \end{aligned} \quad (4.64)$$

where A is independent of both n and θ_0, and $\alpha + 2\epsilon \leq \theta_0 \leq \beta - 2\epsilon$.

From (4.63) we obtain

$$|\varphi_n^*(e^{i\theta_0})| \leqslant |\pi(e^{i\theta})|\cdot\left(A + \sqrt{A^2+1}\right) =$$

$$= \frac{A + \sqrt{A^2+1}}{\sqrt{p(\theta_0)}} \leqslant \frac{A + \sqrt{A^2+1}}{\sqrt{m}} = C, \quad (4.65)$$

where C is also independent of both n and $\theta_0 \in [\alpha + 2\epsilon, \beta - 2\epsilon]$

4.6. Let us turn to yet one other general method for obtaining local estimates.

Theorem 4.10. If the integral (4.35) exists, then in the interior of the arc $[e^{i\alpha}, e^{i\beta}]$ we have

$$|\varphi_n(e^{i\theta})| \leqslant (C_1 + C_2\sqrt{n}\,\delta_n) \max|\pi(re^{i\theta})|,$$
$$\alpha + \eta \leqslant \theta \leqslant \beta - \eta, \quad \eta > 0, \quad r \leqslant 1 - \frac{1}{2An}, \tag{4.66}$$

where C_1, C_2, and A are independent of both n and θ.

To prove this consider the points $M_1, \ldots, M_6$ (see Fig. 1) whose coordinates are given by the complex numbers

$$\left.\begin{aligned} z_1 &= \rho_1 e^{i(\alpha+\delta)}, & z_2 &= \rho_2 e^{i(\alpha+\delta)}, \\ z_3 &= e^{i(\alpha+\delta_1)}, & z_4 &= e^{i(\beta-\delta_1)}, \\ z_5 &= \rho_2 e^{i(\beta-\delta)}, & z_6 &= \rho_1 e^{i(\beta-\delta)}, \end{aligned}\right\} \tag{4.67}$$

such that

$$0 < \delta < \delta_1, \quad \rho_1 < \rho_2 < 1.$$

We connect the pairs of points (M_2, M_3), (M_4, M_5), and (M_6, M_1) by curves of bounded curvature so as to obtain a closed convex smooth curve Γ which does not leave the region defined by $\rho_0 \leq |z| \leq 1$, $\alpha + \delta \leq \theta \leq \beta - \delta$; the arc M_3M_4 of the circumference and the intervals M_1M_2 and M_5M_6 of the radii form parts of Γ.

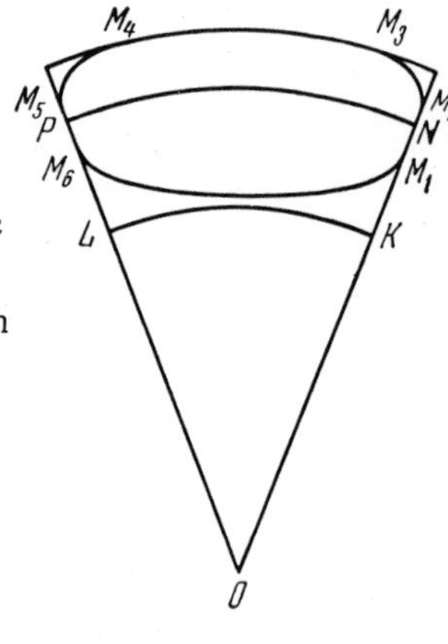

Fig. 1.

$$OM_1 = OM_6 = \rho_1,$$
$$OM_2 = OM_5 = \rho_2,$$
$$OM_3 = OM_4 = 1,$$
$$ON = OP = 1 - \frac{1}{2An},$$
$$OK = OL = \rho_0.$$

We now introduce the notation

$$\mu'_n = \max_{z\in\Gamma} |\varphi_n^*(z)| = |\varphi_n^*(z_0)|, \quad z_0 \in \Gamma. \tag{4.68}$$

Then throughout the closed region $\overline{B}$ bounded by Γ we have $|\varphi_n^*(z)| \leq \mu'_n$.

Now at every point z' of Γ let us construct a tangent circle $\gamma(z')$ lying in $\overline{B}$ and with radius r'; then at every point of $\gamma(z')$ we have $|\varphi_n^*(z)| \leq \mu'_n$. According to a theorem due to Szász [1],

we then have

$$\left|\frac{d\varphi_n^*(z)}{dz}\right| \leqslant \frac{n\mu_n'}{r'}, \quad z \in \gamma(z'), \tag{4.69}$$

which is thus also valid at z'. Now we have constructed Γ in a way that makes it possible to name its minimum radius of curvature $r' = r_0$, so that we may set $r' = r_0$ for all z'. Hence on every point of Γ, and therefore also throughout the closed region $\overline{B}$ we obtain*

$$\left|\frac{d\varphi_n^*(z)}{dz}\right| \leqslant An\mu_n', \quad z \in \overline{B}, \tag{4.70}$$

where $A = 1/r_0$ is independent of both n and z.

Let us choose n so large that $1 - \frac{1}{4An} \geqslant \rho_0$, in which case we find from (3.38) that if $r \leqslant 1 - \frac{1}{2An}$, then

$$|\varphi_n^*(re^{i\theta})| \leqslant \frac{\alpha}{\alpha_0} |\pi(re^{i\theta})| \cdot \left(1 + \sqrt{2An}\,\delta_n\right). \tag{4.71}$$

First, assume that $|z_0| \leqslant 1 - \frac{1}{2An}$. Then using the last inequality we have

$$\mu_n' = |\varphi_n^*(z_0)| \leqslant \frac{\alpha}{\alpha_0} |\pi(re^{i\theta_0})| \left(1 + \sqrt{2An}\,\delta_n\right),$$

and therefore on $[\alpha + \delta, \beta - \delta_1]$ we obtain the inequality

$$\begin{gathered} |\varphi_n^*(e^{i\theta})| \leqslant \mu_n' \leqslant \frac{\alpha}{\alpha_0}\left(1 + \sqrt{2An}\,\delta_n\right) \max|\pi(re^{i\theta})|, \\ \alpha + \delta \leqslant \theta \leqslant \beta - \delta, \quad r \leqslant 1 - \frac{1}{2An}. \end{gathered} \tag{4.72}$$

Second, assume that $1 - \frac{1}{2An} < |z_0| \leqslant 1$. Repeating the considerations of Theorem 3.6 and using (4.70), we arrive simply at

$$\begin{gathered} |\varphi_n^*(z_0) - \varphi_n^*(z')| \leqslant |z_0 - z'| \cdot An\mu_n', \\ z_0 = r_0 e^{i\theta_0}, \quad z' = r' e^{i\theta_0}, \quad r' < r_0, \end{gathered}$$

from which, setting $r_0 - r' = 1/2An$, we obtain

* The method here used to obtain (4.70) is that of D. Jackson [2]. See also G. Szegö [4], and W. Sewell [1], Section 2.1.

$$|\varphi_n^*(z') - \varphi_n^*(z_0)| \leqslant \frac{\mu_n'}{2}, \quad |\varphi_n^*(z')| \geqslant \frac{\mu_n'}{2}.$$

Now since

$$r' = |z'| = r_0 - \frac{1}{2An} \leqslant 1 - \frac{1}{2An},$$

we may apply (4.71) at z', which leads to

$$\frac{\mu_n'}{2} \leqslant |\varphi_n^*(z')| \leqslant \frac{\alpha}{\alpha_0}(1 + \sqrt{2An}\,\delta_n)\,|\pi(r'e^{i\vartheta_0})|.$$

Therefore in this case also we have

$$|\varphi_n^*(e^{i\theta})| \leqslant \mu_n' \leqslant \frac{2\alpha}{\alpha_0}(1 + \sqrt{2An}\,\delta_n)\max|\pi(re^{i\theta})|,$$
$$\alpha + \delta_1 \leqslant \theta \leqslant \beta - \delta_1,$$

where we maximize the modulus of $\pi(z)$ in the closed region

$$\alpha + \delta \leqslant \theta \leqslant \beta - \delta, \quad r \leqslant 1 - \frac{1}{2An}.$$

The theorem we have proved implies the following: if an orthonormal set is such that $\delta_n = O(1/n)$, the increase of the $\{\varphi_n^*(z)\}$ on an arc $[e^{i\alpha}, e^{i\beta}]$ depends solely on the values of $p(\theta)$ on the interval $[\alpha, \beta]$, since the function $\ln|\pi(z)|$ is defined in terms of the Poisson integral (2.16').

Theorem 4.11. If (4.35) exists and if on the interval $[\alpha, \beta]$ we have

$$\sigma(\theta_2) - \sigma(\theta_1) \geqslant m(\theta_2 - \theta_1), \quad \alpha \leqslant \theta_1 < \theta_2 \leqslant \beta, \quad m > 0, \tag{4.73}$$

then in the interior of the arc $[e^{i\alpha}, e^{i\beta}]$ we have

$$|\varphi_n^*(e^{i\theta})| \leqslant C_1 + C_2\sqrt{n}\,\delta_n, \quad \alpha + \eta \leqslant \theta \leqslant \beta - \eta,$$
$$\eta > 0, \quad n \geqslant n_0. \tag{4.74}$$

To prove this we note that (4.73) implies that $p(\theta) \geqslant m > 0$, $\theta \in [\alpha, \beta]$. Using known properties of Poisson's integral,* we find

* See, for instance, A. Zygmund [1], Section 3.42; see also the note to 4.1 at the end of the book.

that for every $\delta > 0$ there exist a $\rho < 1$ such that if $\rho \le r < 1$, $\alpha + \delta \le \theta \le \beta - \delta$, then $\ln|\pi(z)| \le a$, where $\underline{a}$ is a constant depending on δ. This leads us to the inequality

$$|\pi(re^{i\theta})| \leqslant e^{a}, \quad \alpha+\delta \leqslant \theta \leqslant \beta-\delta, \quad \rho \leqslant r < 1. \tag{4.75}$$

Remark 4.2. Let us turn to a certain necessary condition for local boundedness of an orthonormal set, namely, the following: if condition (3.53) of Theorem 3.10 holds only on the arc $[e^{i\alpha}, e^{i\beta}]$, then the conclusion in (3.54) follows only on the interval $[\alpha, \beta]$. The proof of this assertion is the same as that used in (3.10).

Let us consider the behavior of the orthonormal set not on an interval, but at a point; we have

Theorem 4.12. Let $E' \subset [0, 2\pi]$ be a set of points such that

$$\begin{gathered}\int_0^h |d_t\{\sigma(\theta_0+t)-\sigma(\theta_0-t)-2t\sigma'(\theta_0)\}| = o(h),\\ \theta_0 \in E', \quad \operatorname{Mes} E' = 2\pi.\end{gathered} \tag{4.76}$$

If at some point $\theta_0 \in E'$ we have

$$\frac{1}{n+1} K_n(e^{i\theta_0}, e^{i\theta_0}) \leqslant C, \qquad (n=0, 1, 2, \ldots)$$

(in particular, if the orthonormal set is bounded at this point), then $\sigma'(\theta_0) \ge 1/C$, and therefore $\sigma'(\theta_0) = 0$, $\theta_0 \in E'$ implies

$$\varlimsup_{n\to\infty} |\varphi_n^*(e^{i\theta_0})| = \infty. \tag{4.77}$$

To prove this we use known results of Fejèr's method of summing Fourier-Stieltjes series:* from (4.16), (4.17), and the conditions stated in the theorem, we obtain the inequality

---

* See, for instance, A. Zygmund [1], Section 3.8.

$$\left.\begin{aligned}
&\frac{1}{C} \leqslant \frac{n+1}{K_n(e^{i\theta_0}, e^{i\theta_0})} \leqslant \frac{2\nu+1}{2\nu} \cdot \frac{1}{4\pi\nu} \int_0^{2\pi} \left\{ \frac{\sin \nu(\theta-\theta_0)}{\sin \frac{1}{2}(\theta-\theta_0)} \right\}^2 d\sigma(\theta), \\
&\qquad\qquad\qquad\qquad\qquad\qquad\qquad\qquad 2\nu - 1 \leqslant n, \\
&\frac{1}{C} \leqslant \lim_{\nu\to\infty} \left(\frac{2\nu+1}{2\nu}\right) \cdot \lim_{\nu\to\infty} \frac{1}{4\pi\nu} \int_0^{2\pi} \left\{ \frac{\sin \nu(\theta-\theta_0)}{\sin \frac{1}{2}(\theta-\theta_0)} \right\}^2 d\sigma(\theta) = \sigma'(\theta_0).
\end{aligned}\right\} \tag{4.78}$$

In Table III we present a list of those local estimates for orthonormal polynomials with which we are familiar.

Condition II is due to Steklov [1]; condition I has been studied by Erdos and Turan [1]. Condition III is the most general, for it places no restrictions on $\sigma(\theta)$ outside of $[\alpha, \beta]$; it is a consequence of Theorem 4.2.

Condition IV, sufficient for the validity of the uniform estimate $o(\sqrt{n})$ is a consequence of Theorem 4.10, and the existence of the integral (4.35) is necessary and sufficient for the existence of the limit $\lim_{n\to\infty} \delta_n = 0$. In conditions VIII and IX greater restrictions are placed on $\sigma(\theta)$ outside of $[\alpha, \beta]$ than in IV, but under these conditions the estimates are expressed in terms of the integral moduli of continuity of $p(\theta)$ only over the interval $[\alpha, \beta]$, whereas δ_n depends on the behavior of $\sigma(\theta)$ throughout $[0, 2\pi]$.

The only local estimate known to us in which no restrictions are placed on $p(\theta)$ outside of $[\alpha, \beta]$ are those given by Shohat ([4], Table C). In the derivation of these conditions, however, there is a mistake (p. 548), in view of which the entire derivation is seen to be incorrect.

CHAPTER V

ASYMPTOTIC FORMULAS AND LIMIT RELATIONS

5.1. As was shown at the end of Chapter I, the limit relation

$$\lim_{n\to\infty} \varphi_n^*(z) = \frac{1}{\alpha}\sum_{k=0}^{\infty} \overline{\varphi_k(0)}\,\varphi_k(z) = \pi(z), \qquad |z| < 1, \tag{5.1}$$

is equivalent to the existence of the integral of (1.26). Consequently the problem of the existence of the limit

$$\lim_{n\to\infty} \varphi_n^*(e^{i\theta}) = \pi(e^{i\theta}), \tag{5.2}$$

i.e., the question of whether the asymptotic formula

$$\varphi_n(e^{i\theta}) \simeq e^{in\theta}\overline{\pi(e^{i\theta})} \tag{5.2'}$$

is valid, brings us to Tauber's problem: *given the existence of the radial boundary value $\pi(e^{i\theta})$, deduce the convergence properties of the sequence $\{\varphi_n^*(e^{i\theta})\}$.*

Theorem 5.1. If the integral of (4.35) exists, if $\delta_n = o\left(\frac{1}{\sqrt{n}}\right)$ and if

$$\sigma(\theta_2) - \sigma(\theta_1) \geqslant m(\theta_2 - \theta_1), \qquad 0 \leqslant \theta_1 < \theta_2 \leqslant 2\pi, \; m > 0, \tag{5.3}$$

then throughout the interval $[0, 2\pi]$ we have*

$$\left.\begin{aligned} |\varphi_n^*(e^{i\theta}) - \pi(e^{i\theta})| \leqslant |\pi(e^{i\theta}) - \pi(re^{i\theta})| + C\sqrt[3]{n\delta_n^2}, \\ r = 1 - \left(\frac{\delta_n}{n}\right)^{\frac{2}{3}}, \end{aligned}\right\} \tag{5.4}$$

and hence on a set $E_0 \subset E$ of points of $[0, 2\pi]$ on which the radial

* Here C and in the sequence $C_1, C_2 \ldots$ are constants independent of n and θ.

boundary values

$$\pi(e^{i\theta}) = \lim_{r \to 1-0} \pi(re^{i\theta})$$

exist, the limit relation (5.2) and the asymptotic formula (5.2') are valid.

If particular, in view of condition I of Table I, the theorem is valid if $\sigma(\theta) \in A$ and $\omega_2(\delta; p) = o(\sqrt{\delta})$.

To prove the theorem we evaluate

$$|\pi(e^{i\theta}) - \varphi_n^*(e^{i\theta})| \leqslant |\pi(e^{i\theta}) - \pi(re^{i\theta})| + |\pi(re^{i\theta}) - \varphi_n^*(re^{i\theta})| + \\ + |\varphi_n^*(re^{i\theta}) - \varphi_n^*(e^{i\theta})|, \quad \theta \in E_0. \tag{5.5}$$

Since according to Theorem 3.7 we have $|\varphi_n^*(z)| \leq C$, $|z| \leq 1$, (n = = 0, 1, 2, . . .), it follows, setting $M_n = C$ in (3.42), that

$$|\varphi_n^*(e^{i\theta}) - \varphi_n^*(re^{i\theta})| \leqslant Cn(1-r), \quad 0 \leqslant \theta \leqslant 2\pi. \tag{5.6}$$

Further, (3.37) states that

$$|\alpha_n \varphi_n^*(re^{i\theta}) - \alpha\pi(re^{i\theta})| \leqslant \frac{\alpha\delta_n}{\sqrt{1-r}} |\pi(re^{i\theta})|, \tag{5.7}$$

which, with (2.8), leads to

$$|\varphi_n^*(re^{i\theta}) - \pi(re^{i\theta})| \leqslant \left| \varphi_n^*(re^{i\theta}) - \frac{\alpha}{\alpha_n}\pi(re^{i\theta}) \right| + \\ + \left(\frac{\alpha}{\alpha_n} - 1\right) |\pi(re^{i\theta})| \leqslant |\pi(re^{i\theta})| \left\{ \frac{\alpha\delta_n}{\alpha_n\sqrt{1-r}} + \frac{\alpha^2\delta_n^2}{\alpha_n(\alpha+\alpha_n)} \right\} \leqslant \\ \leqslant \frac{\alpha\delta_n}{\alpha_0} |\pi(re^{i\theta})| \cdot \left\{ \frac{1}{\sqrt{1-r}} + \frac{\alpha\delta_n}{\alpha+\alpha_0} \right\}. \tag{5.7'}$$

We thus have

$$|\varphi_n^*(re^{i\theta}) - \pi(re^{i\theta})| \leqslant \frac{C_1|\pi(re^{i\theta})|}{\sqrt{1-r}} \delta_n, \quad r < 1. \tag{5.8}$$

From (5.5), (5.6), and (5.8) we obtain

$$|\pi(e^{i\theta}) - \varphi_n^*(e^{i\theta})| \leqslant |\pi(e^{i\theta}) - \pi(re^{i\theta})| + Cn(1-r) + \\ + \frac{C_1\delta_n}{\sqrt{1-r}} |\pi(re^{i\theta})|. \tag{5.9}$$

If $\theta \in E_0$, then

$$\pi(e^{i\theta}) - \pi(re^{i\theta}) = \varepsilon(r, \theta), \qquad |\pi(re^{i\theta})| \leqslant |\varepsilon(r, \theta)| + |\pi(e^{i\theta})|,$$

where

$$\lim_{r \to 1-0} \varepsilon(r, \theta) = 0.$$

Further, by (2.17) we have

$$|\pi(re^{i\theta})| \leqslant \frac{1}{\sqrt{m}}$$

for $r < 1$. Let us choose r according to

$$n(1-r) = \frac{\delta_n}{\sqrt{1-r}}, \tag{5.10}$$

which means that $1 - r = \left(\frac{\delta_n}{n}\right)^{\frac{2}{3}}$, and as a result

$$n(1-r) = \frac{\delta_n}{\sqrt{1-r}} = \sqrt[3]{n\delta_n^2} = o(1), \tag{5.11}$$

because $\delta_n^2 = o\left(\frac{1}{n}\right)$.

Finally, we arrive at

$$|\pi(e^{i\theta}) - \varphi_n^*(e^{i\theta})| \leqslant \varepsilon(r, \theta) + C_2 \sqrt[3]{n\delta_n^2}, \qquad \theta \in E_0, \tag{5.12}$$

where $\epsilon(r, \theta)$ tends to zero with $1 - r$, i.e., with $1/n$.

Remark 5.1. One cannot claim uniform convergence, since $\epsilon(z, \theta)$ depends on θ; if, however, $\pi(e^{i\theta})$ were continuous on some interval $[\alpha, \beta]$, we could obtain an expression for $\epsilon(r, \theta)$ independent of θ.*

5.2. Theorem 5.2. If $\sigma(\theta) \in A$ and if

$$\int_0^a x^{-\frac{3}{2}} \omega_2(x; p)\, dx < \infty, \tag{5.13}$$

* See, for instance, Zygmund [1], Section 3.4.

then in the closed region $|z| \leq 1$ we have, uniformly,*

$$|\varphi_n^*(z) - \pi(z)| \leqslant \varepsilon_n, \quad \varepsilon_n \leqslant C \int_0^{\frac{1}{n}} x^{-\frac{3}{2}} \omega_2(x;\, p)\, dx. \tag{5.14}$$

Equation (5.13) implies the existence of the integral

$$\int_{\frac{1}{a}}^{\infty} y^{-\frac{1}{2}} \omega_2\left(\frac{1}{y};\, p\right) dy, \tag{5.15}$$

and therefore also the convergence of the series

$$\sum_{n=1}^{\infty} \frac{1}{\sqrt{n}} \omega_2\left(\frac{1}{n};\, p\right). \tag{5.16}$$

From the property**

$$\sum_{n=1}^{\infty} |a_n| \leqslant C \sum_{n=1}^{\infty} \frac{\sqrt{|a_n|^2 + |a_{n+1}|^2 + \dots}}{\sqrt{n}} \tag{5.17}$$

of numerical series, (2.8), and condition I of Table I, we have

$$\sum_{n=1}^{\infty} |\varphi_n(0)| \leqslant C \sum_{n=1}^{\infty} \frac{1}{\sqrt{n}} \sqrt{\sum_{k=n}^{\infty} |\varphi_k(0)|^2} \leqslant$$

$$\leqslant C' \sum_{n=1}^{\infty} \frac{1}{\sqrt{n}} \omega_2\left(\frac{1}{n};\, p\right) < \infty. \tag{5.18}$$

A necessary sequence of (5.13) is $\omega_2(\delta;\, p) = o(\sqrt{\delta})$, and therefore from Theorem 3.8 we have $|\varphi_n^*(z)| \leq C$, $|z| \leq 1$, $(n = 0, 1, \dots)$.

---

* See a previous communication [5] by the present author, where this theorem is proved in a different way; in Chapter VIII we prove the more general Theorem 8.6.

** This property was obtained by Copson (see, for instance, Hardy, Littlewood, and Polya [1], p. 255 of the English-language edition, Theorem 345. Here C is an absolute constant. The deviation of (5.17) and (5.20) is given in the note to 5.2 at the end of the book.

(3.36) implies that

$$|\alpha\pi(z)-\alpha_n\varphi_n^*(z)|\leqslant C\sum_{k=n+1}^{\infty}|\varphi_k(0)|,\qquad |z|\leqslant 1. \qquad (5.19)$$

For $2^{r-1} \leq n+1 < 2^r$ in (5.18) we have

$$\sum_{k=n+1}^{\infty}|\varphi_k(0)|\leqslant C_1\sum_{\nu=2^{r-2}}^{\infty}\frac{1}{\sqrt{\nu}}\sqrt{\sum_{k=\nu}^{\infty}|\varphi_k(0)|^2}\leqslant$$

$$\leqslant C_1'\sum_{\nu=2^{r-2}-1}^{\infty}\frac{1}{\sqrt{\nu}}\omega_2\left(\frac{1}{\nu};p\right)\leqslant C_2\int_n^{\infty}\frac{\omega_2\left(\frac{1}{y};p\right)dy}{\sqrt{y}}=$$

$$=C_2\int_0^{\frac{1}{n}}x^{-\frac{3}{2}}\omega_2(x;p)\,dx. \qquad (5.20)$$

Using (2.17), (2.20), and (5.20), we obtain from (5.19)

$$|\varphi_n^*(z)-\pi(z)|\leqslant\left|\varphi_n^*(z)-\frac{\alpha}{\alpha_n}\pi(z)\right|+\left(\frac{\alpha}{\alpha_n}-1\right)|\pi(z)|\leqslant$$

$$\leqslant\frac{C_3}{\alpha_0}\int_0^{\frac{1}{n}}x^{-\frac{3}{2}}\omega_2(x;p)\,dx+\frac{1}{\sqrt{m}}C_4\left[\omega_2\left(\frac{1}{n};p\right)\right]^2, \qquad (5.21)$$

and since $\omega_2\left(\frac{1}{n};p\right)=o\left(\frac{1}{\sqrt{n}}\right)$, this in turn implies (5.14).

Note that $\pi(z)$ is given by a series converging absolutely and uniformly in the closed region $|z| \leq 1$, and is therefore continuous in this region. We have shown in a roundabout way that $p(\theta)$, which satisfies (5.13), is equivalent to a function continuous on $[0, 2\pi]$. Now if we assume that $\omega_2(\delta;p) < C\delta^{\alpha}$, $\alpha > 1/2$, this assertion would have followed Theorem 5 of Hardy and Littlewood [1]; but (5.13) is satisfied, for instance, if $\omega_2(\delta;p)\leqslant C\sqrt{\delta}\left(\ln\frac{1}{\delta}\right)^{-\gamma}$, $\gamma>1$, and in this case the result we have obtained is a new one, not a consequence of the above theorem.

Table IV lists the sufficient conditions known to the author for the validity of the asymptotic formula on the entire circumference, with estimates of the errors involved. Condition I has been studied by Bernshtein [1] and Szegő [1], Sections 12.1, 12.4; condition IV is analyzed by Kuz'mina [1], and is contained in our more general condition II. To see this, note that (2.8) implies that

$$\delta_n \leqslant \|\pi(e^{i\theta}) - G_n(e^{i\theta})\|_2^\sigma \leqslant M \|\pi(e^{i\theta}) - G_n(e^{i\theta})\|_2,$$

and note that if we take $G_n(z)$ to be a partial sum of the Maclaurin series for $\pi(z)$ and use the fact that this is an absolutely continuous function, we have $\delta_n = o\left(\frac{1}{\sqrt{n}}\right)$. This implies the validity of Theorem 5.1 with the corresponding uniform estimate of the error, since in Kuz'mina's case the boundary function $\pi(e^{i\theta})$ is continuous on the entire circumference.

5.3. Let us now investigate the limit relation under local conditions.

Theorem 5.3. Let the conditions of Theorem 4.8 be fulfilled. Then at every point θ_0 in the interior of $[\alpha, \beta]$

$$\lim_{n\to\infty} \varphi_n^*(e^{i\theta_0}) = \pi(e^{i\theta_0}), \quad \alpha+\varepsilon \leqslant \theta_0 \leqslant \beta-\varepsilon, \quad \varepsilon > 0. \tag{5.22}$$

To see the truth of this assertion it is sufficient to recall (4.53).

Remark 5.2. The limit relation under the local conditions was first obtained by Szegö.* He considers, namely a weight $p(\theta)$ of the form

$$p(\theta) = p_0(\theta) \prod_{k=1}^{s} |e^{i\theta} - e^{i\theta_k}|^{\sigma_k}, \quad \sigma_k > 0, \tag{5.23}$$

where $0 < m \le p_0(\theta) \le M$ on $[0, 2\pi]$, and $p_0(\theta)$ is assumed differentiable at a point $\theta_0 \neq \theta_k$ $(k = 1, 2, \ldots, s)$ and such that the fraction

$$\frac{p(\theta) - p(\theta_0) - p'(\theta_0)(\theta - \theta_0)}{(\theta - \theta_0)^2}$$

is bounded in a neighborhood e' of θ_0.

5.4 Since $\pi(e^{i\theta})$ in Theorem 5.3 is continuous if $\theta \in [\alpha, \beta]$, convergence on $[\alpha, \beta]$ is quasi-uniform.** We shall show that under more restrictive conditions imposed on $p(\theta)$ on the interval $[\alpha, \beta]$,

* See G. Szegö [1], Sections 10.4, 12.6.

** See the definition in the note to 5.4 at the back of the book.

one can prove that the convergence in (5.22) is uniform in the interior of $[\alpha, \beta]$. To do this we shall need the following

Theorem 5.4. Let the conditions of Theorem 4.8 be fulfilled and let $p(\theta)$ have a continuous second derivative $p''(\theta)$ on $[\alpha, \beta]$; further let this second derivative satisfy the Dini-Lipschitz condition

$$\omega(\delta; p'') \leqslant C\left(\ln \frac{1}{\delta}\right)^{-\lambda}, \qquad \lambda > 1. \tag{5.24}$$

Then $\pi(z)$ has a bounded second derivative in the interior of the arc $[e^{i\alpha}, e^{i\beta}]$*.

Using this theorem, it is a simple matter to obtain the following

Lemma 5.1. Under the conditions of the preceding theorem the functions $\{b_n(\theta_0)\}$ of (4.52) are equicontinuous in the interior of $[\alpha, \beta]$.

We have

$$b_n(\theta_1) - b_n(\theta_2) =$$

$$= \frac{1}{2\pi}\int_0^{2\pi}\left\{\frac{\pi_0(\theta) - \pi(z_1)}{z - z_1} - \frac{\pi_0(\theta) - \pi(z_2)}{z - z_2}\right\}\overline{\varphi_n(e^{i\theta})}\, d\sigma(\theta),$$

$$z = e^{i\theta}, \quad z_1 = e^{i\theta_1}, \quad z_2 = e^{i\theta_2}, \quad \alpha + 2\varepsilon \leqslant \theta_1 < \theta_2 \leqslant \beta - 2\varepsilon,$$
$$\varepsilon > 0,$$

whence

$$|b_n(\theta_1) - b_n(\theta_2)| \leqslant$$

$$\leqslant \sqrt{\frac{1}{2\pi}\int_0^{2\pi}\left|\frac{\pi_0(\theta) - \pi(z_1)}{z - z_1} - \frac{\pi_0(\theta) - \pi(z_2)}{z - z_2}\right|^2 d\sigma(\theta)}. \tag{5.25}$$

Let us divide the integral into two parts, one over the interval $[\alpha + \epsilon, \beta - \epsilon]$, and one over its compliment e.

* See Ya. L. Geronimus [6], Theorem 4.

We note that*

$$\frac{\pi_0(\theta)-\pi(z_1)}{z-z_1}-\frac{\pi_0(\theta)-\pi(z_2)}{z-z_2}=$$

$$=\mu(z_1-z_2)\cdot\frac{\pi_0(\theta)-\pi(\zeta)-(z-\zeta)\pi'(\zeta)}{(z-\zeta)^2}, \quad (5.26)$$

where $|\mu| \leq \pi/2$, $\zeta = e^{i\varphi}$, $\alpha + 2\epsilon \leq \theta_1 < \varphi < \theta_2 \leq \beta - 2\epsilon$. For the integral over $\underline{e}$, therefore, we have**

$$\sqrt{\frac{1}{2\pi}\int_e} \leqslant \frac{\pi}{2}\cdot\frac{|z_1-z_2|}{4\sin^2\frac{\varepsilon}{2}}\left[\sqrt{\frac{1}{2\pi}\int_0 |\pi_0(0)|^2 d\sigma(0)}+\right.$$

$$\left.+\{|\pi(\zeta)|+2|\pi'(\zeta)|\}\sqrt{\frac{1}{2\pi}\int_e d\sigma(\theta)}\right]\leqslant C_1|\theta_1-\theta_2|.$$

On the other hand, for $\alpha + \epsilon \leq \theta \leq \beta - \epsilon$ we have $\pi_0(\theta) = \pi(z)$,

$$\pi(z)=\pi(\zeta)+(z-\zeta)\pi'(\zeta)+\mu_1(z-\zeta)^2\pi''(\eta), \quad \eta=e^{i\gamma},$$

$$|\mu_1|\leqslant\left(\frac{\pi}{2}\right)^2,$$

where γ lies between θ and φ.

Hence

$$\left|\frac{\pi(z)-\pi(z_1)}{z-z_1}-\frac{\pi(z)-\pi(z_2)}{z-z_2}\right|\leqslant$$

$$\leqslant\left(\frac{\pi}{2}\right)^3|z_1-z_2||\pi''(\eta)|=C_2|\theta_1-\theta_2|.$$

Finally, then, for all n = 1, 2, 3, . . . we have

$$|b_n(\theta_1)-b_n(\theta_2)|\leqslant C_3|\theta_1-\theta_2|, \quad \alpha+2\varepsilon\leqslant\theta_1<\theta_2\leqslant\beta+2\varepsilon. \quad (5.27)$$

Lemma 5.2. Under the conditions of Theorem 5.4 we have

$$\lim_{n\to\infty} b_n(\theta_0)=0, \quad (5.28)$$

and the convergence is uniform in the interior of $[\alpha, \beta]$.

---

* See W. Sewell [1] p. 72.

** Here $C_1, C_2, C_3, \ldots$, are constants independent of θ_1, θ_2.

According to (4.53) the limit relation expressed in (5.28) holds at every point of $[\alpha + 2\epsilon, \beta - 2\epsilon]$. Then by using the fact that the sequence $\{b_n(\theta)\}$ is equicontinuous on this interval, we show that the convergence is uniform.

Let there be given an $\eta > 0$ arbitrarily small, and let us choose a $\delta > 0$ such that for all n = 1, 2, . . . we have

$$|b_n(\theta_1) - b_n(\theta_2)| \leqslant \frac{1}{3}\eta, \qquad \alpha + 2\varepsilon \leqslant \theta_1 < \theta_2 \leqslant \beta - 2\varepsilon, \tag{5.29}$$

for $|\theta_1 - \theta_2| < \delta$. Let the interval $[\alpha + 2\epsilon, \beta - 2\epsilon]$ be divided by points $\{\beta_i\}_1^m$ so that $\beta_{i+1} - \beta_i < \delta$, (i = 1, 2, . . . , m − 1). Let θ be on $[\beta_i, \beta_{i+1}]$, i.e., $|\theta - \beta_i| < \delta$. Then

$$|b_{n+k}(\theta) - b_n(\theta)| \leqslant |b_{n+k}(\theta) - b_{n+k}(\beta_i)| + |b_{n+k}(\beta_i) - b_n(\beta_i)| + \\ + |b_n(\beta_i) - b_n(\theta)| < \frac{2}{3}\eta + |b_{n+k}(\beta_i) - b_n(\beta_i)|.$$

Now choose n_i large enough so that

$$|b_{n+k}(\beta_i) - b_n(\beta_i)| < \frac{1}{3}\eta, \qquad n > n_i.$$

Then

$$|b_{n+k}(\theta) - b_n(\theta)| < \eta, \qquad n > n_i.$$

Now let $n_0 \geq \max\{n_1, n_2, \ldots, n_{m-1}\}$; and then for $n > n_0$ we have

$$|b_{n+k}(\theta) - b_n(\theta)| < \eta$$

for arbitrary θ on $[\alpha + 2\epsilon, \beta - 2\epsilon]$, which proves the uniformity of the convergence (5.28).

As a consequence of the above we have

Theorem 5.5. Let the integral of (4.35) exist, and assume that on $[\alpha, \beta]$ the function $\sigma(\theta)$ is absolutely continuous, while $p(\theta)$ satisfies $0 < m \leq (\theta)$ (i.e., is bounded from below) and has a continuous second derivative $p''(\theta)$ satisfying the Dini-Lipschitz condition (5.24). Then in the interior of $[\alpha, \beta]$ the limit relation (5.22) holds, and the convergence is uniform.

As is seen from (4.46) it is sufficient to show that the convergence in (4.34) is uniform, which has already been done in Lemma 5.2 for the $\{b_n(\theta_0)\}$ sequence. For the $\{a_n(\theta_0)\}$ we have

$$a_n(\theta_0)=\frac{1}{2\pi}\int_0^{2\pi} z\frac{\pi_0(\theta)-\pi_0(\theta_0)}{z-z_0}\overline{\varphi_n^*(z)}\,d\sigma(\theta)=$$

$$=\frac{1}{2\pi}\int_0^{2\pi} z\frac{\pi_0(\theta)-\pi_0(\theta_0)}{z-z_0}\left\{\left[\overline{\varphi_n^*(z)}-\frac{\alpha}{\alpha_n}\overline{\pi_0(\theta)}\right]+\frac{\alpha}{\alpha_n}\overline{\pi_0(\theta)}\right\}d\sigma(\theta),$$

$$z=e^{i\theta},\quad z_0=e^{i\theta}.$$

Since $\frac{1}{\pi(z)}\in H_2$,

$$\frac{1}{2\pi}\int_0^{2\pi} z\frac{\pi_0(\theta)-\pi_0(\theta_0)}{z-z_0}\overline{\pi_0(\theta)}\,d\sigma(\theta)=$$

$$=-\frac{\pi(z_0)}{2\pi i}\int_{|z|=1}\frac{\frac{1}{\pi(z)}-\frac{1}{\pi(z_0)}}{z-z_0}\,dz=0,$$

whence, using the Bunyakovskii-Schwarz inequality, we arrive at

$$|a_n(\theta_0)|\leqslant\left\|\frac{\pi_0(\theta)-\pi_0(\theta_0)}{e^{i\theta}-e^{i\theta_0}}\right\|_2^\sigma\cdot\frac{1}{\alpha_n}\|\alpha\pi_0(\theta)-\alpha_n\varphi_n^*(e^{i\theta})\|_2^\sigma.\quad(5.30)$$

According to (4.44) and (4.47) the first integral can be appraised independently of θ_0; the second integral is independent of θ_0 and tends to zero with $1/n$.

Thus we have obtained conditions I and II of Table V. Condition III has been studied by Szegö[1] (Sections 12.1, 12.6), and the limit relation holds at any point θ_0 in the neighborhood of which condition III is fulfilled.

5.5. In the sequel we shall need

<u>Lemma 5.3</u>. Let $f(\theta)\in L_1$ be continuous on $[\alpha,\beta]$ with modulus of continuity $\omega(\delta;f)$. Then the Jackson sum $u_\nu(\theta)$ [see (3.1)] has the following property in the interior of $[\alpha,\beta]$:

$$|u_\nu(\theta_0)-f(\theta_0)|\leqslant C\omega\left(\frac{1}{\nu};f\right),\quad \alpha+\varepsilon\leqslant\theta_0\leqslant\beta-\varepsilon,\quad(5.31)$$

where C is independent of <u>n</u> and θ_0.

Let t_0 denote the maximum value of t for which

$$[\theta_0 - 2t,\ \theta_0 + 2t] \subset \left[\alpha + \frac{\varepsilon}{2},\ \beta - \frac{\varepsilon}{2}\right], \tag{5.32}$$

and let us break up the integral in (3.7) into the two integrals

$$\int_0^{\frac{\pi}{2}} = \int_0^{t_0} + \int_{t_0}^{\frac{\pi}{2}} \tag{5.33}$$

Since $t \geq t_0$ in the second of these integrals,

$$\frac{3}{\pi\nu(2\nu^2+1)} \int_{t_0}^{\frac{\pi}{2}} \left(\frac{\sin \nu t}{\sin t}\right)^4 |f(\theta_0 + 2t) + f(\theta_0 - 2t) - 2f(\theta_0)|\, dt \leqslant$$

$$\leqslant \frac{3}{\pi\nu(2\nu^2+1)\sin^4 t_0} \cdot \left\{ \int_0^{2\pi} |f(t)|\, dt + \pi |f(\theta_0)| \right\} = O\left(\frac{1}{\nu^3}\right). \tag{5.34}$$

A consequence of (5.32) is that in the integrand of the first integral

$$|f(\theta_0 + 2t) + f(\theta_0 - 2t) - 2f(\theta_0)| \leqslant 2\omega(2|t|;\ f),$$

from which we obtain

$$\frac{3}{\pi\nu(2\nu^2+1)} \int_0^{t_0} \left(\frac{\sin \nu t}{\sin t}\right)^4 |A(t,\ \theta_0)|\, dt \leqslant$$

$$\leqslant \frac{6}{\pi\nu(2\nu^2+1)} \int_0^{t_0} \left(\frac{\sin \nu t}{\sin t}\right)^4 \omega(2t;\ f)\, dt \leqslant$$

$$\leqslant \frac{6\omega\left(\frac{1}{\nu};\ f\right)}{\pi\nu(2\nu^2+1)} \int_0^{t_0} \left(\frac{\sin \nu t}{\sin t}\right)^4 (2\nu t + 1)\, dt \leqslant 6\omega\left(\frac{1}{\nu};\ f\right) \tag{5.35}$$

if in the (3.4) we again write $\lambda = 2\nu t$, $\delta = 1/\nu$. This brings us to

Theorem 5.6. Let $\frac{1}{p(\theta)} \in L_2$ and $p(\theta) \leq M$ for $0 \leq \theta \leq 2\pi$; let $\frac{1}{p_0(\theta)} \leqslant \frac{1}{m}$ for $\theta \in E_h$; assume that on $[\alpha, \beta]$ the function $\sigma(\theta)$ is absolutely continuous, while $p(\theta) \geq m > 0$ is continuous and satisfies the Dini-Lipschitz condition

$$\omega(\delta;\ p) \leqslant C\left(\ln \frac{1}{\delta}\right)^{-\gamma}, \quad \gamma > 1. \tag{5.36}$$

Then in the interior of $[e^{i\alpha}, e^{i\beta}]$ we have

$$|\varphi_n^*(e^{i\theta_0}) - \pi(e^{i\theta_0})| \leqslant C_1\omega_2\left(\frac{1}{n}; \frac{1}{p}\right) + C_2(\ln n)^{1-\gamma} + C_3\delta_{n-1},^{*}$$

$$\alpha + \varepsilon \leqslant \theta_0 \leqslant \beta - \varepsilon, \qquad \varepsilon > 0, \tag{5.37}$$

where C, C_1, C_2, . . . are constants independent of δ, of n, and of θ_0.

We note first that according to Theorem 4.5, the orthonormal set is uniformly bounded in the interior of $[\alpha, \beta]$, that is to say

$$|\varphi_n(e^{i\theta_0})| \leqslant A, \quad \alpha < \alpha' \leqslant \theta_0 \leqslant \beta' < \beta. \tag{5.37'}$$

Set $f(\theta) = \frac{1}{p(\theta)} \in L_2$ in (3.1) and let ν be the largest integer for which $r = 2\nu - 2 \leq n$; then from Lemmas 3.1 and 5.3 we have

$$\left\| u_\nu(\theta) - \frac{1}{p(\theta)} \right\|_2 \leqslant 6\omega_2\left(\frac{1}{\nu}; \frac{1}{p}\right),$$

$$\left| u_\nu(\theta) - \frac{1}{p(\theta)} \right| \leqslant C\omega\left(\frac{1}{\nu}; \frac{1}{p}\right), \quad \alpha + \varepsilon \leqslant \theta \leqslant \beta - \varepsilon, \tag{5.38}$$

Because $n - 1 \leq 2\nu - 2$, it follows that $\frac{1}{\nu} \leqslant \frac{2}{n+1} < \frac{2}{n}$, and therefore

$$\left\| u_\nu(\theta) - \frac{1}{p(\theta)} \right\|_2 \leqslant 12\omega_2\left(\frac{1}{n}; \frac{1}{p}\right),$$

$$\left| u_\nu(\theta) - \frac{1}{p(\theta)} \right| \leqslant C'\omega\left(\frac{1}{n}; \frac{1}{p}\right), \qquad \alpha + \varepsilon \leqslant \theta \leqslant \beta - \varepsilon. \tag{5.38'}$$

Recall further that on $[\alpha, \beta]$ we have $p\theta \geq m > 0$, so that if $\alpha + \epsilon \leq \theta \leq \beta - \epsilon$ and $|\delta| < \epsilon$ we obtain

$$\left| \frac{1}{p(\theta+\delta)} - \frac{1}{p(\theta)} \right| = \frac{|p(\theta+\delta) - p(\theta)|}{p(\theta+\delta)\,p(\theta)} \leqslant \frac{1}{m^2}\,|p(\theta+\delta) - p(\theta)|,$$

as a consequence of which $\alpha + \epsilon \leq \theta \leq \beta - \epsilon$ means that

$$\left| u_\nu(\theta) - \frac{1}{p(\theta)} \right| \leqslant C_1\omega\left(\frac{1}{n}; p\right) \leqslant C_2(\ln n)^{-\gamma}. \tag{5.38''}$$

---

* In the special case for which $\sigma(\theta)$ is absolutely continuous throughout $[0, 2\pi]$, we may set $C_3 = 0$.

We now introduce the polynomials

$$\lambda_n(z) = \beta_n z^n + \ldots, \qquad n = 0, 1, 2, \ldots,$$

orthonormal with respect to the weight

$$p_1(\theta) = \frac{1}{u_\nu(\theta)},$$

and recall that Jackson polynomials have the property that $0 < 1/M \leq \leq u_\nu(\theta)$ $(0 \leq \theta \leq 2\pi)$. It is clear from (1.20) that all the polynomials $\{\lambda_k(z)\}_0^r$ will be the same as those obtained if we replace the weight $p_1(\theta)$ by $\frac{1}{|\lambda_r(e^{i\theta})|^2}$; hence

$$u_\nu(\theta) = |\lambda_r(e^{i\theta})|^2, \quad r = 2\nu - 2 \leqslant n. \tag{5.39}$$

From this we obtain the inequality

$$|\lambda_r(e^{i\theta})| = \sqrt{u_\nu(\theta)} \leqslant C, \quad \alpha + \varepsilon \leqslant \theta \leqslant \beta - \varepsilon, \tag{5.40}$$

since (5.38) asserts that for $\alpha + \epsilon \leq \theta \leq \beta - \epsilon$,

$$u_\nu(\theta) \leqslant \frac{1}{p(\theta)} + C_1\omega\left(\frac{1}{n};\ p\right) \leqslant \frac{1}{m} + C_1\omega\left(\frac{1}{n};\ p\right) = C.$$

Expanding $\varphi_r(z)$ in the $\{\lambda_s(z)\}_0^r$, we arrive, in analogy with (4.25), at

$$\varphi_r(e^{i\theta_0}) = \frac{\alpha_r}{\beta_r}\lambda_r(e^{i\theta_0}) +$$

$$+ \frac{1}{2\pi}\int_0^{2\pi}\left\{\frac{1}{u_\nu(\theta)} - p(\theta)\right\}\varphi_r(e^{i\theta})\,K'_{r-1}(e^{i\theta_0}, e^{i\theta})\,d\theta - d_r, \tag{5.41}$$

$$\left.\begin{aligned} d_r &= \frac{1}{2\pi}\int_0^{2\pi}\varphi_r(e^{i\theta})\,K'_{r-1}(e^{i\theta}, e^{i\theta})\,d\sigma_1(\theta), \\ K'_{r-1}(z_0, z) &= \frac{\lambda_r^*(z_0)\,\overline{\lambda_r^*(z)} - \lambda_r(z_0)\,\overline{\lambda_r(z)}}{1 - z_0\bar{z}}. \end{aligned}\right\} \tag{5.42}$$

To evaluate d_r we note that according to (5.39), (5.40), and (2.23), we have, for $\theta \in [\alpha, \beta]$ and $\alpha + \epsilon \leq \theta_0 \leq \beta - \epsilon$,

$$|K'_{r-1}(e^{i\theta_0}, e^{i\theta})| \leqslant \frac{2|\lambda_r(e^{i\theta})\,\lambda_r(e^{i\theta})|}{|e^{i\theta} - e^{i\theta_0}|} \leqslant \frac{\sqrt{u_\nu(\theta)\,u_\nu(\theta_0)}}{\sin\frac{\varepsilon}{2}} = A'\sqrt{u_\nu(\theta)}, \tag{5.43}$$

$$|d_r| \leqslant A' \| \sqrt{u_\nu(\theta)} \|_2^{\sigma_1} \| \varphi_r(e^{i\theta}) \|_2^{\sigma_1} = B\delta_r \sqrt{\| u_\nu(\theta) \|_1^{\sigma_1}} .^*$$

If in (3.1) we were to replace $f(t)$ by $1/p_0(t)$ or $1/p(t)$, we would not change $u_\nu(\theta)$, since these functions are equivalent; thus, making use of Lemma 3.1, we have

$$\| u_\nu(\theta) \|_1^{\sigma_1} \leqslant \left\| u_\nu(\theta) - \frac{1}{p_0(\theta)} \right\|_1^{\sigma_1} + \left\| \frac{1}{p_0(\theta)} \right\|_1^{\sigma_1} \leqslant C\omega_1^{\sigma_1}\left(\frac{1}{\nu}; \frac{1}{p_0}\right) \leqslant$$

$$\leqslant C \sup_{|\delta| \leqslant \frac{1}{\nu}} \left\| \frac{1}{p_0(\theta+\delta)} - \frac{1}{p_0(\theta)} \right\|_1^{\sigma_1} = C \sup_{|\delta| \leqslant \frac{1}{\nu}} \left\| \frac{1}{p_0(\theta+\delta)} \right\|_1^{\sigma_1} =$$

$$= C \sup_{|\delta| \leqslant \frac{1}{\nu}} \sqrt{\| \pi_0(\theta+\delta) \|_2^{\sigma_1}}.$$

Then from (3.9') we obtain

$$\| u_\nu(\theta) \|_1^{\sigma_1} \leqslant C_1,$$

and hence, using (5.43), we arrive at

$$|d_r| \leqslant C_2\delta_r \leqslant C_2\delta_{n-1}, \quad n-1 \leqslant r = 2\nu - 2 \leqslant n, \quad \delta_r \leqslant \delta_{n-1}. \tag{5.44}$$

Let us now obtain an appraisal for the integral in (5.41).

Throughout $[0, 2\pi]$ we know that $p(\theta) \leq M$ and $u_\nu(\theta) \geq 1/M$, so that

$$\sqrt{\frac{p(\theta)}{u_\nu(\theta)}} \leqslant M, \qquad 0 \leqslant \theta \leqslant 2\pi. \tag{5.45}$$

From (5.41) we are led to

$$\left| \varphi_r(e^{i\theta_0}) - \frac{\alpha_r}{\beta_r}\lambda_r(e^{i\theta_0}) \right| \leqslant$$

$$\leqslant \frac{M}{2\pi}\int_0^{2\pi} \left| u_\nu(\theta) - \frac{1}{p(\theta)} \right| \cdot \sqrt{p(\theta)}\, |\varphi_r(e^{i\theta})| \cdot \frac{|K'_{r-1}(e^{i\theta_0}, e^{i\theta})|}{\sqrt{u_\nu(\theta)}}\, d\theta + |d_r|. \tag{5.46}$$

* A, A', B, . . . are constants independent of θ and $\underline{n}$.

Let $\alpha' + 2\epsilon \leq \theta_0 \leq \beta' - 2\epsilon$ and let us introduce the intermediate points

$$0 < \alpha' + \varepsilon < \theta_0 - \frac{1}{n} < \theta_0 + \frac{1}{n} < \beta' - \varepsilon < 2\pi,$$

in terms of which we break up the integral in (5.46) into five integrals, $i_1, \ldots, i_5$, and proceed to obtain an appraisal for each of them.

From the Cauchy-Bunyakovskii inequality we have

$$|K'_{r-1}(e^{i\theta_0}, e^{i\theta})| \leqslant K'_{r-1}(e^{i\theta_0}, e^{i\theta_0}) \cdot K'_{r-1}(e^{i\theta}, e^{i\theta}).$$

Since, according to (5.40), $\frac{1}{u_\nu(\theta)} \geqslant \frac{1}{C^2}$ on $[\alpha' + \epsilon, \beta' - \epsilon]$, we arrive with the aid of (4.8) at

$$\left.\begin{array}{c} K'_{r-1}(e^{i\theta_0}, e^{i\theta_0}) \leqslant Cr \leqslant C_1 n, \quad K'_{r-1}(e^{i\theta}, e^{i\theta}) \leqslant C_1 n, \\ \alpha' + \varepsilon \leqslant \theta, \quad \theta_0 \leqslant \beta - \varepsilon. \end{array}\right\} \tag{5.47}$$

In this way, using (5.37'), (5.45), and (5.38"), we obtain the following estimate for i_3 in (5.46):

$$i_3 = \frac{M}{2\pi} \int_{\theta_0 - \frac{1}{n}}^{\theta_0 + \frac{1}{n}} \left| u_\nu(\theta) - \frac{1}{p(\theta)} \right| \sqrt{p(\theta)} \, |\varphi_r(e^{i\theta})| \times$$

$$\times \frac{|K'_{r-1}(e^{i\theta_0}, e^{i\theta})|}{\sqrt{u_\nu(\theta)}} d\theta \leqslant \frac{M}{2\pi} C_2 (\ln n)^{-\gamma} MAC_1 n \cdot \frac{2}{n} = C'_2 (\ln n)^{-\gamma}. \tag{5.48}$$

For the remaining integrals, we use (5.39) and (5.40), according to which

$$\frac{|K'_{r-1}(e^{i\theta_0}, e^{i\theta})|}{\sqrt{u_\nu(\theta)}} \leqslant \frac{2\,|\lambda_r(e^{i\theta})\,\lambda_r(e^{i\theta_0})|}{|e^{i\theta} - e^{i\theta_0}|\sqrt{u_\nu(\theta)}} \leqslant$$

$$\leqslant \frac{|\lambda_r(e^{i\theta_0})|}{\left|\sin\frac{\theta - \theta_0}{2}\right|} \leqslant \frac{\pi C}{|\theta - \theta_0|}.$$

Since $|\theta - \theta_0| \geq \epsilon$ for $0 \leq \theta \leq \alpha' + \epsilon$, we arrive at

$$i_1 \leqslant \frac{M\pi C}{2\pi\varepsilon}\int\limits_0^{\alpha'+\varepsilon}\left|u_\nu(\theta)-\frac{1}{p(\theta)}\right|\cdot\sqrt{p(\theta)}\,|\varphi_r(e^{i\theta})|\,d\theta \leqslant$$

$$\leqslant \frac{MC\pi}{\varepsilon}\left\|u_\nu(\theta)-\frac{1}{p(\theta)}\right\|_2\|\varphi_r(e^{i\theta})\|_2^{\sigma} \leqslant C_3\omega_2\left(\frac{1}{n};\ \frac{1}{p}\right), \quad (5.49)$$

and a similar expression for i_5.

Finally, i_2 satisfies the inequality

$$i_2 = \frac{M}{2\pi}\int\limits_{\alpha'+\varepsilon}^{\theta_0-\frac{1}{n}} \leqslant \frac{M}{2\pi}C_2(\ln n)^{-\gamma}\sqrt{M}\,A\int\limits_{\alpha'+\varepsilon}^{\theta_0-\frac{1}{n}}\frac{d\theta}{\theta_0-\theta} \leqslant C_4(\ln n)^{1-\gamma}; \quad (5.50)$$

a similar expression holds for i_4.

Summing up, therefore, from (5.46)–(5.50) we obtain

$$\left|\varphi_r(e^{i\theta_0})-\frac{\alpha_r}{\beta_r}\lambda_r(e^{i\theta_0})\right| \leqslant C_5(\ln n)^{1-\gamma}+C_6\omega_2\left(\frac{1}{n};\ \frac{1}{p}\right)+C_7\delta_{n-1},$$

$$\alpha'+2\varepsilon \leqslant \theta_0 \leqslant \beta'-2\varepsilon. \quad (5.51)$$

Further,

$$\left|u_\nu(\theta)-\frac{1}{p(\theta)}\right| = \left|\,|\lambda_r^*(e^{i\theta})|^2-|\pi(e^{i\theta})|^2\,\right| =$$

$$= \left|\,|\lambda_r^*(e^{i\theta})|-|\pi(e^{i\theta})|\,\right|\cdot\left|\,|\lambda_r^*(e^{i\theta})|+|\pi(e^{i\theta})|\,\right|,$$

and, using (5.38'), we obtain the following inequality for the difference of the moduli:

$$\left|\,|\lambda_r^*(e^{i\theta_0})|-|\pi(e^{i\theta_0})|\,\right| \leqslant \frac{C\omega\left(\frac{1}{n};\,p\right)}{|\lambda_r^*(e^{i\theta_0})|+|\pi(e^{i\theta_0})|} \leqslant C(\ln n)^{-\gamma},$$

$$\alpha'+2\varepsilon \leqslant \theta_0 \leqslant \beta'-2\varepsilon. \quad (5.52)$$

In deriving this we used the fact that according to (5.45)

$$|\pi(e^{i\theta_0})| = \frac{1}{\sqrt{p(\theta_0)}} \geqslant \frac{1}{\sqrt{M}}, \quad |\lambda_r^*(e^{i\theta_0})| = \sqrt{u_\nu(\theta_0)} \geqslant \frac{1}{\sqrt{M}},$$

$$0 \leqslant \theta_0 \leqslant 2\pi. \tag{5.52'}$$

We now use (2.6) to evaluate the difference of the arguments

$$\arg \lambda_r^*(e^{i\theta_0}) - \arg \pi(e^{i\theta_0}) = \frac{1}{4\pi}\int_0^{2\pi}\left\{\ln u_\nu(\theta) - \ln\frac{1}{p(\theta)}\right\}\operatorname{ctg}\frac{\theta_0-\theta}{2}\,d\theta,$$

$$\alpha' + 2\varepsilon \leqslant \theta_0 \leqslant \beta' - 2\varepsilon. \tag{5.53}$$

We now introduce the points

$$0 < \alpha' + \varepsilon < \theta_0 - \varepsilon_n < \theta_0 + \varepsilon_n < \beta' - \varepsilon < 2\pi,$$

$$\varepsilon_n = \frac{1}{n(\ln n)^{\gamma-1}},$$

to break up the integral in (5.53) into the five integrals $I_1, \ldots, I_5$. To obtain an appraisal for I_1 we note that $|\theta - \theta_0| \geq \epsilon$, which according to (5.38), implies that

$$|I_1| = \left|\frac{1}{4\pi}\int_0^{\alpha'+\varepsilon}\right| \leqslant \frac{1}{4\pi\sin\frac{\varepsilon}{2}}\int_0^{\alpha'+\varepsilon}\left|\ln u_\nu(\theta) - \ln\frac{1}{p(\theta)}\right|d\theta \leqslant$$

$$\leqslant \frac{1}{2\sin\frac{\varepsilon}{2}}\left\|\ln u_\nu(\theta) - \ln\frac{1}{p(\theta)}\right\|_2 \leqslant D_1\omega_2\left(\frac{1}{n};\ \frac{1}{p}\right)^*, \tag{5.54}$$

since the conditions $\frac{1}{p(\theta)} \geqslant \frac{1}{M}$ and $u_\nu(\theta) \geqslant \frac{1}{M}$ lead to

$$\left|\ln u_\nu(\theta) - \ln\frac{1}{p(\theta)}\right| \leqslant M\left|u_\nu(\theta) - \frac{1}{p(\theta)}\right|, \quad 0 \leqslant \theta \leqslant 2\pi; \tag{5.54'}$$

a similar expression is obtained for I_5.

* Here $D_1, D_2, \ldots$ are constants independent of $\underline{n}$ and θ_0.

For I_2, we use (5.38"), according to which

$$|I_2| = \left| \frac{1}{4\pi} \int_{\alpha'+\varepsilon}^{\theta_0-\varepsilon_n} \right| \leqslant C\omega\left(\frac{1}{n};\ p\right) \int_{\alpha'+\varepsilon}^{\theta_0-\varepsilon_n} \frac{d\theta}{\theta_0-\theta} = \tag{5.55}$$
$$= C\omega\left(\frac{1}{n};\ p\right)\left[\ln\frac{1}{\varepsilon_n} + \ln(\beta'-\alpha'-3\varepsilon)\right] \leqslant D_2(\ln n)^{1-\gamma};$$

a similar expression is obtained for I_4.

Finally, for I_3 we use the fact that

$$\int_{\theta_0-\varepsilon_n}^{\theta_0+\varepsilon_n} \operatorname{ctg}\frac{\theta_0-\theta}{2}\, d\theta = 0,$$

so that we may write

$$I_3 = \frac{1}{4\pi} \int_{\theta_0-\varepsilon_n}^{\theta_0+\varepsilon_n} \left\{ [\ln u_\nu(\theta) - \ln u_\nu(\theta_0)] + \left[\ln\frac{1}{p(\theta_0)} - \ln\frac{1}{p(\theta)}\right] \right\} \operatorname{ctg}\frac{\theta_0-\theta}{2}\, d\theta.$$

This then leads us to

$$|I_3| \leqslant \frac{1}{4} \int_{\theta_0-\varepsilon_n}^{\theta_0+\varepsilon_n} \frac{|\ln u_\nu(\theta) - \ln u_\nu(\theta_0)| + |\ln p(\theta) - \ln p(\theta_0)|}{|\theta-\theta_0|}\, d\theta. \tag{5.56}$$

Since on $[\alpha, \beta]$ the function $\ln p(\theta)$ has a modulus of continuity of the same order as that of $p(\theta)$, we have

$$|\ln p(\theta) - \ln p(\theta_0)| \leqslant C'\omega(|\theta-\theta_0|;\ p),$$

whence

$$\frac{1}{4\pi} \int_{\theta_0-\varepsilon_n}^{\theta_0+\varepsilon_n} \left| \frac{\ln p(\theta) - \ln p(\theta_0)}{\theta-\theta_0} \right| d\theta \leqslant \frac{C'}{2\pi} \int_0^{\varepsilon_n} \frac{\omega(x;\ p)\, dx}{x} \leqslant D_3(\ln n)^{1-\gamma}. \tag{5.57}$$

Now (5.39) and (5.40) may be rewritten, setting $z = e^{i\theta}$,

$$u_\nu(\theta) = |\lambda_r(z)|^2, \quad |\lambda_r(z)| \leqslant C, \quad \alpha + \varepsilon \leqslant \theta \leqslant \beta - \varepsilon,$$

so that

$$u'_\nu(\theta) = i\left[z\lambda'_r(z)\overline{\lambda_r(z)} - \lambda_r(z)\overline{z\lambda'_r(z)}\right],$$

$$|u'_\nu(\theta)| \leqslant 2|\lambda_r(z)\lambda'_r(z)| \leqslant 2C|\lambda'_r(z)|, \quad \alpha + \varepsilon \leqslant \theta \leqslant \beta - \varepsilon.$$

We may now use the consideration employed by Sewell [1] in Section 2.1 and his Theorem 2.1.4, to assert that*

$$|\lambda'_r(z)| \leqslant C_1 r, \quad \alpha + 2\varepsilon \quad \theta \leqslant \beta - 2\varepsilon,$$

and thus to obtain

$$|u'_\nu(\theta)| \leqslant C_2 n, \quad \alpha + 2\varepsilon \leqslant \theta \leqslant \beta - 2\varepsilon.$$

Hence

$$|u_\nu(\theta) - u_\nu(\theta_0)| = \left|\int_{\theta_0}^{\theta} u'_\nu(\theta)\, d\theta\right| \leqslant C_2 n\,|\theta - \theta_0|,$$
$$\alpha + 2\varepsilon \leqslant \theta, \quad \theta_0 \leqslant \beta - 2\varepsilon,$$

and therefore on the basis of (5.52') and (5.54') we have

$$|\ln u_\nu(\theta) - \ln u_\nu(\theta_0)| \leqslant C_3 n\,|\theta - \theta_0|.$$

We thus obtain

$$\int_{\theta_0 - \varepsilon_n}^{\theta_0 + \varepsilon_n} \left|\frac{\ln u_\nu(\theta) - \ln u_\nu(\theta_0)}{\theta - \theta_0}\right| d\theta \leqslant 2C_3 n\varepsilon_n = 2C_3(\ln n)^{1-\gamma} \quad (5.58)$$

Our final result, therefore, is

$$\left|\arg\lambda^*_r(e^{i\theta_0}) - \arg\pi(e^{i\theta_0})\right| \leqslant D_4\omega_2\left(\frac{1}{n};\ \frac{1}{p}\right) + D_5(\ln n)^{1-\gamma}. \quad (5.59)$$

This and (5.52) lead to the conclusion that for $\alpha' + 2\epsilon \leq \theta_0 \leq \leq \beta' - 2\epsilon$,

$$\left|\lambda^*_r(e^{i\theta_0}) - \pi(e^{i\theta_0})\right| \leqslant D_6\omega_2\left(\frac{1}{n};\ \frac{1}{p}\right) + D_7(\ln n)^{1-\gamma}. \quad (5.60)$$

---

* See also G. Szegö [4].

We now compare this with (5.51) to obtain an estimate for $(\alpha_r/\beta_r) - 1$. from (2.10) we have

$$\frac{\alpha_r}{\beta_r} = \frac{\alpha_r}{\alpha} \cdot \frac{\alpha}{\beta_r}, \quad \alpha = \pi(0) = \exp\left\{ -\frac{1}{4\pi} \int_0^{2\pi} \ln p(\theta)\, d\theta \right\},$$

$$\beta_r = \exp\left\{ -\frac{1}{4\pi} \int_0^{2\pi} \ln \frac{1}{u_\nu(\theta)}\, d\theta \right\},$$

whence

$$\frac{\alpha}{\beta_r} = \exp\left\{ \frac{1}{4\pi} \int_0^{2\pi} \left[\ln \frac{1}{u_\nu(\theta)} - \ln p(\theta) \right] d\theta \right\}.$$

But since

$$\frac{1}{2\pi} \int_0^{2\pi} \left| \ln \frac{1}{u_\nu(\theta)} - \ln p(\theta) \right| d\theta \leqslant \left\| \ln u_\nu(\theta) - \ln \frac{1}{p(\theta)} \right\|_2 \leqslant$$

$$\leqslant A\omega_2\left(\frac{1}{n}, \frac{1}{p}\right),$$

it follows that

$$\left| \frac{\alpha}{\beta_r} - 1 \right| \leqslant B\omega_2\left(\frac{1}{n}; \frac{1}{p}\right). \tag{5.61}$$

On the other hand, $\alpha_r \leq \alpha$; thus finally from (2.20) we have

$$\frac{\alpha_r}{\beta_r} - 1 = \frac{\alpha_r}{\alpha}\left(\frac{\alpha}{\beta_r} - 1\right) + \frac{\alpha_r}{\alpha} - 1,$$

$$\left| \frac{\alpha_r}{\beta_r} - 1 \right| \leqslant B\omega_2\left(\frac{1}{n}, \frac{1}{p}\right) + B'\delta_r^2.$$

Thus we arrive at

$$|\varphi_r^*(e^{i\theta_0}) - \lambda_r^*(e^{i\theta_0})| \leqslant \left|\varphi_r^*(e^{i\theta_0}) - \frac{\alpha_r}{\beta_r}\lambda_r^*(e^{i\theta_0})\right| + \left|\frac{\alpha_r}{\beta_r} - 1\right| |\lambda_r^*(e^{i\theta_0})| \leqslant$$

$$\leqslant D_8 (\ln n)^{1-\gamma} + D_9\omega_2\left(\frac{1}{n}, \frac{1}{p}\right) + D_{10}\delta_{n-1},$$

$$\alpha' + 2\varepsilon \leqslant \theta_0 \leqslant \beta' - 2\varepsilon.$$

Combining this with (5.60), we are led to

$$|\varphi_r^*(e^{i\theta_0}) - \pi(e^{i\theta_0})| \leqslant C_1\omega_2\left(\frac{1}{n}; \frac{1}{p}\right) + C_2(\ln n)^{1-\gamma} + C_3\delta_{n-1}$$

$$\alpha + \eta \leqslant \theta_0 \leqslant \beta - \eta. \tag{5.62}$$

Since $r = 2_\nu - 2 \leq n$, this last inequality has been established only for even r. According to (1.2), however, we may write

$$|\varphi^*_{r+1}(e^{i\theta_0}) - \pi(e^{i\theta_0})| \leqslant \left|\frac{\alpha_{r+1}}{\alpha_r}\varphi^*_r(e^{i\theta_0}) - \pi(e^{i\theta_0})\right| + \\ + \frac{|\varphi_{r+1}(0)|}{\alpha_r}|\varphi_r(e^{i\theta_0})| \leqslant |\varphi^*_r(e^{i\theta_0}) - \pi(e^{i\theta_0})| + \\ + |\varphi^*_r(e^{i\theta_0})|\left\{\left|\frac{\alpha_{r+1}}{\alpha_r} - 1\right| + \frac{|\varphi_{r+1}(0)|}{\alpha_r}\right\}.$$

Now we know that $1/\alpha_r \leq 1/\alpha_0$, and that $|\varphi^*_r(e^{i\theta_0})| = |\varphi_r(e^{i\theta_0})| \leq A$ for $\alpha' \leq \theta_0 \leq \beta'$; further, using (1.5) and (2.8), we find that

$$\frac{\alpha_{r+1} - \alpha_r}{\alpha_r} = \frac{\alpha^2_{r+1} - \alpha^2_r}{\alpha_r(\alpha_{r+1} + \alpha_r)} \leqslant \frac{|\varphi_{r+1}(0)|^2}{2\alpha_0^2} \leqslant \frac{\alpha^2}{2\alpha_0^2}(\delta_r^2 - \delta_{r+1}^2) \leqslant \frac{\alpha^2\delta_r^2}{2\alpha_0^2},$$

so that

$$|\varphi^*_{r+1}(e^{i\theta_0}) - \pi(e^{i\theta_0})| \leqslant C_1\omega_2\left(\frac{1}{n};\ \frac{1}{p}\right) + C_2(\ln n)^{1-\gamma} + C_3\delta_{n-1} + \\ + A\left\{\frac{\alpha^2\delta^2_{n-1}}{2\alpha_0^2} + \frac{\alpha\delta_{n-1}}{\alpha_0}\right\} \leqslant C_1\omega_2\left(\frac{1}{n};\ \frac{1}{p}\right) + C_2(\ln n)^{1-\gamma} + C_3'\delta_{n-1}, \\ \alpha + \eta \leqslant \theta_0 \leqslant \beta - \eta.$$

We thus see that (5.37) is valid for all n, both even and odd.

We thus arrive at condition IV of Table V. Conditions V–X will be treated in Chapter VII.

5.6. Let us consider yet another limit relation of the local type.

Theorem 5.7. Let the integral of (4.35) exist, and assume that on $[\alpha, \beta]$ the function $\sigma(\theta)$ is absolutely continuous, and that $p(\theta) \geq m > 0$ is continuous. Then in the interior of $[\alpha, \beta]$ we obtain the limit relation

$$\lim_{n\to\infty}\frac{K_n(e^{i\theta_0}, e^{i\theta_0})}{n+1} = \frac{1}{p(\theta_0)}, \quad \alpha + \varepsilon \leqslant \theta_0 \leqslant \beta - \varepsilon, \tag{5.63}$$

the convergence being uniform.

We note first that from (4.20) and Fejér's theorem we obtain the inequality

$$\frac{n+1}{K_n(e^{i\theta_0}, e^{i\theta_0})} \leqslant p(\theta_0) + \varepsilon_n', \quad \alpha + \varepsilon \leqslant \theta_0 \leqslant \beta - \varepsilon, \quad \lim_{n\to\infty}\varepsilon_n' = 0. \tag{5.64}$$

To obtain a lower bound let us write the measure $d\sigma(\theta)$ in the form

$$d\sigma(\theta) = p_2(\theta)\, d\sigma_2(\theta), \tag{5.65}$$

where we have set

$$p_2(\theta) = \begin{cases} p(\theta), & \theta \in [\alpha, \beta], \\ 1, & \theta \overline{\in} [\alpha, \beta], \end{cases} \quad \sigma_2(\theta) = \begin{cases} \theta, & \theta \in [\alpha, \beta], \\ \sigma(\theta), & \theta \overline{\in} [\alpha, \beta]. \end{cases} \tag{5.66}$$

Then $p_2(\theta) \geq m' > 0$ throughout $[0, 2\pi]$, and $\sigma_2(\theta)$ satisfies all the conditions of Theorems 5.5 and 4.2. Hence from (5.22) and (4.8) it follows that for the sums and polynomials associated with these functions we have

$$\lim_{n\to\infty} \varphi_n^{(2)*}(e^{i\theta}) = \pi_2(e^{i\theta}), \quad \lim_{n\to\infty} \frac{K_n^{(2)}(e^{i\theta}, e^{i\theta})}{n+1} = \frac{1}{\sigma_2'(\theta)} = 1,$$
$$K_n^{(2)}(e^{i\theta}, e^{i\theta}) \leqslant C(n+1), \quad n \geqslant m, \quad \alpha + \varepsilon \leqslant \theta \leqslant \beta - \varepsilon, \tag{5.67}$$

where the convergence indicated is uniform in the interior of $[\alpha, \beta]$.

We shall now prove that for any $0 < \delta < 1$ and any $0 < \eta < \epsilon$ there exist an $n_0 = n_0(\delta, \eta)$, such that for all $n > n_0$ and for $\alpha + 2\epsilon \leq \theta_0 \leq \beta - 2\epsilon$ we have *

$$\frac{1}{2\pi}\int_{e} |h_n(e^{i\theta}, e^{i\theta_0})|^2\, d\sigma_2(\theta) \geqslant \frac{1-\delta}{C(n+1)}, \quad h_n(z, z_0) = \frac{K_n(z, z_0)}{K_n(z_0, z_0)},$$
$$e = [\theta_0 - \eta, \theta_0 + \eta]. \tag{5.68}$$

We shall prove the assertion by contradiction. Assume that there exists an <u>n</u> such that

$$\frac{1}{2\pi}\int_0^{2\pi} |h_n(e^{i\theta}, e^{i\theta_0})|^2\, d\sigma_2(\theta) < \frac{1-\delta}{C(n+1)}. \tag{5.69}$$

Consider the new polynomial

$$g_\nu(z, z_0) = h_n(z, z_0) \left\{ \frac{9 + \left(\frac{z}{z_0}\right)^2}{10} \right\}^{\left[\frac{1}{4} n\delta\right]}, \quad g_\nu(z_0, z_0) = 1 \tag{5.70}$$

---

* See P. Erdős and P. Turan [1], Section 3.

of degree $\nu \leqslant n\left(1+\frac{\delta}{2}\right)$. We then have

$$|g_\nu(e^{i\theta}, e^{i\theta_0})|^2 = |h_n(e^{i\theta}, e^{i\theta_0})|^2 \left\{1 - \frac{9}{25}\sin^2(\theta-\theta_0)\right\}^{\left[\frac{1}{4}n\delta\right]} <$$

$$< |h_n(e^{i\theta}, e^{i\theta_0})|^2. \quad (5.71)$$

From (1.10) and (4.8) it follows that for $\alpha + 2\epsilon \le \theta_0 \le \beta - 2\epsilon$ we have the inequality

$$\frac{1}{2\pi}\int_0^{2\pi} |g_\nu(e^{i\theta}, e^{i\theta_0})|^2 \, d\sigma_2(\theta) \geqslant \frac{1}{K_\nu^{(2)}(e^{i\theta_0}, e^{i\theta_0})} \geqslant$$

$$\geqslant \frac{1}{C(\nu+1)} \geqslant \frac{1}{C\left[n\left(1+\frac{\delta}{2}\right)+1\right]}. \quad (5.72)$$

On the other hand, if $\theta \overline{\in} e$ then $|\theta - \theta_0| \ge \eta$. so that

$$1 - \frac{9}{25}\sin^2(\theta-\theta_0) \leqslant 1 - \frac{9}{25}\sin^2\eta \leqslant 1 - \lambda^2\eta^2, \quad \lambda = \frac{6}{5\pi}, \quad \theta \overline{\in} e.$$

Thus if we set $e' + e = [0, 2\pi]$, we obtain

$$\frac{1}{2\pi}\int_0^{2\pi} |g_\nu(e^{i\theta}, e^{i\theta_0})|^2 \, d\sigma_2(\theta) < (1-\lambda^2\eta^2)^{\left[\frac{1}{4}n\delta\right]} \times$$

$$\times \frac{1}{2\pi}\int_{e'} |h_n(e^{i\theta}, e^{i\theta_0})|^2 \, d\sigma_2(\theta) + \frac{1}{2\pi}\int_{e} |h_n(e^{i\theta}, e^{i\theta_0})|^2 \, d\sigma_2(\theta),$$

which leads to the inequality

$$\frac{1}{2\pi}\int_0^{2\pi} |h_n(e^{i\theta}, e^{i\theta_0})|^2 \, d\sigma_2(\theta) > \frac{1}{2\pi}\int_{e'} |h_n(e^{i\theta}, e^{i\theta_0})|^2 \, d\sigma_2(\theta) >$$

$$> \frac{1}{(1-\lambda^2\eta^2)^{\left[\frac{1}{4}n\delta\right]}}\left\{\frac{1}{2\pi}\int_0^{2\pi} |g_\nu(e^{i\theta}, e^{i\theta_0})|^2 \, d\sigma_2(\theta) - \right. \quad (5.73)$$

$$\left. - \frac{1}{2\pi}\int_{e} |h_n(e^{i\theta}, e^{i\theta_0})|^2 \, d\sigma_2(\theta)\right\}.$$

By making use of (5.72), (5.69), and (4.8), we arrive at

$$\frac{1}{2\pi}\int_0^{2\pi} |h_n(e^{i\theta}, e^{i\theta_0})|^2 \, d\sigma_2(\theta) >$$

$$> (1+\lambda^2\eta^2)^{\left[\frac{1}{4}n\delta\right]} \left\{\frac{1}{C\left[n\left(1+\frac{\delta}{2}\right)+1\right]} - \frac{1-\delta}{C(n+1)}\right\} =$$

$$= \frac{\delta(1+\lambda^2\eta^2)^{\left[\frac{1}{4}n\delta\right]}}{C(n+1)} \frac{\frac{n}{2}(1+\delta)+1}{n\left(1+\frac{\delta}{2}\right)+1} > \frac{\delta(1+\lambda^2\eta^2)^{\left[\frac{1}{4}n\delta\right]}}{2C(n+1)}.$$

Since $p_2(\theta) \geqslant m' > 0$, $\theta \in [0, 2\pi]$, we finally find that

$$\frac{1}{2\pi}\int_0^{2\pi} |h_n(e^{i\theta}, e^{i\theta_0})|^2 \, d\sigma(\theta) = \frac{1}{K_n(e^{i\theta_0}; e^{i\theta})} >$$

$$> \frac{m'}{2\pi}\int_0^{2\pi} |h_n(e^{i\theta}, e^{i\theta_0})|^2 \, d\sigma_2(\theta) > \frac{m'\delta(1+\lambda^2\eta^2)^{\left[\frac{1}{4}n\delta\right]}}{2C(n+1)}.$$

According to (4.8)

$$\frac{1}{C'(n+1)} \geqslant \frac{1}{K_n(e^{i\theta_0}, e^{i\theta_0})} > \frac{m'\delta(1+\lambda^2\eta^2)^{\left[\frac{1}{4}n\delta\right]}}{2C(n+1)},$$

$$\alpha + 2\varepsilon \leqslant \theta_0 \leqslant \beta - 2\varepsilon,$$

which means that

$$(1+\lambda^2\eta^2)^{\left[\frac{1}{4}n\delta\right]} < \frac{2C}{2C'm'\delta}. \tag{5.74}$$

Now for fixed η and δ and for sufficiently large $n > n_0 = n_0(\delta, \eta)$ this inequality is an impossible one, so that (5.68) holds for all $n > n_0$.

Recalling that $p_2(\theta)$ is continuous for $\theta_0 - \eta \leq \theta \leq \theta_0 + \eta$, we have

$$|p_2(\theta) - p_2(\theta_0)| \leqslant \omega(\eta;\ p_2),$$

whence

$$\min_{\theta \in e} p_2(\theta) \geqslant p_2(\theta_0) - \omega(\eta;\ p_2).$$

Using (5.68), we obtain

$$\frac{1}{K_n(e^{i\theta_0}, e^{i\theta_0})} = \frac{1}{2\pi}\int_0^{2\pi} |h_n(e^{i\theta}, e^{i\theta_0})|^2 p_2(\theta)\, d\sigma_2(\theta) \geqslant$$

$$\geqslant \min_{\theta\in e} p_2(\theta) \cdot \frac{1}{2\pi}\int_e |h_n(e^{i\theta}, e^{i\theta_0})|^2 d\sigma_2(\theta) \geqslant$$

$$\geqslant \frac{p_2(\theta_0) - \omega(\eta, p_2)}{C(n+1)}(1-\delta), \quad (5.75)$$

which leads easily to the inequality

$$\frac{(1-\delta)[p_2(\theta_0) - \omega(\eta, p_2)]}{C} \leqslant \frac{n+1}{K_n(e^{i\theta_0}; e^{i\theta_0})}, \quad \alpha + 2\varepsilon \leqslant \theta_0 \leqslant \beta - 2\varepsilon.$$

From (5.67) it follows that

$$K_n^{(2)}(e^{i\theta_0}, e^{i\theta_0}) \leqslant (n+1)[1+o(1)]$$

and thus C can be made arbitrarily close to unity by choosing n sufficiently large. Since δ and η are independent of n and of each other, it is possible, given $\mu > 0$ no matter how small, to choose δ and η so small, and n so large, as to ensure the validity of the inequality

$$p_2(\theta_0) - \mu \leqslant \frac{(1-\delta)\{p_2(\theta_0) - \omega(\eta; p_2)\}}{C} \leqslant \frac{n+1}{K_n(e^{i\theta_0}, e^{i\theta_0})}$$

on $[\alpha + 2\epsilon, \beta - 2\epsilon]$. By comparing this with (5.64) and using the arbitrariness of μ and the fact that $\varepsilon_n' = o(1)$, we arrive at (5.63).

Remark 5.3. The theorem just proved has been treated by several authors, but not in its local form and only for the case in which $\sigma(\theta)$ is absolutely continuous on the entire interval of orthogonality.

Our theorem is valid, in particular, if the derivative $\sigma'(\theta)$, existing almost everywhere on $[0, 2\pi]$, is such that

$$p(\theta) = \sigma'(\theta) = \prod_{k=1}^{s} |e^{i\theta} - e^{i\theta_k}|^{\nu_k} \varphi(\theta), \quad \nu_k > -1; \quad (5.76)$$

In this case $\sigma(\theta)$ satisfies all the conditions of the theorem on any interval $[\alpha, \beta]$ between θ_k and θ_{k+1}, where it is absolutely continuous, and $\varphi(\theta)$ is continuous and bounded from below by a positive number.

The theorem was first proved for the case $s = 2$, $\theta_2 = \theta_1 + \pi$ by Szegö [3] with the unnecessary assumption that $\varphi(\theta)$ be twice differentiable. It was proved for the same case by Akhiezer [3] without this assumption.

The theorem is also a consequence of Grenader's and Rosenblatt's [1] Theorem 3; their Theorem 3, however, is based on their Theorem 2, and this latter cannot be considered rigorously proved. Finally, the theorem is proved by Erdös and Turan [1] in a somewhat different formulation, namely, as an asymptotic formula for the Christoffel numbers.

5.7. We now turn to some limit relations in the metrics of the space L_1 and L_2.

Theorem 5.8. Assume the existence of (4.35). Then

$$\lim_{n\to\infty}\left\|\frac{\varphi_n^*(e^{i\theta})}{\pi(e^{i\theta})}-1\right\|_2=0, \tag{5.77}$$

$$\lim_{n\to\infty}\left\|\frac{K_n(e^{i\theta},e^{i\theta})\,p(\theta)}{n+1}-1\right\|_1=0, \tag{5.78}$$

and this implies that there exist subsequences $\{n_s\}$ and $\{n_\nu\}$ such that almost everywhere in $[0, 2\pi]$

$$\lim_{s\to\infty}\varphi_{n_s}^*(e^{i\theta})=\pi(e^{i\theta}),\qquad \lim_{\nu\to\infty}\frac{K_{n_\nu}(e^{i\theta},e^{i\theta})}{n_\nu+1}=\frac{1}{p(\theta)}. \tag{5.79}$$

From (2.8) we have

$$\delta_n=\left\|\frac{\alpha_n}{\alpha}\varphi_n^*(e^{i\theta})-\pi_0(\theta)\right\|_2^{\sigma}\geqslant\left\|\frac{\alpha_n\varphi_n^*(e^{i\theta})}{\alpha\pi(e^{i\theta})}-1\right\|_2,$$

$$\left\|\frac{\varphi_n^*(e^{i\theta})}{\pi(c^{i\theta})}-1\right\|_2\leqslant\left\|\frac{\alpha_n}{\alpha}\cdot\frac{\varphi_n^*(e^{i\theta})}{\pi(e^{i\theta})}-1\right\|_2+$$

$$+\left(1-\frac{\alpha_n}{\alpha}\right)\left\|\frac{\varphi_n^*(e^{i\theta})}{\pi(e^{i\theta})}\right\|_2\leqslant\delta_n+\frac{\alpha\delta_n^2}{\alpha+\alpha_0},$$

and this implies (5.77).

Further,

$$\left\| \left|\frac{\varphi_n^*(e^{i\theta})}{\pi(e^{i\theta})}\right|^2 - 1 \right| = \left\| \frac{\varphi_n^*(e^{i\theta})}{\pi(e^{i\theta})} \right| - 1 \right| \cdot \left\| \frac{\varphi_n^*(e^{i\theta})}{\pi(e^{i\theta})} \right| + 1 \right| \leqslant$$

$$\leqslant \left| \frac{\varphi_n^*(e^{i\theta})}{\pi(e^{i\theta})} - 1 \right| \left\{ \left| \frac{\varphi_n^*(e^{i\theta})}{\pi(e^{i\theta})} \right| + 1 \right\},$$

which leads to

$$\left\| \left|\frac{\varphi_n^*(e^{i\theta})}{\pi(e^{i\theta})}\right|^2 - 1 \right\|_1 \leqslant \left\| \frac{\varphi_n^*(e^{i\theta})}{\pi(e^{i\theta})} - 1 \right\|_2 \cdot \left\{ \left\| \frac{\varphi_n^*(e^{i\theta})}{\pi(e^{i\theta})} \right\|_2 + 1 \right\} \leqslant$$

$$\leqslant 2 \left\| \frac{\varphi_n^*(e^{i\theta})}{\pi(e^{i\theta})} - 1 \right\|_2,$$

so that

$$\lim_{n\to\infty} \| p(\theta) \, | \varphi_n^*(e^{i\theta}) |^2 - 1 \|_1 = 0.$$

Now from the fact that

$$\left\| \frac{K_n(e^{i\theta}, e^{i\theta})\, p(\theta)}{n+1} - 1 \right\|_1 \leqslant \frac{1}{n+1} \sum_{s=0}^{n} \| p(\theta) \, | \varphi_s(e^{i\theta}) |^2 - 1 \|_1,$$

we are led, using the theorem on the limit of the arithmetic mean, to

$$\overline{\lim_{n\to\infty}} \left\| \frac{K_n(e^{i\theta}, e^{i\theta})\, p(\theta)}{n+1} - 1 \right\|_1 \leqslant$$

$$\leqslant \lim_{n\to\infty} \frac{1}{n+1} \sum_{s=0}^{n} \| p(\theta) \, | \varphi_s(e^{i\theta}) |^2 - 1 \|_1 = 0.$$

Remark 5.4. We call attention to an inequality obtained by Freud [1]:

$$\left\| \frac{K_n(e^{i\theta}, e^{i\theta})\, p(\theta)}{n+1} - 1 \right\| \leqslant C_1 I\left(\frac{1}{n}\right). \tag{5.80}$$

5.8. Let us now turn to some necessary conditions for the validity of the limit relations. We first consider necessary conditions for the existence of the limit on the right-hand side of (5.22), namely,

$$\pi(e^{i\theta_0}) = \lim_{r\to 1-0} \pi(re^{i\theta_0}) \neq 0.$$

This requires that the boundary value

$$\ln \pi (e^{i\theta}) = \ln \frac{1}{\sqrt{p(\theta_0)}} + \arg \pi (e^{i\theta_0})$$

exist, and this in turn means that the Fourier series for the function

$$\ln \frac{1}{\sqrt{p(\theta)}} \sim \frac{a_0}{2} + \sum_{k=0}^{\infty} (a_k \cos k\theta + b_k \sin k\theta)$$

and the conjugate series

$$\sum_{k=1}^{\infty} (a_k \sin k\theta - b_k \cos k\theta)$$

must be summable by Abel's (or Poisson's) method at $\theta = \theta_0$. The necessary condition for the existence of the limit of the left-hand side of (5.22) gives the following

Theorem 5.9. If there exists a subsequence of orthonormal polynomials such that on a set of points of positive measure on the circumference $|z| = 1$ this subsequence converges in measure to a function which is measurable and finite almost everywhere on this set, then the integral (4.35) exists.

Let the subsequence $\{\varphi^*_{n_\nu}(e^{i\theta})\}$ converge in measure to the function $f(\theta) \neq \infty$, $\theta \in e$. From the obvious inequality $\ln^+ x < x$, $x > 0$, we find that any function $f_\nu(z) \in H_2$ satisfies the inequality

$$\frac{1}{2\pi}\int_0^{2\pi} \ln^+ |f_\nu(re^{i\theta})|\, d\theta \leqslant \|f_\nu(re^{i\theta})\|_1 \leqslant \leqslant \|f_\nu(re^{i\theta})\|_2 \leqslant \|f_\nu(e^{i\theta})\|_2, \quad r < 1, \tag{5.81}$$

since the integral is a nondecreasing function of r. On the other hand, (1.20) asserts that

$$\frac{1}{2\pi}\int_0^{2\pi} \frac{d\theta}{|\varphi^*_n(e^{i\theta})|^2} = c_0 \qquad (n = 0, 1, 2, \ldots). \tag{5.82}$$

Setting $f_\nu(z) = \dfrac{1}{\varphi^*_{n_\nu}(z)}$ in (5.81), we arrive at the inequality

$$\frac{1}{2\pi}\int_0^{2\pi} \ln^+ \frac{1}{|\varphi^*_{n_\nu}(re^{i\theta})|}\, d\theta \leqslant \sqrt{c_0}, \quad r < 1 \quad (\nu = 1, 2, \ldots). \tag{5.83}$$

According to 1.2, in the region $|z| < 1$ we are assured of the existence of $\lim_{\nu \to \infty} \varphi^*_{n_\nu}(z) = \pi(z)$, where $\pi(z) \equiv \infty$, if the integral of (4.35) does not exist. Applying the generalized Khinchin-Ostrovskii theorem* to the subsequence $\left\{\frac{1}{\varphi^*_{n_\nu}(e^{i\theta})}\right\}$, we may assert that this subsequence converges in measure on the set $\underline{e}$ to the boundary values $1/\pi(z)$, and hence that $1/\pi(e^{i\theta})$ and $1/f(\theta)$ are equivalent on $\underline{e}$. If, therefore, the integral of (4.35) does not exist, $1/f(\theta)$ is equivalent to zero on $\underline{e}$, contrary to assumption.

Thus if the integral of (4.35) does not exist, then:

1) In the region $|z| < 1$ the limit

$$\lim_{n \to \infty} \varphi^*_n(z) = \infty \tag{5.84}$$

exists.

2) On the circumference $|z| = 1$ there can exist no subsequence converging in measure on a set of positive measure to a function finite almost everywhere on this set. A sequence may, however, be bounded, as for instance in (4.14').

3) On a set of measure zero on the circumference $|z| = 1$ a sequence may converge; for instance, at points of concentrated mass forming a countable set, the series $\sum_{k=0}^{\infty} |\varphi_k(z)|^2$ converges, and therefore $\lim_{n \to \infty} \varphi_n(z) = 0$. **

5.9. We have been considering limit relations on the circumference $|z| = 1$; let us now turn to the relations in the region $|z| < 1$.

Theorem 5.10. If condition (4.35) is fulfilled, then

$$\left|\frac{\varphi^*_n(z)}{\pi(z)} - 1\right| \leqslant \frac{C\delta_n}{\sqrt{1 - |z|}}, \quad |z| < 1. \tag{5.85}$$

* See, for instance, I. I. Privalov [1], Chap. II, Section 7.

** See Ya. L. Geronimus, [1], Section 20.

For $|z| \leq r < 1$, we have, uniformly,

$$|\varphi_n^*(z) - \pi(z)| = o(\delta_n). \tag{5.86}$$

From (5.7'), for $|z| < 1$ we have

$$|\varphi_n^*(z) - \pi(z)| \leqslant \left|\varphi_n^*(z) - \frac{\alpha}{\alpha_n}\pi(z)\right| + \frac{\alpha - \alpha_n}{\alpha_n}|\pi(z)| \leqslant$$

$$\leqslant \frac{1}{\alpha_n}\sqrt{\sum_{k=n+1}^{\infty}|\varphi_k(z)|^2 \cdot \sum_{k=n+1}^{\infty}|\varphi_k(0)|^2} + |\pi(z)| \cdot \frac{\alpha^2\delta_n^2}{\alpha_n(\alpha+\alpha_n)} \leqslant$$

$$\leqslant \frac{|\pi(z)|\,\alpha\delta_n}{\alpha_0}\left\{\frac{1}{\sqrt{1-|z|}} + \frac{\alpha\delta_n}{\alpha+\alpha_0}\right\}, \tag{5.87}$$

which leads to (5.85).

In view of the convergence of

$$\sum_{k=0}^{\infty}|\varphi_k(z)|^2 = \frac{|\pi(z)|^2}{1-|z|^2}, \qquad |z| < 1$$

to a function continuous for $|z| \leq r < 1$, we have

$$\sum_{k=n+1}^{\infty}|\varphi_k(z)|^2 = o(1), \qquad |z| \leqslant r < 1,$$

uniformly, which, with (5.87), leads to (5.86).

Using Table I and (3.9)-(3.9"), it is possible to evaluate the errors involved in (5.86) for $|z| < 1$.

CHAPTER VI

ORTHOGONAL SERIES

6.1. We shall concern ourselves with series of the form

$$\sum_{k=0}^{\infty} g_k \varphi_k(z) \tag{6.1}$$

in orthogonal polynomials. We first place some restrictions on the measure $d\sigma(\theta)$ so that the series should have properties analogous to those of power series.

We shall denote by $a(\delta)$ the so-called modulus of increase* of $\sigma(\theta)$, i.e.,

$$a(\delta) = \inf \int_{e} d\sigma(\theta), \qquad \text{Mes } e = \delta, \qquad e \in [0, 2\pi]. \tag{6.2}$$

We then have the following

Theorem 6.1. If

$$\lim_{\delta \to 0} \{\delta \ln a(\delta)\} = 0, \tag{6.3}$$

then the limit

$$\lim_{n \to \infty} \sqrt[n]{|\varphi_n(z)|} = |z|, \qquad |z| > 1 \tag{6.4}$$

exists.

We write

$$\Phi_n(z) = \frac{\varphi_n(z)}{a_n} = z^n + \ldots \qquad (n = 0, 1, 2, \ldots),$$

* See J. Shohat [1, 2]; Ya. L. Geronimus [7, 8].

and then obtain

$$\frac{1}{\alpha_n^2}=\frac{1}{2\pi}\int_0^{2\pi}|\Phi_n(e^{i\theta})|^2\,d\sigma(\theta)\leqslant\frac{1}{2\pi}\int_0^{2\pi}|e^{in\theta}|^2\,d\sigma(\theta)=c_0.$$

On the other hand, let

$$m_n=\max_{0\leqslant\theta\leqslant 2\pi}|\Phi_n(e^{i\theta})|=|\Phi_n(e^{i\theta_0})|. \tag{6.5}$$

Then using (3.42) with $z_1 = e^{i\theta}$, $z_0 = e^{i\theta}$, we have

$$|\Phi_n(e^{i\theta_0})-\Phi_n(e^{i\theta_1})|=$$

$$=\left|\int_{z_1}^{z_0}\Phi_n'(z)\,dz\right|\leqslant nm_n|z_0-z_1|\leqslant nm_n|\theta_0-\theta_1|.$$

Proceeding in the same way as in the proof of Theorem 3.6, we obtain for $\theta\in e=\left[\theta_0-\frac{1}{2n},\ \theta_0+\frac{1}{2n}\right]$

$$|\Phi_n(e^{i\theta})|\geqslant\frac{m_n}{2}.$$

This leads to

$$\frac{1}{2\pi}\int_0^{2\pi}|\Phi_n(e^{i\theta})|^2\,d\sigma(\theta)\geqslant\frac{m_n^2}{8\pi}\int_e d\sigma(\theta)\geqslant\frac{m_n^2}{8\pi}\,a\left(\frac{1}{n}\right)\geqslant\frac{1}{8\pi}\,a\left(\frac{1}{n}\right),$$

since $m_n \geq 1$ as a consequence of the fact that z^n is the polynomial whose deviation from zero on the circumference $|z| = 1$ is less than that of any other polynomial of the form $z^n + \ldots$.

We thus have the double inequality

$$\frac{1}{8\pi}\,a\left(\frac{1}{n}\right)\leqslant\frac{m_n^2}{8\pi}\,a\left(\frac{1}{n}\right)\leqslant\frac{1}{\alpha_n^2}\leqslant c_0, \tag{6.6}$$

$$\sqrt[2n]{\frac{1}{8\pi}\,a\left(\frac{1}{n}\right)}\leqslant\sqrt[n]{m_n}\cdot\sqrt[2n]{\frac{1}{8\pi}\,a\left(\frac{1}{n}\right)}\leqslant\frac{1}{\sqrt[n]{\alpha_n}}\leqslant\sqrt[2n]{c_0},$$

and therefore

$$\frac{1}{2n}\ln\frac{a\left(\frac{1}{n}\right)}{8\pi}\leqslant\frac{1}{n}\ln m_n+\frac{1}{2n}\ln\frac{a\left(\frac{1}{n}\right)}{8\pi}\leqslant-\frac{1}{n}\ln\alpha_n\leqslant\frac{1}{2n}\ln c_0.$$

Now going to the limit $n \to \infty$, we obtain

$$\frac{1}{2} \lim_{n\to\infty} \left\{\frac{1}{n} \ln a\left(\frac{1}{n}\right)\right\} \leqslant - \overline{\lim_{n\to\infty}} \left\{\frac{1}{n} \ln \alpha_n\right\} \leqslant$$

$$\leqslant - \underline{\lim_{n\to\infty}} \left\{\frac{1}{n} \ln \alpha_n\right\} \leqslant 0,$$

which, together with (6.3), implies the existence of the limit

$$\lim_{n\to\infty} \left\{\frac{1}{n} \ln \alpha_n\right\} = 0, \quad \lim_{n\to\infty} \sqrt[n]{\alpha_n} = \lim_{n\to\infty} \sqrt[n]{m_n} = 1. \quad (6.7)$$

Consider the sequence of functions

$$f_n(z) = \frac{1}{2}\left\{\sqrt[n]{\frac{\varphi_n^*(z)}{\alpha_n m_n}} - 1\right\}, \quad |z| < 1 \quad (n = 0, 1, 2, \ldots).$$

In the region $|z| < 1$ all these functions are regular, bounded (for $|f_n(z)| < 1$), and nonvanishing, and for all of them the limit

$$\lim_{n\to\infty} f_n(0) = \frac{1}{2}\left\{\lim_{n\to\infty} \frac{1}{\sqrt[n]{m_n}} - 1\right\} = 0$$

exists. As a consequence we have the limit relation

$$\lim_{n\to\infty} f_n(z) = 0, \quad \lim_{n\to\infty} \sqrt[n]{\varphi_n^*(z)} = 1, \quad |z| < 1,$$

the convergence being uniform for $|z| \leq r < 1$*).

Now for $z_0 = 1/z$ with $|z_0| > 1$, we have $\varphi_n(z_0) = z_0^n \overline{\varphi}_n^*(z)$, which implies (6.4).

Remark 6.1. A limit relation analogous to (6.4) can be obtained for polynomials $\{\Phi_n(z)\}$, as the author has shown [7], from the conditions that $\sigma'(\theta) > 0$ almost everywhere in $[0, 2\pi]$. For absolutely continuous $\sigma(\theta)$ this has been shown by Erdős and Turan [1].

From the theorem just proved we obtain the following further

Theorem 6.2. Assume (6.3) to hold. Then 1) if (6.1) converges at a point z_0 such that $|z_0| > 1$, then it converges absolutely for

---

* See G. Pólya and G. Szegö [1], Part III, Problem 256. Our equation (6.4) is a consequence also of a theorem of Walsh [1], Section 7.4.

$|z| < |z_0|$, and uniformly for $|z| \le r < |z_0|$, and 2) if

$$\overline{\lim_{n \to \infty}} \sqrt[n]{|g_n|} = \frac{1}{R} < 1, \qquad (6.8)$$

then R is the radius of convergence of the series.

From convergence at a point z_0 one deduces (just as one proves Abel's first theorem in the theory of power series) that (6.1) converges absolutely for $|z| < |z_0|$ and uniformly on a circumference $1 < |z| = r < |z_0|$. Then Weierstrass's theorem implies that the convergence is uniform throughout the closed region $|z| \le r < |z_0|$.

The proof of the second assertion is similar to the derivation of the Cauchy-Hadamard formula, of which it is a generalization.*

Remark 6.2. The condition stated in Theorem 6.1 can sometimes be put in a different form.

Let $\sigma(\theta)$ be a strictly increasing continuous function with derivative $\sigma'(\theta)$ positive almost everywhere. Further, let the image $\sigma(e)$ of the set $\underline{e}$ of points on which $\sigma'(\theta) = +\infty$ be of measure zero. Then the inverse function $\sigma^{-1}(\lambda)$ is also strictly increasing, and both functions are absolutely continuous.

Obviously $a(\delta)$ is an increasing function such that $a(0) = 0$. If we write

$$\sigma(\theta) = \lambda, \quad a(\delta) = \gamma,$$

both inverse functions

$$\theta = \sigma^{-1}(\lambda), \quad \delta = a^{-1}(\gamma), \quad a^{-1}(0) = 0 \qquad (6.9)$$

are also increasing.

For $\theta_1 < \theta_2$ (6.2) tells us that

$$\sigma(\theta_2) - \sigma(\theta_1) \geqslant a(\theta_2 - \theta_1),$$

which can also be written in the form

$$\lambda_2 - \lambda_1 \geqslant a(\theta_2 - \theta_1), \quad \theta_2 - \theta_1 = \sigma^{-1}(\lambda_2) - \sigma^{-1}(\lambda_1) \leqslant a^{-1}(\lambda_2 - \lambda_1), \qquad (6.10)$$

---

* Szegö [5] has proved (6.8) on the assumption that $\sigma(\theta)$ is an absolutely continuous function, (4.35) holds, and the series $\sum_{k=0}^{\infty} |g_k|^2$ converges.

so that $a^{-1}(\delta)$ is the analogy of the modulus of continuity for the inverse function $\sigma^{-1}(\lambda)$.

Then using (6.9) we may rewrite (6.3) in the form

$$\lim_{\gamma \to 0} \{a^{-1}(\gamma) \ln \gamma\} = 0, \tag{6.11}$$

which shows that it is the analog of the Dini condition for the inverse function.

In just the same way, we can rewrite (3.18), a condition we have used several times, in the form

$$\theta_2 - \theta_1 = \sigma^{-1}(\lambda_2) - \sigma^{-1}(\lambda_1) \leqslant \frac{1}{m}(\lambda_2 - \lambda_1), \tag{6.12}$$

which shows that it is the analog of the classification Lip 1 for the inverse function.

6.2. We now place some more severe restrictions on $\sigma(\theta)$ and the sequence $\{g_n\}$, namely we assume the existence of the integral (4.35) and that the series $\sum_{n=1}^{\infty} |g_n|^2$ converges.

In view of the inequality

$$\left| \sum_{k=n}^{m} g_k \varphi_k(z) \right| \leqslant \sqrt{\sum_{k=n}^{m} |g_k|^2} \sqrt{\sum_{k=n}^{m} |\varphi_k(z)|^2},$$

the series of (6.1) converges absolutely for $|z| < 1$, uniformly for $|z| \leq r < 1$, and its sum

$$F(z) = \sum_{k=0}^{\infty} g_k \varphi_k(z), \quad |z| < 1, \tag{6.13}$$

is an analytic function, regular for $|z| < 1$.

We now turn to a theorem which is to some extent an analog of Tauber's theorem and Abel's second theorem for power series.

Theorem 6.3. Assume that (4.35) exists, and let E be the set of points of $[0, 2\pi]$ on which the derivative $\sigma'(\theta) > 0$ exists; let $|\varphi_n(z)| \leq M_n$, $|z| \leq 1$, and the sequence $\{M_n\}$ be nondecreasing. Then

$$g_n = o\left\{ \frac{1}{n \sqrt[3]{M_n}} \right\} \tag{6.14}$$

is a sufficient condition, in the notation of (6.13), for the existence of the radial boundary value

$$F(e^{i\theta_0}) = \lim_{r \to 1-0} F(re^{i\theta_0}), \quad \theta_0 \in E \tag{6.15}$$

to be equivalent to the convergence of

$$\sum_{k=0}^{\infty} g_k \varphi_k(e^{i\theta_0}) = F(e^{i\theta_0}), \quad \theta_0 \in E \tag{6.16}$$

to this value.*

Remark 6.3. Consider the two limits

$$\left.\begin{array}{c} \lim\limits_{n \to \infty} \left\{ \lim\limits_{r \to 1-0} s_n(re^{i\theta_0}) \right\}, \qquad \lim\limits_{r \to 1-0} \left\{ \lim\limits_{n \to \infty} s_n(re^{i\theta_0}) \right\}, \\ s_n(z) = \sum\limits_{k=0}^{n} g_k \varphi_k(z); \end{array}\right\} \tag{6.17}$$

condition (6.14) is sufficient for the existence of one of these to imply the existence of the other and their equality.

To prove the theorem we evaluate

$$| F(re^{i\theta_0}) - s_n(e^{i\theta_0}) | \leqslant \left| \sum_{k=0}^{n} g_k [\varphi_k(re^{i\theta_0}) - \varphi_k(e^{i\theta_0})] \right| +$$

$$+ \left| \sum_{k=n+1}^{\infty} g_k \varphi_k(re^{i\theta_0}) \right| \leqslant \sum_{k=0}^{n} | g_k | \cdot | \varphi_k(re^{i\theta_0}) - \varphi_k(e^{i\theta_0}) | +$$

$$+ \sqrt{\sum_{k=n+1}^{\infty} | g_k |^2} \cdot \sqrt{\sum_{k=n+1}^{\infty} | \varphi_k(re^{i\theta_0}) |^2} .$$

Now according to (3.42')

$$| \varphi_k(re^{i\theta_0}) - \varphi_k(e^{i\theta_0}) | \leqslant kM_k(1 - r),$$

---

* The theorem retains its validity if (6.14) is replaced by

$$\sum_{n=1}^{\infty} n \, | g_n |^2 M_n^{\frac{2}{3}} < \infty,$$

as has been shown in an article by the author [9]. If $\{M_n\}_0^\infty \leqslant C$ we obtain Fejèr's generalizations of Tauber's theorem (see E. Landau [1], Section 13).

and therefore

$$\sum_{k=0}^{n} |g_k| \cdot |\varphi_k(re^{i\theta_0}) - \varphi_k(e^{i\theta_0})| \leqslant (1-r) \sum_{k=1}^{n} k |g_k| M_k. \quad (6.18)$$

From (6.14) we have

$$\lim_{k \to \infty} \frac{k |g_k| M_k}{M_k^{\frac{2}{3}}} = 0.$$

Now

$$\sum_{k=1}^{n} M_k^{\frac{2}{3}} \leqslant n M_n^{\frac{2}{3}},$$

so that it follows from Cesàro's theorem that

$$\sum_{k=1}^{n} k |g_k| M_k = o\left(n M_n^{\frac{2}{3}}\right)$$

and therefore that

$$\sum_{k=0}^{n} |g_k| \cdot |\varphi_k(re^{i\theta_0}) - \varphi_k(e^{i\theta_0})| = o(1)(1-r)\, n\, M_n^{\frac{2}{3}}. \quad (6.19)$$

Further, according to (1.7) and (2.1) we have

$$\sum_{k=n+1}^{\infty} |\varphi_k(re^{i\theta_0})|^2 \leqslant \sum_{k=0}^{\infty} |\varphi_k(re^{i\theta_0})|^2 = \frac{|\pi(re^{i\theta_0})|^2}{1-r^2}, \quad r < 1.$$

Since the derivative

$$\sigma'(\theta_0) = p(\theta_0) = \frac{1}{|\pi(e^{i\theta_0})|^2} > 0$$

exists at the point θ_0, it follows from the properties of Poisson's integral and (2.16') that

$$\ln |\pi(re^{i\theta_0})|^2 - \ln \frac{1}{p(\theta_0)} = \varepsilon(r, \theta_0), \qquad \lim_{r \to 1-0} \varepsilon(r, \theta_0) = 0.$$

We thus obtain

$$\sum_{k=n+1}^{\infty} |\varphi_k(re^{i\theta_0})|^2 < \frac{e^{\varepsilon(r, \theta_0)}}{(1-r^2)\, p(\theta_0)} < \frac{C}{1-r}, \quad (6.20)$$

where C is independent of both r and θ_0.

Further, from (6.14),

$$\sum_{k=n+1}^{\infty} |g_k|^2 = o(1) \sum_{k=n+1}^{\infty} \frac{1}{k^2 M_k^{\frac{2}{3}}} \leqslant \frac{o(1)}{M_n^{\frac{2}{3}}} \sum_{k=n+1}^{\infty} \frac{1}{k^2} = \frac{o(1)}{n M_n^{\frac{2}{3}}}. \quad (6.21)$$

Finally, combining (6.19), (6.20), and (6.21), we obtain

$$|F(re^{i\theta_0}) - s_n(e^{i\theta_0})| \leqslant o(1)(1-r) n M_n^{\frac{2}{3}} + \frac{o(1)}{\sqrt{n(1-r)}\, M_n^{\frac{1}{3}}}. \quad (6.22)$$

We choose r from the condition that

$$n M_n^{\frac{2}{3}} (1-r) = \frac{1}{\sqrt{n(1-r)}\, M_n^{\frac{1}{3}}}, \quad 1 - r = \frac{1}{n M_n^{\frac{2}{3}}}. \quad (6.23)$$

Writing

$$F(re^{i\theta_0}) - F(e^{i\theta_0}) = \mu(r, \theta_0),$$

$$\sum_{k=0}^{n} g_k \varphi_k(e^{i\theta_0}) - F(e^{i\theta_0}) = \eta(n; \theta_0),$$

we are led from (6.22) and (6.23) to

$$\mu(r, \theta_0) - \eta(n, \theta_0) = o(1).$$

Clearly $r \to 1 - 0$ as $n \to \infty$. Hence

$$\lim_{n \to \infty} [\mu(r, \theta_0) - \eta(n, \theta_0)] = 0$$

and therefore separately

$$\lim_{r \to 1-0} \mu(r, \theta_0) = 0, \quad \lim_{n \to \infty} \eta(n, \theta_0),$$

which means that (6.15) and (6.16) are equivalent.

By placing more severe restrictions on $\sigma(\theta)$, we can obtain some sufficient conditions which must be satisfied by the sequence $\{g_n\}$ in order that (6.15) and (6.16) be equivalent.

Theorem 6.4. 1) Let $\sigma(\theta_2) - \sigma(\theta_1) \geqslant m(\theta_2 - \theta_1)$, $\theta_1, \theta_2 \in [0, 2\pi]$. Then in order for (6.15) and (6.16) to be equivalent it is sufficient that

$$g_n = o\left(n^{-\frac{7}{6}}\right). \quad (6.24)$$

2) Let $\sigma(\theta) \in A$. Then it is sufficient that

$$g_n = o\left\{ n^{-\frac{7}{6}} \left[\omega_2\left(\frac{1}{n};\ p\right)\right]^{-\frac{1}{3}} \right\}. \tag{6.25}$$

In particular, if $p(\theta) \in \mathrm{Lip}(\alpha,\ 2)$, $0 < \alpha < \frac{1}{2}$, then

$$g_n = o\left\{ n^{\frac{2\alpha - 7}{6}} \right\}; \tag{6.26}$$

if, on the other hand, $1/2 \leq \alpha \leq 1$, then it is sufficient that

$$g_n = o\left(\frac{1}{n}\right). \tag{6.27}$$

The proof follows from the conditions of Table II.

Remark 6.4. We note that (6.27) is a direct generalization of Tauber's condition for power series.

Let us now turn to some estimates for the partial sums

$$s_n(z) = \sum_{k=0}^{n} g_k \varphi_k(z)$$

of the series

$$F(z) = \sum_{k=0}^{\infty} g_k \varphi_k(z), \quad |z| < 1.$$

Theorem 6.5. Under the conditions stated in Theorem 6.3, if

$$g_n = O\left(\frac{1}{n\sqrt[3]{M_n}}\right) \tag{6.28}$$

then

$$|s_n(e^{i\theta_0})| \leqslant C + |F(re^{i\theta_0})|, \quad 1 - r = \frac{1}{nM_n^{\frac{2}{3}}}. \tag{6.29}$$

To prove this it is sufficient to reproduce the proof of Theorem 6.3 with o replaced by O. In particular, if

$$\sigma(\theta_2) - \sigma(\theta_1) \geqslant m(\theta_2 - \theta_1), \quad 0 \leqslant \theta_1 < \theta_2 \leqslant 2\pi, \quad m > 0,$$

then the condition that $g_n = O\left(n^{-\frac{7}{6}}\right)$ implies (6.29), with $1 - r = n^{-4/3}$; if $\sigma(\theta) \in A$, $p(\theta) \in \mathrm{Lip}\left(\frac{1}{2},\ 2\right)$ then the condition that $g_n = O\left(\frac{1}{n}\right)$ implies (6.29) with $1 - r = 1/n$.

Theorem 6.5 is to a certain extent an analog of theorems of Hardy and Littlewood* and of Landau;** for instance, if at $\theta_0 = 0$ and as $z \to 1-0$ we have

$$F(z) = O\left(\frac{1}{1-z}\right), \tag{6.30}$$

then (6.29) gives

$$|s_n(1)| \leqslant C_1 + C_2 n M_n^{\frac{2}{3}} \qquad (n = 1, 2, \ldots). \tag{6.31}$$

6.3. We now consider a simple theorem, the analog of Luzin's theorem [1] for trigonometric series.

Theorem 6.6. 1) If the orthogonal series

$$\sum_{k=0}^{\infty} g_k \varphi_k(z) \tag{6.32}$$

converge on a set $\underline{e}$ of positive measure of points on the circumference $|z| = 1$, then the limit $\lim_{n \to \infty} g_n = 0$ exists.

2) If the series (6.32) converges absolutely on $\underline{e}$, then $\sum_{n=0}^{\infty} |g_n|$ converges.***

Assume the series converges for the points $z = e^{i\theta}$, $\theta \in e'$; we then have

$$\lim_{n \to \infty} g_n \varphi_n(e^{i\theta}) = 0, \quad \theta \in e'.$$

If we assume that $\overline{\lim_{n \to \infty}} |g_n| > 0$, then there exists a subsequence $\{g_{n_i}\}$ such that $|g_{n_i}| \geqslant \lambda > 0$ $(i = 1, 2, \ldots)$; hence it must be true that

$$\lim_{i \to \infty} |\varphi_{n_i}(e^{i\theta})| = 0, \quad \theta \in e'. \tag{6.33}$$

According to a known theorem of Egorov, given an arbitrary $\delta > 0$, one can find a set $e'' \subset e'$ such that Mes e'' > Mes $e' - \delta$ on which the convergence of (6.33) is uniform; choosing $\epsilon > 0$ arbitrarily small, we have

* G. Hardy and J. Littlewood [2].

** E. Landau [1], Section 1, Theorem B.

*** The proof we present is that of Luzin, generalized appropriately.

$$|\varphi_{n_i}(e^{i\theta})| \leqslant \varepsilon, \qquad \frac{1}{|\varphi_{n_i}(e^{i\theta})|^2} \geqslant \frac{1}{\varepsilon^2},$$
$$\theta \in e'', \qquad i \geqslant i_0.$$

From (1.20) we obtain

$$c_0 = \frac{1}{2\pi}\int_0^{2\pi} \frac{d\theta}{|\varphi_{n_i}(e^{i\theta})|^2} \geqslant \frac{1}{2\pi}\int_{e''} \frac{d\theta}{|\varphi_{n_i}(e^{i\theta})|^2} \geqslant \frac{\text{Mes } e''}{2\pi\varepsilon^2} \qquad (6.34)$$

whence

$$\text{Mes } e' - \delta < \text{Mes } e'' \leqslant 2\pi\varepsilon^2 c_0, \quad \delta + 2\pi\varepsilon^2 c_0 > \text{Mes } e',$$

which is impossible, since ϵ and δ are arbitrary.

We have thus proved assertion 1). Therefore if $\overline{\lim\limits_{n\to\infty}} |g_n| > 0$ the series (6.32) diverges almost everywhere on the circumference $|z| = 1$.

To prove 2), again using Egorov's theorem, we have uniform convergence of

$$\sum_{n=0}^{\infty} |g_n \varphi_n{}'e^{i\theta})| = F(\theta)$$

on some set $\bar{e} \subset e'$ such that Mes $\bar{e}$ > Mes e' − δ, with $F(\theta) \geq 0$ and continuous on $\bar{e}$. Then integrating term by term we arrive easily at

$$\sum_{n=0}^{\infty} |g_n| \cdot \int_{\bar{e}} |\varphi_n(e^{i\theta})|\, d\theta = \int_{\bar{e}} F(\theta)\, d\theta. \qquad (6.35)$$

Let us choose $\epsilon > 0$ to satisfy the condition $\epsilon \leq 1/\sqrt{c_0}$ and $2\pi\epsilon^2 c_0 + \delta <$ Mes e' and let $\bar{e} = e_0^{(n)} + e_1^{(n)}$ such that

$$|\varphi_n(e^{i\theta})| \leqslant \varepsilon, \quad \theta \in e_0^{(n)}; \quad |\varphi_n(e^{i\theta})| > \varepsilon, \quad \theta \in e_1^{(n)}.$$

Using (6.34), we have Mes $e_0^{(n)} \leq 2\pi\epsilon^2 c_0$, and therefore

$$\text{Mes } e_1^{(n)} = \text{Mes } \bar{e} - \text{Mes } e_0^{(n)} \geqslant \text{Mes } e' - \delta - 2\pi\varepsilon^2 c_0 > 0.$$

Further,

$$\int_{\bar{e}} |\varphi_n(e^{i\theta})|\, d\theta \geqslant \int_{e_1^{(n)}} |\varphi_n(e^{i\theta})|\, d\theta > \varepsilon \operatorname{Mes} e_1^{(n)} \geqslant$$

$$\geqslant \varepsilon(\operatorname{Mes} e' - \delta - 2\pi\varepsilon^2 c_0) = a > 0,$$

which, with (6.35), implies

$$\sum_{n=0}^{\infty} |g_n| \leqslant \frac{1}{a} \int_{\bar{e}} F(\theta)\, d\theta < \infty.$$

Remark 6.5. For an arbitrary orthogonal system the theorem was proved by Placherel and by Privalov [2]; in the general case, one requires that (6.32) converge almost everywhere and that the orthonormal system be uniformly bounded on the interval or orthogonality. The fact that these restrictions are not required in our case makes it the more interesting.

The theorem just proved can be greatly generalized. Consider an infinite sequence of point functions $\{f_n(P)\}$ in a space of an arbitrary number of dimensions. We will say that this sequence possesses property L if on any subset $e \subset E$ there is at least one point P_0, such that $\varliminf_{n\to\infty} |f_n(P_0)| > 0$. We will say it possesses property L' if there exists no point P_0 at which at least one infinite subsequence $\{f_{n_i}(P_0)\}$ vanishes.

Theorem 6.7. Consider the series

$$\sum_{n=1}^{\infty} g_n f_n(P). \tag{6.36}$$

1) In order that its convergence on some set E imply the existence of the limit $\lim_{n\to\infty} g_n = 0$, it is sufficient that the sequence $\{f_n(P)\}$ possess property L on E and necessary that it possess property L'.

2) In order that the absolute convergence of the series (6.36) on E imply the convergence of the numerical series $\sum_{n=1}^{\infty} |g_n|$, it is sufficient that the function sequence $\{f_n(P)\}$ have property L on E, and necessary that it have property L'.

If (6.36) converges, the assumption that $\overline{\lim\limits_{n\to\infty}}|g_n| > 0$ leads to the existence of a subsequence $\{f_{n_i}(P)\}$ such that

$$\lim_{i\to\infty} f_{n_i}(P) = 0, \quad P \in E. \tag{6.37}$$

In view of property L, however, there exists at least one point P_0 such that

$$\underline{\lim_{i\to\infty}}|f_{n_i}(P_0)| > 0, \tag{6.38}$$

and this contradicts (6.37); thus the sufficiency in assertion 1) is proved.

Now let (6.36) converge absolutely:

$$\sum_{n=1}^{\infty} |g_n f_n(P)| < \infty, \quad P \in E. \tag{6.39}$$

In view of property L of the function sequence and the properties of the lower bound, we may assert that for every $\epsilon > 0$ there exists an n_0 such that if $n \geq n_0$, then

$$|f_n(P_0)| > \underline{\lim_{n\to\infty}}|f_n(P_0)| - \varepsilon = a > 0.$$

But in this case (6.39) implies that

$$a \sum_{n=n_0}^{\infty} |g_n| < \infty,$$

and this, in turn, implies the convergence of $\sum\limits_{n=1}^{\infty}|g_n|$.

If $\{f_n(P)\}$ does not possess property L', there exists a point P_0 and a subsequence of functions such that $f_{n_i}(P_0) = 0$ $(i = 1, 2, \ldots)$. But then $\sum\limits_{i=1}^{\infty} g_{n_i} f_{n_i}(P_0)$ converges, and furthermore absolutely, for arbitrary coefficients $\{g_{n_i}\}$; this proves the necessity in both assertions 1) and 2).

Privalov [2] has given the following example: Let the set of functions orthonormal on the interval [0, 1] be

$$f_k(x) = \begin{cases} \sqrt{2^k}, & x \in e_k = \left[\frac{1}{2^k}, \quad \frac{1}{2^{k-1}}\right], \\ 0, & x \overline{\in} e_k \end{cases} \qquad (k = 1, 2, \ldots).$$

Then $\sum_{k=1}^{\infty} g_k f_k(x)$ converges, and furthermore absolutely, throughout [0, 1] for any arbitrary coefficients. From this Privalov concludes the necessity of the uniform boundedness of the orthonormal system on the entire interval of orthogonality. It is easy to see, however, that in this example the functions do not possess property L', for at every point x of [0, 1], either one function fails to vanish (if $x \neq 1/2k$), or two (if $x = 1/2k$). All the remaining functions vanish.

CHAPTER VII

THE CONVERGENCE OF FOURIER-CHEBYSHEV EXPANSION

7.1. By the well-known Riesz-Fischer theorem to every sequence of numbers $\{g_n\}$ such that

$$\sum_{n=0}^{\infty} |g_n|^2 < \infty \qquad (7.1)$$

there corresponds uniquely a function $f_0(\theta) \in L_2^{\sigma}$ for which these numbers are the Fourier-Chebyshev coefficients

$$f_0(\theta) \sim \sum_{k=0}^{\infty} g_k \varphi_k(e^{i\theta}), \quad g_k = \frac{1}{2\pi} \int_0^{2\pi} f_0(\theta)\, \overline{\varphi_k(e^{i\theta})}\, d\sigma(\theta) \qquad (7.2)$$

and for which the closure condition

$$\sqrt{\sum_{k=0}^{\infty} |g_k|^2} = \|f_0\|_2^{\sigma} \qquad (7.3)$$

is fulfilled, i.e.,

$$\lim_{n\to\infty} \min_{G_n} \| f_0(\theta) - G_n(e^{i\theta}) \|_2^{\sigma} = 0. \qquad (7.4)$$

We shall consider in detail the case for which

$$\int_0^{2\pi} \ln \sigma'(\theta)\, d\theta > -\infty \qquad (7.5)$$

and thus the set of polynomials $\{\varphi_n(e^{i\theta})\}$ is not closed in L_2^{σ}.

To every given function $f(\theta) \in L_2^{\sigma}$ there corresponds a uniquely determined sequence $\{g_n\}$ of its Fourier-Chebyshev coefficients

$$g_n = \frac{1}{2\pi}\int_0^{2\pi} f(\theta)\overline{\varphi_n(e^{i\theta})}\,d\sigma(\theta) \quad (n=0, 1, 2, \ldots) \tag{7.6}$$

for which, in view of Bessel's inequality,

$$\sum_{n=0}^{\infty} |g_n|^2 < \infty.$$

We now use these coefficients to construct the partial sums

$$s_n(f; z) = \sum_{k=0}^{n} g_k\varphi_k(z) \quad (n=0, 1, 2, \ldots) \tag{7.7}$$

of the Fourier-Chebyshev expansion for the given function, and then under condition (7.5), as described in 6.2, for $|z| < 1$ we have

$$\lim_{n\to\infty} s_n(f; z) = \sum_{k=0}^{\infty} g_k\varphi_k(z) = F(z), \tag{7.8}$$

where F(z) is an analytic function, regular for $|z| < 1$. Now if one starts not from a function $f(\theta)$, but from a sequence $\{g_n\}$ of complex numbers such that $\sum_{n=0}^{\infty} |g_n|^2 < \infty$, then one first obtains the corresponding well-defined analytic function F(z) of (7.8). Further, according to the Riesz-Fischer theorem one can construct a function $f_0(\theta) \in L_2^\sigma$ with the given $\{g_n\}$ for coefficients and satisfying the closure condition; all other functions $f(\theta)$ with the same coefficients are given, according to (2.22), by

$$f(\theta) = f_0(\theta) + \pi_0(\theta)\,\overline{e^{i\theta}\mu(e^{i\theta})}, \quad \mu(z) \in H_2. \tag{7.9}$$

Let us clarify the properties of $f_0(\theta)$, its relation to the boundary values of F(z), and the convergence conditions for the series $\sum_{k=0}^{\infty} g_k\varphi_k(e^{i\theta})$ in terms of the metrics in the spaces L_2^σ and C.

We define the subclass $M \subset L_2^\sigma$ as follows: $f(\theta) \in M$ if $f(\theta)$ is equivalent to boundary values $\varphi(e^{i\theta})$ of some analytic function $\varphi(z)$ regular for $|z| < 1$, such that $\frac{\varphi(z)}{\pi(z)} \in H_2$.

7.2. We first consider a function $f(\theta) \in L_2^\sigma$.

Theorem 7.1. If condition (7.5) is fulfilled, and if the closure condition holds for $f(\theta) \in L_2^\sigma$, then $f(\theta) \in M$; further, $\frac{F(z)}{\pi(z)} \in H_2$ and $\varphi(z) \equiv F(z)$, which is to say that $f(\theta)$ is equivalent to $F(e^{i\theta})$.* From the closure condition we obtain

$$\lim_{n\to\infty} \frac{1}{2\pi} \int_0^{2\pi} |f(\theta) - s_n(f; e^{i\theta})|^2 p(\theta)\, d\theta =$$

$$= \lim_{n\to\infty} \frac{1}{2\pi} \int_0^{2\pi} \left| \frac{f(\theta)}{\pi(e^{i\theta})} - \frac{s_n(f; e^{i\theta})}{\pi(e^{i\theta})} \right|^2 d\theta = 0.$$

Therefore in $[0, 2\pi]$, the sequence $\left\{\frac{s_n(f; e^{i\theta})}{\pi(e^{i\theta})}\right\}$ converges in measure to the function $f(\theta)/\pi(e^{i\theta})$.**

Now we have

$$\frac{1}{2\pi} \int_0^{2\pi} \left| \frac{s_n(f; e^{i\theta})}{\pi(e^{i\theta})} \right|^2 d\theta \leqslant \frac{1}{2\pi} \int_0^{2\pi} |s_n(f; e^{i\theta})|^2 d\sigma(\theta) =$$

$$= \sum_{k=0}^{n} |g_k|^2 \leqslant \sum_{k=0}^{\infty} |g_k|^2 = B < \infty.$$

Setting

$$f_n(z) = \frac{s_n(f; z)}{\pi(z)},$$

in (5.81), we arrive at the inequality

$$\frac{1}{2\pi} \int_0^{2\pi} \ln^+ \left| \frac{s_n(re^{i\theta})}{\pi(re^{i\theta})} \right| d\theta \leqslant \sqrt{B}, \quad r < 1 \quad (n = 0, 1, 2 \ldots), \tag{7.10}$$

where B is independent of r and of n.

---

* This theorem has been proved by V. I. Smirnov [3] for absolutely continuous $\sigma(\theta)$; it is also contained in the general results of M. G. Krein [1] and G. Ts. Tumarkin [1].

** See I. I. Privalov [1], Introduction, Section 1.

According to the generalized theorem of Khinchin and Ostrovskii[*]
and (7.8), this last equation means that the sequence $\left\{\dfrac{s_n(f;\,z)}{\pi(z)}\right\}$ con-
verges uniformly for $|z| < 1$, i.e.,

$$\lim_{n\to\infty} \frac{s_n(z)}{\pi(z)} = \frac{F(z)}{\pi(z)} = \psi(z) \tag{7.11}$$

and that $\psi(z)$ is an analytic function regular for $|z| < 1$. If in the in-
equality

$$\frac{1}{2\pi} \int_0^{2\pi} \left|\frac{s_n(f;\,re^{i\theta})}{\pi(re^{i\theta})}\right|^2 d\theta \leqslant B, \quad r < 1, \tag{7.12}$$

we fix $\underline{r}$ and go to the limit $n \to \infty$, we obtain

$$\psi(z) \in H_2, \qquad |z| < 1. \tag{7.13}$$

Now furthermore, by the same theorem, the function $f(\theta)/\pi(e^{i\theta})$
to which $\left\{\dfrac{s_n(f;\,e^{i\theta})}{\pi(e^{i\theta})}\right\}$ converges in measure on $[0,\,2\pi]$ must be equivalent to the boundary values $\psi(e^{i\theta}) = F(e^{i\theta})/\pi(e^{i\theta})$; hence if (7.3) holds
for $f(\theta) \in L_2^\sigma$ it follows that $f(\theta) \in M \subset L_2^\sigma$ and that the function
$f(\theta)$ is equivalent to $F(e^{i\theta})$.

Remark 7.1. From the theorem we have just proved it follows
that the closure condition can be fulfilled for at least one function
$f(\theta) \in L_2^\sigma$, $f(\theta) \overline{\in} M$ only if the set of polynomials is closed in L_2^σ, and
this explains the role of the particular function $\psi_0(\theta) = e^{-i\theta}$ in studying
closure and the equivalence of conditions a) and b) in 2.1.

Theorem 7.2. The assertion of the preceding theorem is valid
if the closure condition for $f(\theta) \in L_2^\sigma$ is replaced by the condition that
its Fourier-Chebyshev expansion converges to it in measure on a set
$e \subset [0,\,2\pi]$ of positive measure.

Indeed, under this condition the sequence $\left\{\dfrac{s_n(f;\,e^{i\theta})}{\pi(e^{i\theta})}\right\}$, satisfying
(7.10), converges in measure on a set of positive measure to the func-
tion $f(\theta)/\pi(e^{i\theta})$. Then again using the Khinchin-Ostrovskii theorem, it

---

[*] See I. I. Privalov [1], Chapter II, Section 7.

is easily shown that the assertion holds. This implies that under condition (7.5) the Fourier-Chebyshev expansion of a function $f(\theta) \in L_2^\sigma$, $f(\theta) \bar{\in} M$ diverges almost everywhere $[0, 2\pi]$, and further, that if the Fourier-Chebyshev expansion of a function $f(\theta) \in L_2^\sigma$ converges to zero on some set $e \subset [0, 2\pi]$, then Mes e = 0 or Mes e = 2π. Indeed, if Mes e > 0, then as a consequence of Theorem 7.2 the function $f(\theta)$ is equivalent to a boundary function $\varphi(e^{i\theta})$ vanishing on a set of positive measure, in which case $\varphi(z) \equiv 0$, so that $\varphi(e^{i\theta}) = 0$ almost everywhere in $[0, 2\pi]$.

Theorem 7.3. Assume (7.5) to be fulfilled, and let $d\sigma(\theta) = p(\theta)\,d\theta + d\sigma_1(\theta)$. If two functions $f_1, f_2 \in L_2^\sigma$ differ from each other only on the set E' of points of increase of $\sigma_1(\theta)$, then for $|z| < 1$ we have identically

$$F_1(z) \equiv F_2(z). \tag{7.14}$$

To prove this, recall that

$$g_n^{(1)} - g_n^{(2)} = \frac{1}{2\pi} \int_{E'} \{f_1(\theta) - f_2(\theta)\} \overline{\varphi_n(e^{i\theta})}\, d\sigma_1(\theta),$$

whence

$$s_n(f_1; z) - s_n(f_2; z) = \\ = \frac{1}{2\pi} \int_{E'} \{f_1(\theta) - f_2(\theta)\} K_n(z, e^{i\theta})\, d\sigma_1(\theta), \quad |z| < 1. \tag{7.15}$$

Now from (1.7)

$$|K_n(z, e^{i\theta})| \leqslant \frac{2|\varphi_n^*(z)| \cdot |\varphi_n(e^{i\theta})|}{1 - |z|}, \qquad |z| < 1,$$

so that if $|z| \leq r < 1$, we obtain

$$s_n(f_1; z) - s_n(f_2; z) \leqslant \frac{2|\varphi_n^*(z)|}{1 - |z|} \|f_1 - f_2\|_2^\sigma \cdot \|\varphi_n(e^{i\theta})\|_2^{\sigma_1}.$$

Equation (2.23) implies that

$$s_n(f_1; z) - s_n(f_2; z)| \leqslant \frac{C\delta_n}{1 - r} |\varphi_n^*(z)|, \quad |z| \leqslant r < 1, \tag{7.16}$$

where C is independent of both r and n; then fixing r and going into the limit as $n \to \infty$, we arrive at (7.14).

Thus by changing the values of a function $f(\theta) \in L_2^\sigma$ on E', we change its Fourier-Chebyshev coefficients, yet F(z) remains unchanged.

Theorem 7.4. If (7.5) is fulfilled and $f(\theta) \in M$, then the closure equation holds for this function.

Let us find the Fourier-Chebyshev coefficients $\{g_n\}$ of $f(\theta)$ and use the Riesz-Fischer theorem to construct the function $f_0(\theta) \in L_2^\sigma$ with the same coefficients, the closure condition holding for this latter function. According to Theorem 7.1 $f_0(\theta) \in M$, so that $f(\theta) - f_0(\theta)$ is a function of class M with all of its Fourier-Chebyshev coefficients vanishing. Consequently, according to (2.22) the function

$$\frac{f(\theta) - f_0(\theta)}{\pi_0(\theta)} = \overline{e^{i\theta}\mu(e^{i\theta})}$$

must be equivalent to the boundary value $\psi(e^{i\theta})$ of some analytic function $\psi(z) \in H_2$, so that for $|z^*| > 1$, we may write

$$\frac{1}{2\pi}\int_0^{2\pi} \frac{\overline{\mu(e^{i\theta})}\, d\theta}{e^{i\theta} - z^*} \equiv 0.$$

Setting $z^* = 1/\bar{z}$, $|z| < 1$, $\zeta = e^{i\theta}$, we find that

$$\frac{1}{2\pi}\int_0^{2\pi} \frac{\overline{\mu(e^{i\theta})}\, d\theta}{e^{i\theta} - \frac{1}{\bar{z}}} = -\frac{\bar{z}}{2\pi}\int_0^{2\pi} \frac{\overline{\mu(e^{i\theta})}\, d\theta}{1 - \bar{z}e^{i\theta}} =$$

$$= -\frac{z}{2\pi}\int_0^{2\pi} \frac{\mu(e^{i\theta})\, d\theta}{1 - ze^{-i\theta}} = -z\frac{1}{2\pi i}\int_{|\zeta|=1} \frac{\mu(\zeta)\, d\zeta}{\zeta - z} = 0$$

throughout the region $|z| < 1$. Then since $\mu(z) \in H_2$, we have

$$\mu(z) = \frac{1}{2\pi i}\int_{|\zeta|=1} \frac{\mu(\zeta)\, d\zeta}{\zeta - z} = 0, \qquad |z| < 1,$$

and therefore $\psi(z) \equiv \mu(z) \equiv 0$ and $f(\theta) \equiv f_0(\theta)$.

Remark 7.2. A consequence of Theorem 7.4 is that a function of the form $e^{im\theta}\pi(e^{i\theta})$, where m is a positive integer, satisfies the closure condition; exactly similarly, if $\Phi(z)$ is a function regular in the closed region $|z| \leq 1$, then $\Phi(e^{i\theta})$ satisfies the closure condition.* Further, we have the following

Theorem 7.5. If the Fourier-Chebyshev expansion for a function $f(\theta) \in L_2^\sigma$ converges on a set $e \subset [0, 2\pi]$ of positive measure, the condition of closure holds for this function (i.e., convergence in the metric C on $\underline{e}$, for $\text{Mes}\, e > 0$, implies convergence in the metric L_2^σ).

Indeed, if condition (7.5) is satisfied, the theorem follows from Theorems 7.4 and 7.2; if it is not satisfied, the closure condition holds for every function $f(\theta) \in L_2^\sigma$.

7.3. We will now proceed on the basis of a given sequence $\{g_n\}$ of coefficients or of a given function F(z).

Theorem 7.6. Given a sequence of complex numbers $\{g_n\}$ such that

$$\sum_{n=0}^{\infty} |g_n|^2 < \infty,$$

it follows that all functions $f(\theta) \in L_2^\sigma$ for which these numbers will serve as Fourier-Chebyshev coefficients are of the form, under condition (7.5),

$$f(\theta) = f_0(\theta) + e^{-i\theta}\pi_0(\theta)\overline{\mu(e^{i\theta})} = f_0(\theta) + \varphi(\theta),$$

where $\mu(z)$ is an arbitrary function of class H_2 and $f_0(\theta)$, the only one of all functions with the given coefficients for which the closure condition is satisfied and which belongs to class M, is given by the Riesz-Fischer theorem and is equivalent to a function $F(e^{i\theta})$ where F(z) is given by (7.8); further

$$\lim_{n\to\infty} \min_{G_n} \|f(\theta) - G_n(e^{i\theta})\|_2^\sigma =$$

$$= \sqrt{\frac{1}{2\pi}\int_0^{2\pi} |f(\theta)|^2\, d\sigma(\theta) - \sum_{n=0}^{\infty} |g_n|^2} = \|\mu(e^{i\theta})\|_2. \quad (7.17)$$

* For absolutely continuous $\sigma(\theta)$, the first assertion was proved by V. I. Smirnov [3], and the second by G. Szegö [5], Theorem 34.

To prove (7.17) we need only remark that

$$\frac{1}{2\pi}\int_0^{2\pi} f_0(\theta)\overline{\varphi(\theta)}\,d\sigma(\theta)=\frac{1}{2\pi}\int_0^{2\pi}\frac{f_0(\theta)\,e^{i\theta}\mu(e^{i\theta})\,d\theta}{(e^{i\theta})}=$$

$$=\frac{1}{2\pi i}\int_{|z|=1}\frac{F(z)\,\mu(z)}{\pi(z)}\,dz=0,$$

so that

$$\frac{1}{2\pi}\int_0^{2\pi}|f(\theta)|^2\,d\sigma(\theta)=\frac{1}{2\pi}\int_0^{2\pi}|f_0(\theta)|^2\,d\sigma(\theta)+\frac{1}{2\pi}\int_0^{2\pi}|\varphi(\theta)|^2\,d\sigma(\theta)=$$

$$=\sum_{n=0}^{\infty}|g_n|^2+\frac{1}{2\pi}\int_0^{2\pi}|\mu(e^{i\theta})|^2\,d\theta.$$

Theorem 7.6'. Under condition (7.5) let there be an analytic function $F(z)$ regular for $|z| < 1$, such that $\frac{F(z)}{\pi(z)}\in H_2$. Complementing its boundary values $F(e^{i\theta})$ in an arbitrary way on E', we obtain an infinite number of functions $f(\theta)\in M$, for each of which the closure condition is satisfied. These functions have different sequences of Fourier-Chebyshev coefficients, but any two sequences $\{g_n^{(1)}\}$, $\{g_n^{(2)}\}$ are related by

$$\sum_{n=0}^{\infty} g_n^{(1)}\varphi_n(z)=\sum_{n=0}^{\infty} g_n^{(2)}\varphi_n(z)=F(z),\quad |z|<1. \tag{7.18}$$

To prove this we note that $F(z)$ has radial boundary values

$$F(e^{i\theta})=\lim_{r\to 1-0}F(re^{i\theta})$$

almost everywhere on the circumference $|z| = 1$. In calculating integrals involving a function equivalent to $F(e^{i\theta})$, we break up each integral into two parts, namely, a Lebesgue integral over E, and a Lebesgue-Stieltjes integral over E'. To carry out the first integration it is sufficient to know the values of $F(e^{i\theta})$ almost everywhere on $[0, 2\pi]$, but the second requires assigning values to the function on E'; in the sequel, when examining in more detail the convergence of the Fourier-Chebyshev process for $f(\theta)$, a function equivalent to the boundary values $F(e^{i\theta})$ we may set for example $f(\theta) \equiv 0$ for $\theta \in E'$.

For the special case in which $\sigma(\theta)$ is absolutely continuous, the $\{g_n\}$ coefficients can be found from the boundary values of F(z).*

As an illustration, consider a function $\pi(z)$ satisfying the conditions of Theorem 7.6. If we proceed on the basis of this function, to find the Fourier-Chebyshev coefficients of a function $f(\theta)$ equivalent to $\pi(e^{i\theta})$ is not a well-defined problem, for they depend on the values we assign to our function on E'. But we have defined $\pi(z)$ by going to the limit

$$\pi(z) = \lim_{n\to\infty} \varphi_n^*(z) = \frac{1}{\alpha} \sum_{k=0}^{\infty} \overline{\varphi_k(0)}\, \varphi_k(z), \quad |z| < 1,$$

which means that we know its Fourier-Chebyshev coefficients $\left\{g_n = \frac{1}{\alpha}\overline{\varphi_n(0)}\right\}$. By constructing $\pi_0(\theta)$, defined by $\pi_0(\theta) \equiv \pi(e^{i\theta})\gamma_E(\theta)$, we find that it has just these coefficients, as was shown in 2.1.

7.4 Let us now consider a special case of Theorem 7.5.

Theorem 7.7. Assume the existence of the integral (7.5), and let a function $f(\theta) \in L_2^\sigma$ coincide on $[0, 2\pi]$ with the boundary values of a function $f_1(z)$, meromorphic for $|z| < 1$ and continuous in the closed region $|z| \leq 1$, except for the poles

$$\alpha_1, \alpha_2, \ldots, \alpha_s, \quad |\alpha_k| < 1.$$

Then

$$\lim_{n\to\infty} \min_{G_n} \|f(\theta) - G_n(e^{i\theta})\|_2^\sigma = \|H(e^{i\theta})\|_2, \tag{7.19}$$

* See V. I. Smirnov [3].

where H(z) is the principal part of $f_1(z)/\pi(z)$, i.e.,

$$H(z)=\sum_{k=1}^{s} H_k\left(\frac{1}{z-\alpha_k}\right), \quad H_k(\zeta)=\sum_{r=1}^{\nu_k} a_r^{(k)}\zeta^r. \tag{7.20}$$

We have

$$f(\theta)\sim\sum_{k=0}^{\infty} g_k\varphi_k(e^{i\theta}), \quad \sum_{k=0}^{\infty}|g_k|^2<\infty,$$

and note that according to Theorem 7.1 the condition of closure is not fulfilled for $f(\theta)$. According to Theorem 7.6 we may write

$$\left.\begin{aligned} f(\theta)&=F(e^{i\theta})+e^{-i\theta}\overline{\mu(e^{i\theta})}\,\pi_0(\theta)=f_1(e^{i\theta}),\\ F(z)&=\sum_{k=0}^{\infty} g_k\varphi_k(z), \quad |z|<1. \end{aligned}\right\} \tag{7.21}$$

Further, (7.17) states that

$$\lim_{n\to\infty}\min_{G_n}\|f(\theta)-G_n(e^{i\theta})\|_2^{\sigma}=$$

$$=\sqrt{\frac{1}{2\pi}\int_0^{2\pi}|f(\theta)|^2\,d\sigma(\theta)-\sum_{k=0}^{\infty}|g_k|^2}=\|\mu(e^{i\theta})\|_2.$$

Now using (7.21) we can find the boundary values for $\mu(z)\in H_2$, and then from them we can find $\mu(z)$ itself.

Let

$$\frac{f_1(z)}{\pi(z)}=H(z)+R(z), \tag{7.22}$$

where R(z) is the regular part of $f_1(z)/\pi(z)$, continuous in $|z|\leq 1$.

We have

$$H(e^{i\theta})=\sum_{k=1}^{s} H_k\left(\frac{1}{e^{i\theta}-\alpha_k}\right)=\sum_{k=1}^{s}\overline{H_k\left(\frac{e^{i\theta}}{1-\overline{\alpha}_k e^{i\theta}}\right)}=e^{-i\theta}\overline{h(e^{i\theta})}, \tag{7.23}$$

where the rational function

$$h(z)=\sum_{k=1}^{s}\sum_{r=1}^{\nu_k}\frac{\bar{a}_r^k z^{r-1}}{(1-\bar{\alpha}_k z)^r}$$

is regular in the region $|z| < 1$.

From (7.21), using (7.22) and (7.23), we obtain

$$\frac{F(e^{i\theta})}{\pi_0(\theta)}-R(e^{i\theta})=e^{-i\theta}\{\overline{h(e^{i\theta})}-\overline{\mu(e^{i\theta})}\};$$

since the left side is the boundary value of some function of class H_2, we may reproduce the arguments used in proving Theorem 7.4 to obtain

$$h(z)\equiv\mu(z), \qquad |z|<1;$$

$$\|\mu(e^{i\theta})\|_2=\|h(e^{i\theta})\|_2=\|H(e^{i\theta})\|_2.$$

For the special case in which $f_1(z) = z^{-m}$, where $\underline{m}$ is a positive integer, the theorem has been proved by Kolmogorov [1, 2] by the theory of stationary random sequences.

Expanding $\ln p(\theta)$ in a Fourier series

$$\ln p(\theta)\sim\sum_{k=0}^{\infty}(a_k\cos k\theta+b_k\sin k\theta), \quad a_0=\frac{1}{2\pi}\int_0^{2\pi}\ln p(\theta)\,d\theta, \tag{7.24}$$

we find, from (2.6), that

$$\ln D(z)=\ln\frac{1}{\pi(z)}=\frac{1}{2}\sum_{k=0}^{\infty}(a_k-ib_k)z^k=\frac{1}{2}\sum_{k=0}^{\infty}c_k z^k,$$

so that

$$z^{-m}D(z)=z^{-m}e^{\frac{a_0}{2}}\cdot e^{\frac{1}{2}\sum_{k=1}^{\infty}c_k z^k} \tag{7.25}$$

We now introduce the notation

$$\exp\left\{\frac{1}{2}\sum_{k=1}^{\infty}c_k z^k\right\}=1+\sum_{k=1}^{\infty}r_k z^k, \tag{7.26}$$

in terms of which

$$H(z)=e^{\frac{a_0}{2}}\left\{\frac{1}{z^m}+\frac{r_1}{z^{m-1}}+\ldots+\frac{r_{m-1}}{z}+r_m\right\},$$

which leads to Kolmogorov's result

$$\lim_{n\to\infty}\min_{G_n}\|e^{-im\theta}-G_n(e^{i\theta})\|_2^{\sigma}=$$

$$=\sqrt{1+\sum_{k=1}^{m}|r_k|^2}\cdot\exp\left\{\frac{1}{4\pi}\int_0^{2\pi}\ln p(\theta)\,d\theta\right\}. \tag{7.27}$$

Another interesting special case is that for which

$$f_1(z)=\frac{1}{z-\alpha},\quad |\alpha|<1. \tag{7.28}$$

For this case we have

$$\mu(z)=\frac{1}{\overline{\pi(\alpha)}\,(1-\bar{\alpha}z)},\qquad \|\mu(e^{i\theta})\|_2=\frac{1}{|\pi(\alpha)|\sqrt{1-|\alpha|^2}},$$

whence

$$\lim_{n\to\infty}\min_{G_n}\left\|\frac{1}{e^{i\theta}-\alpha}-G_n(e^{i\theta})\right\|_2^{\sigma}=\frac{1}{|\pi(\alpha)|\sqrt{1-|\alpha|^2}},\quad |\alpha|<1. \tag{7.29}$$

7.5. So far we have been considering the Fourier-Chebyshev expansion

$$f(\theta)\sim\sum_{k=0}^{\infty}g_k\varphi_k(e^{i\theta}),\quad f(\theta)\in L_2^{\sigma}$$

of the given function discussing convergence in the metric of L_2^{σ}; let us now turn to convergence in the metric of the space C.

We start with the simplest case.

Theorem 7.8. Let $f(z)$ be a function regular for $|z|<r$, $r>1$, and assume that on the circumference $|z|=r$ there exist singular points of $f(z)$. Then under condition (6.3) the Fourier-Chebyshev expansion of $f(z)$ converges absolutely for $|z|<r$ and uniformly for $|z|\le r_1<r$, while for $|z|>r$ the series diverges.*

* This theory has been proved by Szegö [5] on the assumption that $\sigma(\theta)$ is absolutely continuous and the integral of (7.5) exists.

We have

$$g_n = \frac{1}{2\pi} \int_0^{2\pi} \{f(e^{i\theta}) - G_{n-1}(e^{i\theta})\} \overline{\varphi_n(e^{i\theta})}\, d\sigma(\theta),$$

$$|g_n| \leqslant \|f(e^{i\theta}) - G_{n-1}(e^{i\theta})\|_2^{\sigma} \quad (n = 1, 2, \ldots).$$

We choose as $G_{n-1}(z)$ the polynomial which gives the best approximation to $f(z)$ for $|z| \leq r_1$; then, as is well known,

$$|f(z) - G_{n-1}(z)| \leqslant \frac{C}{r_1^{n-1}}, \quad |z| \leqslant r_1; \quad |g_n| \leqslant \frac{C'}{r_1^{n-1}}.$$

Since r_1 can be chosen arbitrarily close to $\underline{r}$, we have

$$\overline{\lim_{n\to\infty}} \sqrt[n]{|g_n|} \leqslant \frac{1}{r},$$

and then by the Theorem 6.2 our assertion is proved.

Let us now pass to the general case in which $f(z)$ is regular only for $|z| < 1$. We will assume that the integral of (7.5) exists and will treat (in agreement with the consequences of Theorem 7.2) only functions of the class M.

We derive some auxiliary formulas from which we can evaluate the remainder of the Fourier-Chebyshev expansion for the given function.

For the integrals of (7.6) to exist, it is sufficient that $f(\theta) \in L_2^{\sigma}$, and then according to Theorem 7.2 the necessary condition for the Fourier-Chebyshev expansion of the function $f(\theta)$ to converge on a set of positive measure in that it belong to the subclass M. In the special case in which the entire orthonormal set is uniformly bounded on the entire circumference, the sufficient condition for the existence of the integrals in (7.6) is that $f(\theta) \in L_1^{\sigma}$.

If $f(z)$ is an analytic function regular in $|z| < 1$ and having radial boundary values almost everywhere on the circumference $|z| = 1$, then we write, in analogy with (2.7),

$$f_0(\theta) = f(e^{i\theta})\, \gamma_E(\theta).$$

Theorem 7.9. Let $f(z) \in H_1$ and assume that for $|h| \leq \epsilon$

$$\|f_0(\theta + h)\|_2^\sigma \leqslant A^*, \tag{7.30}$$

where A is independent of h; let $\sigma(\theta)$ be absolutely continuous on $[\alpha, \beta]$, with $p(\theta) \leq M$, and let $f(e^{i\theta})$ be continuous with modulus of continuity $\omega(\delta; f)$. Then in the interior of $[\alpha, \beta]$ we have**

$$|f(e^{i\theta_0}) - s_n(f;\ e^{i\theta_0})| \leqslant C_1\mu_n\delta_n + C_2\mu_n\omega_2^{\sigma_0}\left(\frac{1}{n};\ f_0\right) + \\ + C_3\mu_n^2 \ln n\omega\left(\frac{1}{n};\ f\right), \quad (n = 1,\ 2,\ \ldots), \tag{7.30'}$$

where $d\sigma_0(\theta) = p(\theta)\,d\theta$,

$$|\varphi_n(e^{i\theta})| \leqslant \mu_n, \quad (n = 0,\ 1,\ 2,\ \ldots),\ \alpha \leqslant \theta \leqslant \beta, \tag{7.30''}$$

with $\{\mu_n\}$ a nondecreasing sequence.

We have

$$s_n(f;\ e^{i\theta_0}) = \sum_{k=0}^{n} g_k\varphi_k(e^{i\theta_0}) = \sum_{k=0}^{n} \varphi_k(e^{i\theta_0}) \cdot \frac{1}{2\pi}\int_0^{2\pi} f_0(\theta)\overline{\varphi_k(e^{i\theta})}\,d\sigma(\theta) =$$

$$= \frac{1}{2\pi}\int_0^{2\pi} f_0(\theta) K_n(e^{i\theta_0},\ e^{i\theta})\,d\sigma(\theta).$$

Let us construct the Jackson sum $u_\nu(\theta)$ of (3.1) for $f_0(\theta)$; in the present case these are polynomials of degree r in $e^{i\theta}$, where $r = 2\nu - 2 \leq n$ is the largest even number no greater than n. Since

$$u_\nu(\theta_0) = \frac{1}{2\pi}\int_0^{2\pi} u_\nu(\theta) K_n(e^{i\theta_0},\ e^{i\theta})\,d\sigma(\theta), \qquad r \leqslant n,$$

we have

$$s_n(f;\ e^{i\theta_0}) - u_\nu(\theta_0) = \frac{1}{2\pi}\int_0^{2\pi} \{f_0(\theta) - u_\nu(\theta)\} K_n(e^{i\theta_0},\ e^{i\theta})\,d\sigma(\theta).$$

---

* This condition guarantees that $\dfrac{f(z)}{\pi(z)} \in H_2$.

** Here $C_1, C_2, C_3, \ldots$ and in the sequel B, D, E, ... are independent of both n and θ_0.

Using (4.42) with $\alpha + 2\epsilon \le \theta_0 \le \beta - 2\epsilon$, we obtain

$$f(e^{i\theta_0}) - u_\nu(\theta_0) = \frac{1}{2\pi}\int_0^{2\pi} \{f_0(\theta_0) - u_\nu(\theta_0)\} K_n(e^{i\theta_0}, e^{i\theta})\, d\sigma(\theta)$$

and finally

$$s_n(f;\ e^{i\theta}) - f(e^{i\theta_0}) = \frac{1}{2\pi}\int_0^{2\pi} \{\gamma_r(\theta) - \gamma_r(\theta_0)\} K_n(e^{i\theta_0}, e^{i\theta})\, d\sigma(\theta),$$

$$\gamma_r(\varphi) = f_0(\varphi) - u_\nu(\varphi), \quad \alpha + 2\varepsilon \leqslant \theta_0 \leqslant \beta - 2\varepsilon. \tag{7.31}$$

We now write $d\sigma(\theta) = d\sigma_0(\theta) + d\sigma_1(\theta) = p(\theta)\, d\theta + d\sigma_1(\theta)$ and break up the integral in (7.31) into two integrals I_1 and I_2, and start by considering the first. Since $|\theta - \theta_0| \ge 2\epsilon$ for $\theta \overline{\in} [\alpha, \beta]$, we have

$$|K_n(e^{i\theta_0}, e^{i\theta})| \leqslant \frac{2\,|\varphi_n(e^{i\theta_0})\,\varphi_n(e^{i\theta})|}{|e^{i\theta_0} - e^{i\theta}|} \leqslant \frac{\mu_n\,|\varphi_n(e^{i\theta})|}{\sin\varepsilon},$$

and therefore

$$|I_2| \leqslant \frac{1}{2\pi}\int_0^{2\pi} |\gamma_r(\theta) - \gamma_r(\theta_0)| \cdot |K_n(e^{i\theta_0}, e^{i\theta})|\, d\sigma_1(\theta) \leqslant$$

$$\leqslant \frac{\mu_n}{\sin\varepsilon} \|\gamma_r(\theta) - \gamma_r(\theta_0)\|_2^{\sigma_1} \|\varphi_n(e^{i\theta})\|_2^{\sigma_1} \leqslant \frac{\mu_n}{\sin\varepsilon}\{\|\gamma_r(\theta)\|_2^{\sigma_1} +$$

$$+ |\gamma_r(\theta_0)| \cdot \sqrt{c_0}\} \cdot \|\varphi_n(e^{i\theta})\|_2^{\sigma_1}.$$

From (3.6), (5.31), and (7.30) we have

$$\|\gamma_r(\theta)\|_2^{\sigma_1} = \|f_0(\theta) - u_\nu(\theta)\|_2^{\sigma_1} \leqslant C\omega_2^{\sigma_1}\left(\frac{1}{\nu};\ f_0\right) \leqslant$$

$$\leqslant C \sup_{|h| \leqslant \frac{1}{\nu}} \|f_0(\theta + h) - f_0(\theta)\|_2^{\sigma_1} \leqslant 2AC, \tag{7.31'}$$

$$|\gamma_r(\theta_0)| = |f_0(\theta_0) - u_\nu(\theta_0)| \leqslant C_1\omega\left(\frac{1}{\nu};\ f\right),$$

$$\alpha + 2\varepsilon \leqslant \theta_0 \leqslant \beta - 2\varepsilon,$$

and thus, according to (2.23), we obtain

$$|I_2| \leqslant \frac{C'\mu_n}{\sin\varepsilon}\delta_n\left\{2AC + C_1\omega\left(\frac{1}{\nu};\ f\right)\right\} \leqslant C''\mu_n\delta_n. \tag{7.32}$$

To calculate the first integral, in which $d\sigma_0(\theta) = p(\theta)d\theta$, we introduce the intermediate points

$$0 < \alpha + \varepsilon < \theta_0 - \frac{1}{n} < \theta_0 + \frac{1}{n} < \beta - \varepsilon < 2\pi,$$

as we did in 5.5, breaking up the integral into five integrals $i_1, \ldots, i_5$ and evaluating each of these.

Since $|\theta - \theta_0| \geq \epsilon$ for $0 \leq \theta \leq \alpha + \epsilon$, we can use (5.31) and (3.6) to obtain

$$|i_1| = \left| \frac{1}{2\pi} \int_0^{\alpha+\varepsilon} \{\gamma_r(\theta) - \gamma_r(\theta_0)\} K_n(e^{i\theta_0}, e^{i\theta}) p(\theta) d\theta \right| \leqslant$$

$$\leqslant \frac{1}{2 \sin \frac{\varepsilon}{2}} \cdot 2\mu_n \frac{1}{2\pi} \int_0^{\alpha+\varepsilon} \{|\gamma_r(\theta)| + |\gamma_r(\theta_0)|\} \cdot |\varphi_n(e^{i\theta})| d\sigma_0(\theta) \leqslant$$

$$\leqslant \frac{\mu_n}{\sin \frac{\varepsilon}{2}} \{\|\gamma_r(\theta)\|_2^{\sigma_0} + |\gamma_r(\theta_0)| \sqrt{c_0}\} \leqslant$$

$$\leqslant \mu_n \left\{ B\omega_2^{\sigma_0}\left(\frac{1}{n}; f_0\right) + B'\omega\left(\frac{1}{n}; f\right) \right\}; \tag{7.33}$$

a similar result obtains for i_5.

Further, according to (5.31),

$$|i_2| = \left| \frac{1}{2\pi} \int_{\alpha+\varepsilon}^{\theta_0 - \frac{1}{n}} \right| \leqslant \frac{2\mu_n^2 \cdot 2C\omega\left(\frac{1}{n}; f\right)}{2\pi} M \int_{\alpha+\varepsilon}^{\theta_0 - \frac{1}{n}} \frac{d\theta}{\theta_0 - \theta} \leqslant$$

$$\leqslant D\mu_n^2 \omega\left(\frac{1}{n}; f\right) \ln n; \tag{7.34}$$

a similar result obtains for i_4.

Finally, if $\alpha + \epsilon \leq \theta \leq \beta - \epsilon$, we have the inequality

$$|K_n(e^{i\theta_0}, e^{i\theta})| \leqslant (n+1)\mu_n^2, \qquad \alpha + 2\varepsilon \leqslant \theta_0 \leqslant \beta - 2\varepsilon,$$

from which we find for i_3 that

$$|i_3| = \left| \frac{1}{2\pi} \int_{\theta_0 - \frac{1}{n}}^{\theta_0 + \frac{1}{n}} \right| \leqslant \frac{2}{n} \cdot \frac{(n+1)\mu_n^2}{2\pi} \cdot 2C\omega\left(\frac{1}{n};\, f\right) \leqslant E\mu_n^2 \omega\left(\frac{1}{n},\, f\right). \tag{7.35}$$

Combining (7.32) – (7.35), we obtain (7.30').

Remark 7.3. If $\sigma(\theta)$ is absolutely continuous on $[0, 2\pi]$, one may write $C_1 = 0$ in (7.30') and replace condition (7.30) by the condition $\frac{f(z)}{\pi(z)} \in H_2$. If on $[0, 2\pi]$ the function $\sigma(\theta)$ is absolutely continuous and $p(\theta) \leq M$, then $\omega_2^{\sigma_0}(\delta;\, f)$ in (7.30') may be replaced by $\omega_2(\delta; f)$ since $\omega_2^{\sigma}(\delta; f) \leq \sqrt{M}\,\omega_2(\delta; f)$. Finally, if on $[0, 2\pi]$ the function $\sigma(\theta)$ is absolutely continuous, $p(\theta) \leq M$, and the orthonormal set is uniformly bounded (i.e., if $|\varphi_n(e^{i\theta})| \leq C$), then in the interior of $[\alpha, \beta]$ we obtain

$$|s_n(f,\, e^{i\theta_0}) - f(e^{i\theta_0})| \leqslant C_1\omega_1\left(\frac{1}{n};\, f\right) + C_2\omega\left(\frac{1}{n};\, f\right) \ln n, \tag{7.36}$$

and in this case it is no longer necessary that $\frac{f(z)}{\pi(z)} \in H_2$. To prove the last assertion we need only change the estimates for i_1 and i_5. Instead of (7.33) we obtain

$$|i_1| \leqslant \frac{1}{2\sin\frac{\varepsilon}{2}} \cdot 2C^2 \frac{M}{2\pi} \int_0^{\alpha+\varepsilon} \{|\gamma_r(\theta)| + |\gamma_r(\theta_0)|\}\, d\theta \leqslant$$

$$\leqslant \frac{C^2 M}{\sin\frac{\varepsilon}{2}} \{\|\gamma_r(\theta)\|_1 + |\gamma_r(\theta_0)|\} \leqslant C_1\omega_1\left(\frac{1}{n};\, f\right) + C_2\omega\left(\frac{1}{n};\, f\right).$$

7.6. Let us now write $f(z) = \pi(z)$ in (7.9), and therefore $s_n(f,\, z) = \frac{a_n}{\alpha} \varphi_n^*(z)$.

Theorem 7.10. Let $\frac{1}{\sqrt{p(\theta)}} \in L_1$ and let $\frac{1}{p_0(\theta)} \leqslant M_1$, $\theta \in E_h$. Let $\sigma(\theta)$ be absolutely continuous on $[\alpha, \beta]$, and $p(\theta) \geq m > 0$ be continuous on the same interval. Then in the interior of $[\alpha, \beta]$ we have*

* Here C_1, C_2, C_3 are constants independent of both n and θ_0.

$$|\varphi_n^*(e^{i\theta_0})-\pi(e^{i\theta_0})|\leqslant C_1\mu_n\delta_n+C_2\mu_n\delta_n'+C_3\mu_n^2\ln n\omega\left(\frac{1}{n};\ \pi\right). \tag{7.37}$$

If $\sigma(\theta)$ is absolutely continuous on the entire interval $[0, 2\pi]$ the condition $\frac{1}{p_0(\theta)}\leqslant M_1,\ \theta\in E_h$ may be dropped and one may write $C_1 = 0$.*

Rewriting (7.30') for this case, we have

$$\left|\pi(e^{i\theta_0})-\frac{\alpha_n}{\alpha}\varphi_n^*(e^{i\theta_0})\right|\leqslant C_1\mu_n\delta_n+C_2\mu_n\omega_2^{\sigma_0}\left(\frac{1}{n};\ \pi\right)+$$
$$+C_3\mu_n^2\ln n\omega\left(\frac{1}{n};\ \pi\right).$$

From (3.8) and (2.8), we find that

$$\omega_2^{\sigma_0}\left(\frac{1}{n};\ \pi\right)=\sup_{|h|\leqslant\frac{1}{n}}\left\|\frac{\pi(e^{i(\theta+h)})-\pi(e^{i\theta})}{\pi(e^{i\theta})}\right\|_2=\delta_n',$$

$$1-\frac{\alpha_n}{\alpha}=\frac{\alpha-\alpha_n}{\alpha}\leqslant\frac{\alpha}{\alpha+\alpha_0}\delta_n^2.$$

In view of the inequality

$$|\varphi_n^*(e^{i\theta_0})-\pi(e^{i\theta_0})|\leqslant\left|\frac{\alpha_n}{\alpha}\varphi_n^*(e^{i\theta_0})-\pi(e^{i\theta_0})\right|+$$
$$+\left(1-\frac{\alpha_n}{\alpha}\right)|\varphi_n^*(e^{i\theta_0})|\leqslant C_1\mu_n\delta_n+C_2\mu_n\delta_n'+$$
$$+C_3\mu_n^2\ln n\omega\left(\frac{1}{n};\ \pi\right)+\frac{\alpha}{\alpha+\alpha_0}\mu_n\delta_n^2,$$

we arrive at (7.37).

Thus for the validity of the limit relation $\lim_{n\to\infty}\varphi_n^*(e^{i\theta_0})=\pi(e^{i\theta_0})$ or the asymptotic formula $\varphi_n(e^{i\theta})\simeq e^{in\theta}\pi(e^{i\theta})$ it is sufficient that the following three conditions be simultaneously fulfilled:

---

* If $\sigma(\theta)$ is absolutely continuous throughout $[0, 2\pi]$, then (3.9) implies that $\delta_n\leq 12\delta_n'$, from which it is clear that we may write $C_1 = 0$.

1. $\lim_{n\to\infty} \delta'_n = 0$, i.e.,

$$\lim_{n\to\infty} \sup_{|h|\leqslant\frac{1}{n}} \left\| \frac{\pi(e^{i(\theta+h)}) - \pi(e^{i\theta})}{\pi(e^{i\theta})} \right\|_2 =$$

$$= \lim_{n\to\infty} \sup_{|h|\leqslant\frac{1}{n}} \left\| \frac{p(\theta+h) - p(\theta)}{p(\theta)} \right\|_1 = 0;$$

in particular, this is true under any one of the conditions of Table 1.

2. $\mu_n = C$ $(n = 0, 1, 2, \ldots)$, which means that the orthonormal system must be uniformly bounded on $[\alpha, \beta]$; in particular, this is true under any one of conditions V-VII of Table III.

3. $\lim_{\delta\to 0} \left\{ \omega(\delta; \pi) \ln \frac{1}{\delta} \right\} = 0$; Theorem 4.7 can be used to write $\omega(\delta; \pi)$ in terms of $\omega(\delta; p)$ as is done, for instance, in the proof of Theorem 4.8.

We have thus obtained conditions V-IX of Table V. To derive condition X let us first consider the polynomials $\{\gamma_n(z)\}$ orthonormal with respect to the measure $d\sigma_0(\theta) = p(\theta)\, d\theta$. In view of condition VII of Table II these polynomials are uniformly bounded on the entire circumference. We obtain the same $\pi(z)$ function for the two orthogonal sets $\{\varphi_n(z)\}$ and $\{\gamma_n(z)\}$, since it depends only on $p(\theta)$ as is clear from (2.5). Therefore as a result of condition I of Table I and (7.37), if $\alpha + 2\epsilon \leq \theta_0 \leq \beta - 2\epsilon$, then

$$\left|\pi(e^{i\theta_0}) - \gamma_n^*(e^{i\theta_0})\right| \leqslant \frac{C_4}{\sqrt{n}} + \frac{C_5}{(\ln n)^{\gamma-1}} \leqslant C_6 (\ln n)^{1-\gamma},$$

$$\gamma_n(z) = \beta_n z^n + \ldots,$$

where, according to (2.9'), $\lim_{n\to\infty} \beta_n = \lim_{n\to\infty} \alpha_n = \alpha$. On the other hand, we may write in analogy with (4.24'),

$$\varphi_n(e^{i\theta_0}) - \frac{\alpha_n}{\beta_n} \gamma_n(e^{i\theta}) = -\frac{1}{2\pi} \int_0^{2\pi} K'_{n-1}(e^{i\theta_0}, e^{i\theta})\, \varphi_n(e^{i\theta})\, d\sigma_1(\theta),$$

$$K'_{n-1}(z_0, z) = \sum_{k=0}^{n-1} \gamma_k(z_0) \overline{\gamma_k(z)} = \frac{\gamma_n^*(z_0)\overline{\gamma_n^*(z)} - \gamma_n(z_0)\overline{\gamma_n(z)}}{1 - z_0\bar{z}}.$$

For $\alpha + 2\epsilon \leq \theta_0 \leq \beta - 2\epsilon$ and $\theta \bar{\in} [\alpha, \beta]$, we clearly have $|\theta - \theta_0| \geq 2\epsilon$, from which we obtain

$$|K'_{n-1}(e^{i\theta_0}, e^{i\theta})| \leqslant C,$$

$$|\varphi_n(e^{i\theta_0}) - \frac{\alpha_n}{\beta_n}\gamma_n(e^{i\theta_0})| \leqslant C \|\varphi_n(e^{i\theta})\|_1^{\sigma_1} \leqslant C_1\delta_n.$$

Consequently we arrive at the inequality

$$|\varphi_n^*(e^{i\theta_0}) - \pi(e^{i\theta_0})| \leqslant |\varphi_n^*(e^{i\theta_0}) - \frac{\alpha_n}{\beta_n}\gamma_n^*(e^{i\theta_0})| +$$
$$+\left(1 - \frac{\alpha_n}{\beta_n}\right)|\gamma_n^*(e^{i\theta_0})| + |\gamma_n^*(e^{i\theta_0}) - \pi(e^{i\theta_0})| \leqslant C_1\delta_n +$$
$$+ C_6(\ln n)^{1-\gamma} + C_7\delta_n^2 + C_8\delta_n'^2 \leqslant C_1'\delta_n + C_2'(\ln n)^{1-\gamma},$$

since, according to (2.8), we have

$$1 - \frac{\alpha_n}{\beta_n} = \frac{(\alpha - \alpha_n) - (\alpha - \beta_n)}{\beta_n} \leqslant \frac{\frac{\alpha^2\delta_n^2}{\alpha + \alpha_0} + \frac{\alpha^2\delta_n'^2}{\alpha + \beta_0}}{\beta_0}.$$

7.7. By the same means as we used to derive (7.30'), we can derive several other estimates which are of interest in their own right, namely an estimate of the Lebesgue constants of the Fourier-Chebyshev process and an estimate for the partial sums.

Theorem 7.11. Let $\sigma(\theta)$ satisfy the condition of Theorem 7.9. Then we obtain the following estimates: 1) a local estimate for the Lebesgue constants of the Fourier-Chebyshev process is

$$\left.\begin{array}{c} L_n(\theta_0) = \frac{1}{2\pi}\int_0^{2\pi} |K_n(e^{i\theta_0}, e^{i\theta})|\, d\sigma(\theta) \leqslant C\mu_n^2 \ln n, \\ \alpha + \varepsilon \leqslant \theta_0 \leqslant \beta - \varepsilon; \end{array}\right\} \quad (7.38)$$

2) if $f(\theta) \in L_2^\sigma$ is bounded on $[\alpha, \beta]$, a local estimate for the partial sums of its Fourier-Chebyshev expansion is

$$|s_n(f; e^{i\theta_0})| \leqslant C_2\mu_n^2 \ln n, \quad \alpha + \eta \leqslant \theta_0 \leqslant \beta - \eta. \quad (7.38')$$

In particular, if the orthonormal set is uniformly bounded on $[\alpha, \beta]$ (for instance, under conditions V-VII of Table III), we obtain*

---

* In this particular case, as has been shown by V. F. Nikolaev [1], the rate of increase of the Lebesgue constants is slowest; the bound for the partial sums is a local form and a generalization to orthogonal series of the corresponding bound for power series.

$$L_n(\theta_0) \leqslant C_3 \ln n, \quad |s_n(f;\ e^{i\theta_0})| \leqslant C_4 \ln n, \quad \alpha + \eta \leqslant \theta_0 \leqslant \beta - \eta. \tag{7.38''}$$

To prove 2) we must study the integral in (7.31).

The estimate (7.30') of the remainder was derived by approximating $f(e^{i\theta})$ by its Jackson sum (3.1); let us now derive another estimate for the remainder by using the function

$$f_1(\theta) = \frac{f_0(\theta) - f_0(\theta_0)}{e^{i\theta} - e^{i\theta_0}}. \tag{7.39}$$

According to (7.1) we may write

$$s_n(f;\ e^{i\theta_0}) - f_0(\theta_0) = \frac{1}{2\pi}\int_0^{2\pi} \{f_0(\theta) - f_0(\theta_0)\}\, K_n(e^{i\theta_0}, e^{i\theta})\, d\sigma(\theta) =$$

$$= \frac{1}{2\pi}\int_0^{2\pi} f_1(\theta)\left\{e^{i\theta}\varphi_n^*(e^{i\theta_0})\overline{\varphi_n^*(e^{i\theta})} - e^{i\theta_0}\varphi_n(e^{i\theta_0})\overline{\varphi_n(e^{i\theta})}\right\} d\sigma(\theta).$$

In the notation of (4.33), we find, in analogy with (4.45),

$$s_n(f;\ e^{i\theta_0}) - f_0(\theta_0) = a_n\varphi_n^*(e^{i\theta_0}) - e^{i\theta_0}b_n\varphi_n(e^{i\theta_0}),$$

and this leads to

$$\left.\begin{array}{c} |s_n(f;\ e^{i\theta_0}) - f(e^{i\theta_0})| \leqslant \mu_n\{|a_n| + |b_n|\}, \\ \alpha + \eta \leqslant \theta_0 \leqslant \beta - \eta. \end{array}\right\} \tag{7.40}$$

Now using (7.30'), (7.36), and (7.40), the estimate (7.38) for the Lebesgue constants, and the estimates for the μ_n obtained in Chapter IV, it is a simple matter to find the sufficient conditions for the convergence of the Fourier-Chebyshev expansion for a function of class M.

In Table VI we give the sufficient conditions for the uniform convergence of such an expansion of the *entire circumference* $|z| = 1$, assuming that $f(z)$ is *continuous in the closed region* $|z| \leq 1$ and thus has radial boundary values on the entire circumference.

Condition I is a consequence of the inequality

$$|s_n(f;\ e^{i\theta_0}) - f(e^{i\theta_0})| \leqslant$$

$$\leqslant \frac{1}{2\pi}\int_0^{2\pi} |\gamma_r(\theta) - \gamma_r(\theta_0)| \cdot |K_n(e^{i\theta_0}, e^{i\theta})|\, d\sigma(\theta) \leqslant$$

$$\leqslant \{\|\gamma_r(\theta)\|_2^\sigma + |\gamma_r(\theta_0)| \sqrt{c_0}\} \sqrt{K_n(e^{i\theta_0}, e^{i\theta_0})} \leqslant$$

$$\leqslant 2C_1\omega\left(\frac{1}{n};\ f\right)\sqrt{C(n+1)} \leqslant C_2\sqrt{n}\,\omega\left(\frac{1}{n};\ f\right), \tag{7.41}$$

which, in turn, is a consequence of (7.32), (3.30), and (5.31). Further, we have the inequality

$$|s_n(f;\ e^{i\theta_0}) - f(e^{i\theta_0})| \leqslant 2C\omega\left(\frac{1}{n};\ f\right)\cdot\frac{1}{2\pi}\int_0^{2\pi} |K_n(e^{i\theta_0}, e^{i\theta})|\, d\sigma(\theta) =$$

$$= 2C\omega\left(\frac{1}{n};\ f\right)L_n(\theta_0) \leqslant C_1\mu_n^2\omega\left(\frac{1}{n};\ f\right)\ln n, \tag{7.42}$$

$$\alpha + \varepsilon \leqslant \theta_0 \leqslant \beta - \varepsilon,$$

which is obtained from the estimate (7.38) for the Lebesgue constants. Under condition III it follows from condition V of Table II that

$$|s_n(f;\ e^{i\theta_0}) - f(e^{i\theta_0})| \leqslant C\omega\left(\frac{1}{n};\ f\right)\omega_r^r\left(\frac{1}{n};\ p\right) n \ln n,$$

$$(r = 1, \quad \text{or} \quad r = 2),$$

and in view of the requirements placed on $f(e^{i\theta})$ and $p(\theta)$, we have

$$\omega\left(\frac{1}{n};\ f\right)\omega_r^r\left(\frac{1}{n};\ p\right) = o\left(\frac{1}{n \ln n}\right).$$

Under condition II, $\mu_n = C$, and then according to (7.42) it is sufficient that the boundary value $f(e^{i\theta})$ satisfy the Dini condition. Condition IV and its special case condition V can be obtained from (7.42) and condition XII of Table II.

7.8. Let us now turn to Table VII, in which we tabulate sufficient conditions for convergence in the interior of an arc $[e^{i\alpha}, e^{i\beta}]$. It is assumed that $f(z) \in M$ is continuous in the sector $0 \leq |z| \leq 1$, $\alpha \leq \arg z \leq \beta$, and thus has radial boundary values at all points of $[e^{i\alpha}, e^{i\beta}]$.

Under condition II the entire orthonormal set is uniformly bounded throughout $[0, 2\pi]$, and therefore using (7.36), we have

$$\left.\begin{array}{c}|s_n(f;\ e^{i\theta_0})-f(e^{i\theta_0})|\leqslant C_1\omega_1\left(\frac{1}{n};\ f\right)+C_2\omega\left(\frac{1}{n};\ f\right)\ln n,\\ \alpha+\eta\leqslant\theta_0\leqslant\beta-\eta.\end{array}\right\}\quad(7.43)$$

In this case $f(z)$ may be in class H_1 rather than H_2, as in the general case.

When conditions XI-XIII of Table VII are fulfilled, the orthonormal set is uniformly bounded on the internal interval $[\alpha', \beta']$, where $\alpha < \alpha' < \beta' < \beta$ (as a result of conditions V-VII of Table III).

Using the notation of (7.39) and setting $z=e^{i\theta}$, we have

$$z_0=e^{i\theta_0},\quad D(z)=\frac{1}{\pi(z)},$$

$$\frac{1}{2\pi}\int_0^{2\pi}\frac{f_1(\theta)\,e^{i\theta}\,d\theta}{\pi_0(\theta)}=\frac{1}{2\pi i}\int_{|z|=1}\frac{D(z)f(z)-D(z_0)f(z_0)}{z-z_0}\,dz-$$
$$-\frac{f(z_0)}{2\pi i}\int_{|z|=1}\frac{D(z)-D(z_0)}{z-z_0}\,dz=0,$$

since by assumption both $D(z)$ and $D(z)f(z)$ are in H_2. Then as in Lemma 4.1, we have

$$b_n=\frac{1}{2\pi}\int_0^{2\pi}f_1(\theta)\,\overline{\varphi_n(e^{i\theta})}\,d\sigma(\theta),$$

$$a_n\alpha_n=\frac{1}{2\pi}\int_0^{2\pi}e^{i\theta}f_1(\theta)\left\{\alpha_n\overline{\varphi_n^*(e^{i\theta})}-\alpha\overline{\pi_0(\theta)}\right\}d\sigma(\theta).$$

Consider now the two functions

$$F_1(\theta)=\begin{cases}f_1(\theta), & \theta\,\overline{\in}\,[\alpha',\ \beta'],\\ 0 & \theta\in[\alpha',\ \beta'],\end{cases}\qquad F_2(\theta)=\begin{cases}0, & \theta\,\overline{\in}\,[\alpha',\ \beta'],\\ f_1(\theta), & \theta\in[\alpha',\ \beta'],\end{cases}$$

and let us write

$$b_n=b_n^{(1)}+b_n^{(2)},\qquad a_n=a_n^{(1)}+a_n^{(2)}.$$

Let

$$\alpha'+\varepsilon\leqslant\theta_0\leqslant\beta'-\varepsilon,\qquad\varepsilon>0.$$

Then for $\theta \bar{\in} [\alpha', \beta']$ we have $|\theta - \theta_0| \geq \epsilon$, from which it follows that

$$|f_1(\theta)| = \left| \frac{f_0(\theta) - f_0(\theta_0)}{e^{i\theta} - e^{i\theta_0}} \right| \leqslant \frac{|f_0(\theta)| + |f_0(\theta_0)|}{2 \sin \frac{\varepsilon}{2}}, \quad \theta \bar{\in} [\alpha', \beta'].$$

Hence $F_1(\theta) \in L_2^{\sigma}$, and according to Lemma 4.1,

$$\lim_{n\to\infty} a_n^{(1)} = \lim_{n\to\infty} b_n^{(1)} = 0.$$

For $\theta \in [\alpha', \beta']$ we arrive easily at

$$|f_1(\theta)| \leqslant \frac{\pi}{2} \left| \frac{f_0(\theta) - f_0(\theta_0)}{\theta - \theta_0} \right| \leqslant \frac{C}{|\theta - \theta_0|} \cdot \left\{ \ln \frac{1}{|\theta - \theta_0|} \right\}^{-\lambda}$$
$$\lambda > 1,$$

from which it follows that $F_2(\theta) \in L_1$.

It is known that the class $L_2(\alpha', \beta')$ is dense in $L_1(\alpha', \beta')$; and therefore, given a $\delta > 0$ arbitrarily small, there always exists a function

$$F_3(\theta) = \begin{cases} 0, & \theta \bar{\in} [\alpha', \beta'], \\ f_3(\theta), & \theta \in [\alpha', \beta'], \quad f_3 \in L_2(\alpha', \beta'), \end{cases}$$

such that

$$\int_{\alpha'}^{\beta'} |f_1(\theta) - f_3(\theta)|\, d\theta < \delta. \tag{7.44}$$

From the measurability and boundedness of $p(\theta)$ on $[\alpha', \beta']$, it follows that $p(\theta) F_3^2(\theta) \in L_1$. Finally, in view of the fact that $F_3(\theta) \equiv 0$, $\theta \bar{\in} [\alpha', \beta']$, we arrive at the conclusion that $F_3(\theta) \in L_2^{\sigma}$.

Setting

$$F_2(\theta) = F_3(\theta) + F_4(\theta), \qquad F_4(\theta) = F_2(\theta) - F_3(\theta),$$

we again have

$$a_n^{(2)} = a_n^{(3)} + a_n^{(4)}, \qquad b_n^{(2)} = b_n^{(3)} + b_n^{(4)}, \qquad \lim_{n\to\infty} a_n^{(3)} = \lim_{n\to\infty} b_n^{(3)} = 0$$

as a result also of Lemma 4.1.

Finally, to obtain an appraisal for the $a_n^{(4)}$, $b_n^{(4)}$, we make use of the boundedness of both $p(\theta)$ and the orthonormal set on $[\alpha', \beta']$.

If

$$0 < m \leqslant p(\theta) \leqslant M, \qquad |\varphi_n(e^{i\theta})| \leqslant C, \quad \theta \in [\alpha', \beta'],$$

then from (7.44) we obtain

$$|b_n^{(4)}| \leqslant \frac{MC}{2\pi}\int_{\alpha'}^{\beta'} |f_1(\theta)-f_3(\theta)|\,d\theta \leqslant \frac{MC}{2\pi}\delta,$$

$$|a_n^{(4)}| \leqslant \frac{1}{2\pi}\left(C+\frac{\alpha}{\alpha_0}\cdot\frac{1}{\sqrt{m}}\right)\int_{\alpha'}^{\beta'} |f_1(\theta)-f_3(\theta)|\,d\theta \leqslant$$

$$\leqslant \frac{1}{2\pi}\left(C+\frac{\alpha}{\alpha_0}\cdot\frac{1}{\sqrt{m}}\right)\delta,$$

and this implies that

$$\lim_{n\to\infty} a_n^{(4)} = \lim_{n\to\infty} a_n = 0, \qquad \lim_{n\to\infty} b_n^{(4)} = \lim_{n\to\infty} b_n = 0.$$

The continuity of $f(e^{i\theta})$ on $[\alpha, \beta]$ implies that under conditions XI-XIII the convergence is quasi-uniform, as was mentioned in paragraphs 4.5 and 5.4. For uniform convergence in the interior of $[\alpha, \beta]$ it is sufficient that $f(e^{i\theta})$ have a bounded second derivative on $[\alpha, \beta]$. To prove this, one uses Lemmas 5.1 and 5.2 and Theorem 5.5. in which $\pi(e^{i\theta})$ is replaced by $f(e^{i\theta})$.

Let us now make use of (7.30'). We start with the following definition: a function $f_0(\theta)$ belongs to class A_h if for any number $N > 0$ there exists another number $h_0 > 0$ such that if $p(\theta) > N$, then

$$|f_0(\theta+h)| \leqslant A,$$

where $|h| \leq h_0$, and A is independent of h.

Lemma 7.1. If $f_0(\theta) \in A_h$, then $f_0 \in L_2$ implies that $f_0 \in L_2^{\sigma}$; further,

$$\lim_{\delta\to 0} \omega_2^{\sigma_0}(\delta; f_0) = 0. \tag{7.45}$$

Since $p(\theta) \in L_1$, the absolute continuity of the Lebesgue integral means that every $\epsilon > 0$ there exists a $\delta > 0$ such that on any measurable set e of measure less than δ,

$$\int_e p(\theta)\,d\theta < \varepsilon. \tag{7.46}$$

Thus given an ϵ and having chosen δ, we find $N > 0$ sufficiently large so that if e is the set on which $p(\theta) > N$, then Mes $e < \delta$. Then setting e + e' = [0, 2π], we obtain

$$\int_0^{2\pi} p(\theta)\,|f_0(\theta)|^2\,d\theta = \int_{e} + \int_{e'} \leqslant \int_{e} p(\theta)\,|f_0(\theta)|^2\,d\theta +$$

$$+ N\int_{e'} |f_0(\theta)|^2\,d\theta \leqslant \int_{e} p(\theta)\,|f_0(\theta)|^2\,d\theta + N\int_0^{2\pi} |f_0(\theta)|^2\,d\theta.$$

For the first integral we know that

$$\int_{e} p(\theta)\,|f_0(\theta)|^2\,d\theta \leqslant A^2 \int_{e} p(\theta)\,d\theta < A^2\varepsilon,$$

from which it follows that $f_0 \in L_2$ implies $f_0 \in L_2^{\sigma_0}$.

Further.

$$\frac{1}{2\pi}\int_0^{2\pi} |f_0(\theta+h) - f_0(\theta)|^2\,p(\theta)\,d\theta = \frac{1}{2\pi}\int_{e} + \frac{1}{2\pi}\int_{e'} \leqslant \frac{1}{2\pi}\int_{e} +$$

$$+ \frac{N}{2\pi}\int_{e'} |f_0(\theta+h) - f_0(\theta)|^2\,d\theta \leqslant \frac{1}{2\pi}\int_{e} +$$

$$+ \frac{N}{2\pi}\int_0^{2\pi} |f_0(\theta+h) - f_0(\theta)|^2\,d\theta \leqslant \frac{1}{2\pi}\int_{e} + N\,[\omega_2(h;\,f_0)]^2.$$

For the first integral we obtain

$$\frac{1}{2\pi}\int_{e} |f_0(\theta+h) - f_0(\theta)|^2\,p(\theta)\,d\theta \leqslant$$

$$\leqslant (2A)^2 \cdot \frac{1}{2\pi}\int_{e} p(\theta)\,d\theta < \frac{2A^2\varepsilon}{\pi}.$$

By choosing h sufficiently small and recalling the h-independence of A, we arrive at the second assertion of the lemma.

Under conditions III-V of Table VII the orthonormal set is uniformly bounded on [α + ϵ, β − ϵ], and we have

$$|s_n(f;\, e^{i\theta_0}) - f(e^{i\theta_0})| \leqslant C_1 \omega_2^{\sigma_0}\left(\frac{1}{n};\, f_0\right) + C_2 \omega\left(\frac{1}{n};\, f\right) \ln n + C_3 \delta_n,$$

$$\alpha + 2\varepsilon \leqslant \theta_0 \leqslant \beta - 2\varepsilon,$$

which implies uniform convergence.

When condition VI if fulfilled, $I_2 = 0$ in (7.31). To evaluate I_1 we use the Bunyakovskii-Schwarz inequality.

$$|I_1| \leqslant \{\|\gamma_r(\theta)\|_2^{\sigma_0} + \sqrt{c_0}\,|\gamma_r(\theta_0)|\} \cdot \|K_n(e^{i\theta_0}, e^{i\theta})\|_2^{\sigma_0} \leqslant$$
$$\leqslant \{\|\gamma_r(\theta)\|_2^{\sigma_0} + \sqrt{c_0}\,|\gamma_r(\theta_0)|\} \sqrt{K_n(e^{i\theta_0}, e^{i\theta_0})} \leqslant$$
$$\leqslant \{\sqrt{M}\,\|\gamma_r(\theta)\|_2 + \sqrt{c_0}\,|\gamma_r(\theta_0)|\} \cdot \sqrt{C(n+1)},$$

from which, using (3.6) and (5.31), we have

$$|s_n(f;\, e^{i\theta_0}) - f(e^{i\theta_0})| \leqslant C_1 \sqrt{n}\, \omega_2\left(\frac{1}{n};\, f_0\right) + C_2 \sqrt{n}\, \omega\left(\frac{1}{n};\, f\right), \tag{7.47}$$

and this implies that the convergence is uniform. This result is interesting in that it does not require the existence of the integral in (7.5).

In order to derive conditions VII and VIII, we will show that a sufficient condition for convergence is that the measure satisfy the conditions

$$\delta_n' = o\left(\frac{1}{\sqrt[4]{n}}\right), \quad \omega'\left(\delta;\, \frac{1}{p_0}\right) = o(\sqrt{\delta}) \quad \text{on} \quad E_h, \tag{7.48}$$

and that the boundary function $f(e^{i\theta})$ satisfy the conditions

$$\omega_2(\delta;\, f_0) = O\left(\sqrt[4]{\delta}\right), \quad \omega(\delta;\, f) = O\left(\frac{\sqrt{\delta}}{\ln \frac{1}{\delta}}\right) \text{ on } [\alpha, \beta]. \tag{7.48'}$$

Indeed, from $0 < m \leqslant p(\theta)$, $\theta \in [\alpha, \beta]$ one obtains, using (4.66), the estimate $\mu_n \leq C\sqrt{n}\delta_n$; from this and (3.9"), we have

$$\mu_n \leqslant C_1 \sqrt{n\omega'\left(\frac{1}{n};\, \frac{1}{p_0}\right)} + C_2 \sqrt{n}\, \delta_n',$$

which leads to the inequalities

$$\mu_n \delta_n \leqslant C_3 \sqrt{n}\, \omega'\left(\frac{1}{n}; \frac{1}{p_0}\right) + C_4 \sqrt{n}\, \delta_n'^2,$$

$$\mu_n \omega_2\left(\frac{1}{n}; f_0\right) \leqslant \left\{ C_5 \sqrt{n\omega'\left(\frac{1}{n}; \frac{1}{p_0}\right)} + C_6 \sqrt{n}\, \delta_n' \right\} \omega_2\left(\frac{1}{n}; f_0\right),$$

$$\mu_n^2 \ln n\omega\left(\frac{1}{n}; f\right) \leqslant \left\{ C_7 n\omega'\left(\frac{1}{n}; \frac{1}{p_0}\right) + C_8 n\delta_n'^2 \right\} \omega\left(\frac{1}{n}; f\right) \ln n.$$

When conditions (7.48) and (7.48') are fulfilled, the right-hand sides of these inequalities approach zero with 1/n, and then from (7.30') we obtain the desired result.

In the special case in which $\sigma(\theta)$ is absolutely continuous throughout $[0, 2\pi]$, we may drop the condition $f_0(\theta + h) \in L_2^\sigma$ in III – V, VII, and VIII, and the condition $\omega'\left(\delta; \frac{1}{p_0}\right) = o(\sqrt{\delta})$ in VII and VIII. If in addition $p(\theta) \leq M$ throughout $[0, 2\pi]$, we may also drop the condition $f \in A_h$ in III – V, VII, and VIII, and replace $\omega_2^{\sigma_0}(\delta; f)$ by $\omega_2(\delta; f)$, since $\omega_2^{\sigma_0}(\delta; f) \leqslant \sqrt{M}\, \omega_2(\delta; f)$. Then the conditions

$$\delta_n' = o\left(\frac{1}{\sqrt[4]{n}}\right), \quad \omega_2(\delta; f) = O(\sqrt[4]{\delta}), \quad \omega(\delta; f) = O\left(\frac{\sqrt{\delta}}{\ln \frac{1}{\delta}}\right)$$

are sufficient for convergence, and these are the conditions fulfilled under IX and X.

Condition I is due to Freud [3]; it is interesting to compare it with our condition VI. From the requirement that

$$\sum_{n=1}^{\infty} \frac{1}{\sqrt{n}} \omega_2\left(\frac{1}{n}; f\right) < \infty \tag{7.49}$$

one obtains $\omega_2(\delta; f) = o(\sqrt{\delta})$, so that it is more general; condition I places no restrictions on $f(e^{i\theta})$ on the interval $[\alpha, \beta]$, while condition VI requires that it be continuous with a definite modulus of continuity. The present author has shown [5], however, that (7.49) implies that $f(e^{i\theta})$ is equivalent on $[0, 2\pi]$ to some function continuous throughout this interval, and therefore condition I imposes a very serious requirement of a *nonlocal* nature on $f(e^{i\theta})$. Nevertheless it is of interest also because it ensures the *absolute* convergence of the Fourier-Chebyshev expansion.* We note also that in III – V we have placed more restrictive requirements on $f(e^{i\theta})$ over the entire interval $[0, 2\pi]$ and less restrictive ones on the internal interval $[\alpha, \beta]$, than in the analogous case of XI-XIII.

Remark 7.4. If an analytic function $f(z)$ is regular on the arc $[e^{i\alpha}, e^{i\beta}]$, then on this arc it is Lip 1. We would have obtained a simple generalization of the Fatou-Riesz theorem if we had been able to prove the convergence of the Fourier-Chebyshev expansion for $g_n = o(1)$; we have been unable to do this, however, and had to place more restrictive conditions on our function. The simplest of these is condition II, under which the orthonormal system is uniformly bounded and $g_n = o(1)$.

7.9. We now turn to a theorem which is very important in principle, the *equiconvergence theorem*, which compares the Fourier-Chebyshev expansion of a single function in two different sets of orthonormal polynomials $\{\varphi_n(z)\}$ and $\{z^n\}$; in particular, we will compare the Fourier-Chebyshev expansion with the Maclaurin expansion.

We introduce the notation

$$\varphi_n^*(z) = \pi_0(\theta) + \varepsilon_n(z), \quad z = e^{i\theta}, \quad 0 \leqslant \theta \leqslant 2\pi, \tag{7.50}$$

and assume that on $[\alpha + \epsilon, \beta - \epsilon]$ we have, uniformly,

$$|\varepsilon_n(z)| \leqslant \varepsilon_n, \quad z = e^{i\theta}, \quad \alpha + \varepsilon \leqslant \theta \leqslant \beta - \varepsilon. \tag{7.50'}$$

Theorem 7.12. Let the integral of (7.5) exist and assume that on $[\alpha, \beta]$ the function $\sigma(\theta)$ is absolutely continuous, and $p(\theta) \geq$ $\geq m > 0$ is continuous, and that

$$\omega(\delta; p) \leqslant C\left(\ln\frac{1}{\delta}\right)^{-\gamma}, \quad \gamma > 2. \tag{7.51}$$

Let F(z) be a function regular for $|z| < 1$, such that $F(z) \in H_2$ and

* See S. B. Stechkin [1].

$\frac{F(z)}{\pi(z)} \in H_2$, and such that it has boundary values at points of the arc $[e^{i\alpha}, e^{i\beta}]$, and that these boundary values satisfy $|F(e^{i\theta})| \leqslant M_1$, $\theta \in [\alpha, \beta]$. If $s_n(F; z)$ and $\sigma_n(F; z)$ are partial sums of the Fourier-Chebyshev and Maclaurin expansions for F(z), then

$$|s_n(F; z_0) - \sigma_n(F; z_0)| \leqslant C_1\delta_{n+1} + C_2\varepsilon_{n+1}\ln n + \lambda_n,$$
$$z_0 = e^{i\theta_0}, \quad \alpha + \eta \leqslant \theta_0 \leqslant \beta - \eta, \tag{7.52}$$

where λ_n tends uniformly to zero as $n \to \infty$.*

Setting $F_0(\theta) = F(e^{i\theta})\gamma_E(\theta)$, we have

$$s_n(F; z_0) = \frac{1}{2\pi}\int_0^{2\pi} F_0(\theta) K_n(z_0, z) p(\theta)\, d\theta,$$

$$\sigma_n(F; z_0) = \frac{1}{2\pi}\int_0^{2\pi} F_0(\theta) \frac{1-(z_0\bar{z})^{n+1}}{1-z_0\bar{z}}\, d\theta,$$

since the partial sum $\sigma_n(F; z)$ corresponds to $p(\theta) \equiv 1$, $\varphi_n(z) = z^n$. In the Lebesgue integral obtained we can replace $F_0(\theta)$ and $\pi_0(\theta)$ by equivalent functions $F(e^{i\theta})$ and $\pi(e^{i\theta})$.

Now in the notation of (7.30"), if $\theta, \theta_0 \in [\alpha+\varepsilon, \beta-\varepsilon]$ then

$$|K_n(z_0, z)| \leqslant (n+1)\mu_n^2, \quad \left|\frac{1-(z_0\bar{z})^{n+1}}{1-z_0\bar{z}}\right| \leqslant n+1,$$

so that for $k > 2$ we have

$$\left|\frac{1}{2\pi}\int_{\theta_0-\frac{1}{n^k}}^{\theta_0+\frac{1}{n^k}} F(z)\left\{p(\theta)K_n(z_0, z) - \frac{1-(z_0\bar{z})^{n+1}}{1-z_0\bar{z}}\right\} d\theta\right| \leqslant$$

$$\leqslant \frac{1}{2\pi}\int_{\theta_0-\frac{1}{n^k}}^{\theta_0+\frac{1}{n^k}} |F(z)|\left\{p(\theta)\cdot|K_n(z_0, z)| + \left|\frac{1-(z_0\bar{z})^{n+1}}{1-z_0\bar{z}}\right|\right\} d\theta \leqslant$$

$$\leqslant \frac{M_1}{2\pi}\cdot\frac{2}{n^k}(n+1)(\mu_n^2+1) \leqslant \frac{C_1}{n^{k-2}}, \tag{7.53}$$

* Here $C_1, C_2, \ldots$ are constants independent of both $\underline{n}$ and z_0.

where we have used the fact (from condition IV of Table III) that $\mu_n = o(\sqrt{n})$. Setting

$$R_n(z_0) = s_n(F;\, z_0) - \sigma_n(F;\, z_0),$$

we obtain, from (1.7),*

$$R_n(z_0) = \frac{1}{2\pi i} \int\limits_{|z|=1} \frac{F(z)}{z - z_0} \left\{ \frac{\overset{*}{\varphi}_{n+1}(z_0)\, \overline{\overset{*}{\varphi}_{n+1}(z)} - \varphi_{n+1}(z_0)\, \overline{\varphi_{n+1}(z)}}{|\pi(z)|^2} - \right.$$
$$\left. - \left[1 - (z_0 \bar{z})^{n+1}\right] \right\} dz. \tag{7.54}$$

Now we make use of (7.50) to obtain

$$R_n(z_0) = \frac{1}{2\pi i} \int\limits_{|z|=1} \frac{F(z)}{z - z_0} \left\{ P(z) - (z_0 \bar{z})^{n+1}\, \overline{P(z)} + Q_n(z) - \right.$$
$$\left. - (z_0 \bar{z})^{n+1}\, \overline{Q_n(z)} \right\} dz, \tag{7.55}$$

where

$$\left.\begin{aligned} P(z) &= \frac{\pi(z_0) - \pi(z)}{\pi(z)}, \\ Q_n(z) &= \frac{\varepsilon_{n+1}(z_0)}{\pi(z)} + \frac{\overline{\varepsilon_{n+1}(z)}\, \pi(z_0)}{|\pi(z)|^2} + \frac{\varepsilon_{n+1}(z_0)\, \overline{\varepsilon_{n+1}(z)}}{|\pi(z)|^2}. \end{aligned}\right\} \tag{7.56}$$

Let us break up $[0, 2\pi]$ into the three subsets

$$\left.\begin{aligned} e_1 &= [0, \alpha + \varepsilon] + [\beta - \varepsilon, 2\pi], \\ e_2 &= \left[\alpha + \varepsilon, \theta_0 - \frac{1}{n^k}\right] + \left[\theta_0 + \frac{1}{n^k}, \beta - \varepsilon\right], \\ e_3 &= \left[\theta_0 - \frac{1}{n^k}, \theta_0 + \frac{1}{n^k}\right], \qquad \alpha + 2\varepsilon \leqslant \theta_0 \leqslant \beta - 2\varepsilon, \end{aligned}\right\} \tag{7.57}$$

and denote by σ_1, σ_2, σ_3 the corresponding sets of points on the circumference $|z| = 1$.

First, from (7.53) we obtain

$$\left| \frac{1}{2\pi} \int\limits_{\sigma_3} \frac{F(z)}{z - z_0} \left\{ P(z) - (z_0 \bar{z})^{n+1}\, \overline{P(z)} + \right.\right.$$
$$\left.\left. + Q_n(z) - (z_0 \bar{z})^{n+1}\, \overline{Q_n(z)} \right\} dz \right| \leqslant \frac{C_1}{n^{k-2}}. \tag{7.58}$$

Further,

$$\frac{1}{2\pi i} \int\limits_{|z|=1} \frac{P(z)\, F(z)}{z - z_0}\, dz = \frac{1}{2\pi i} \int\limits_{|z|=1} \frac{1 - \dfrac{\pi(z_0)}{\pi(z)}}{z - z_0}\, F(z)\, dz = 0, \tag{7.59}$$

* See G. Szegö [1], Sections 13.3, 13.7.

where we have made use of the fact that if $|\zeta| < 1$, then $F(\zeta) \in H_2$, $1 - \frac{\pi(z_0)}{\pi(\zeta)} \in H_2$ and therefore $\left\{1 - \frac{\pi(z_0)}{\pi(\zeta)}\right\} F(\zeta) \in H_1$.

In view of (7.51), Eq. (4.31) gives

$$|\pi(z) - \pi(z_0)| \leqslant C\left\{\ln \frac{1}{|\theta - \theta_0|}\right\}^{1-\gamma}, \quad \alpha + \varepsilon \leqslant \theta, \ \theta_0 \leqslant \beta - \varepsilon. \tag{7.60}$$

We now show that*

$$\lim_{n \to \infty} \frac{1}{2\pi i} \int\limits_{|z|=1} \frac{\overline{P(z)}\, F(z)}{z - z_0} \bar{z}^{n+1}\, dz =$$

$$= \lim_{n \to \infty} \frac{1}{2\pi i} \int\limits_{|z|=1} \frac{\bar{P}(\bar{z})\, \bar{z}^{n+2}}{\bar{z} - \bar{z}_0} F(z)\, dz = 0 \tag{7.61}$$

uniformly for $\alpha + 2\epsilon \leq \theta_0 \leq \beta - 2\epsilon$.

Let us again turn to the Jackson sum $u_\nu(\theta)$ of (3.1) for the function $F(e^{i\theta})$; this sum is a polynomial of degree $r = 2\nu - 2 \leq n$ in $e^{i\theta}$, and we may therefore use the notation

$$u_\nu(\theta) = G_r(z), \quad z = e^{i\theta}; \quad \lambda_n = \frac{1}{2\pi i} \int\limits_{|z|=1} \frac{\overline{P(z)}\, F(z)\, \bar{z}^{n+1}}{z - z_0} dz.$$

From

$$\frac{1}{2\pi i} \int\limits_{|z|=1} \frac{P(z)\, z^\nu\, dz}{z - z_0} = \frac{1}{D(z_0)\, 2\pi i} \int\limits_{|z|=1} \frac{D(z) - D(z_0)}{z - z_0} z^\nu\, dz = 0,$$

$$(\nu = 0, 1, 2, \ldots),$$

it follows obviously that for $k = 0, 1, 2, \ldots, n$,

$$\left.\begin{aligned} &\frac{1}{2\pi i} \int\limits_{|z|=1} \frac{\bar{P}(\bar{z})\, \bar{z}^{n+2}}{\bar{z} - \bar{z}_0} z^k\, dz = 0, \\ &\lambda_n = -\frac{\bar{z}_0}{2\pi i} \int\limits_{|z|=1} \frac{\bar{P}(\bar{z})\, \bar{z}^{n+2}}{\bar{z} - \bar{z}_0} \{F(z) - G_r(z)\}\, dz. \end{aligned}\right\} \tag{7.62}$$

We now choose a small $\mu > 0$ and divide the circumference into two sets

$$E_1 = \text{Ens}\,\{|z - z_0| \leqslant \mu\}, \quad E_2 = \text{Ens}\,\{|z - z_0| > \mu\}.$$

* See G. Szegö [1], Section 13.7.

We then have

$$\left|\frac{1}{2\pi}\int\limits_{E_1}\frac{\overline{P}(\bar{z})\,\bar{z}^{n+2}}{\bar{z}-\bar{z}_0}\{F(z)-G_r(z)\}\,dz\right| \leqslant \{\max_{z\in E_1}|F(z)|+ + \max_{z\in E_1}|G_r(z)|\}\cdot\frac{\sqrt{M}}{2\pi}\int\limits_{E_1}\left|\frac{\pi(z)-\pi(z_0)}{z-z_0}\right|\cdot|dz|,$$

and since $|F(z)|\leqslant M_1$, $z=e^{i\theta}$, $\theta\in[\alpha,\ \beta]$, the polynomial $G_r(z)$ is also bounded on E_1.

Using (7.60), we obtain the following θ_0-independent estimate for the first integral:

$$\left|\frac{1}{2\pi}\int\limits_{E_1}\right| \leqslant C\int\limits_{F_1}\frac{d\theta}{|\theta-\theta_0|\left\{\ln\frac{1}{|\theta-\theta_0|}\right\}^{\gamma-1}} \leqslant C_1\left(\ln\frac{1}{\mu}\right)^{2-\gamma}.$$

If $z\in E_2$ then $|z - z_0| > \mu$, and we obtain

$$\left|\frac{1}{2\pi}\int\limits_{E_2}\right| < \frac{1}{\mu}\cdot\frac{1}{2\pi}\int\limits_{F_2}\left|1-\frac{\pi(z_0)}{\pi(z)}\right|\cdot|F(z)-G_r(z)|\cdot|dz| \leqslant$$

$$\leqslant\frac{1}{\mu}\left\{1+|\pi(z_0)|\left\|\frac{1}{\pi(z)}\right\|_2\right\}\|F(z)-G_r(z)\|_2\leqslant\frac{C_2}{\mu}\,\omega_2\left(\frac{1}{n};\ F\right).$$

Hence

$$|\lambda_n|\leqslant C_1\left(\ln\frac{1}{\mu}\right)^{2-\gamma}+\frac{C_2}{\mu}\,\omega_2\left(\frac{1}{n};\ F\right), \qquad \alpha+2\varepsilon\leqslant\theta_0\leqslant\beta-2\varepsilon. \tag{7.63}$$

We now choose $\mu > 0$ so small that $C_1\left(\ln\frac{1}{\mu}\right)^{2-\gamma}<\frac{\delta}{2}$, where $\delta > 0$ is any arbitrary small quantity. Fixing μ we now choose n_0 so large that if $n > n_0$, then $\frac{C_2}{\mu}\,\omega_2\left(\frac{1}{n};\ F\right)<\frac{\delta}{2}$, and consequently $|\lambda_n| < \delta$ for $n > n_0$. This means that

$$\lim_{n\to\infty}\lambda_n=\lim_{n\to\infty}\frac{1}{2\pi i}\int\limits_{|z|=1}\frac{\overline{P(z)}\,F(z)}{z-z_0}\,\bar{z}^{n+1}\,dz=0 \tag{7.64}$$

uniformly for $\alpha + 2\epsilon \leq \theta_0 \leq \beta - 2\epsilon$. We thus obtain

$$\frac{1}{2\pi i}\int\limits_{|z|=1}\{P(z)-(z_0\bar{z})^{n+1}\,\overline{P(z)}\}\,\frac{F(z)\,dz}{z-z_0}=\gamma_n, \qquad \lim_{n\to\infty}\gamma_n=0. \tag{7.65}$$

We may now write

$$R_n(z_0)=\frac{1}{2\pi i}\int\limits_{\sigma_1+\sigma_2+\sigma_3}\{[P(z)-(z_0\bar{z})^{n+1}\overline{P(z)}]+$$
$$+[Q_n(z)-(z_0\bar{z})^{n+1}\overline{Q_n(z)}]\}\frac{F(z)\,dz}{z-z_0}=$$
$$=\gamma_n-\frac{1}{2\pi i}\int\limits_{\sigma_3}[P(z)-(z_0\bar{z})^{n+1}\overline{P(z)}]\frac{F(z)\,dz}{z-z_0}+$$
$$+\frac{1}{2\pi i}\int\limits_{\sigma_1+\sigma_2}[Q_n(z)-(z_0\bar{z})^{n+1}\overline{Q_n(z)}]\frac{F(z)\,dz}{z-z_0}+\frac{C_1}{n^{k-2}}. \quad (7.66)$$

Let us consider the first integral on the right side: using (7.60), we arrive at

$$\left|\frac{1}{2\pi}\int\limits_{\sigma_3}\frac{P(z)\,F(z)}{z-z_0}\,dz\right|\leqslant$$
$$\leqslant\frac{M_1\sqrt{M}}{2\pi}\cdot C\int\limits_{\theta_0-\frac{1}{n^k}}^{\theta_0+\frac{1}{n^k}}\frac{d\theta}{|\theta-\theta_0|\left\{\ln\frac{1}{|\theta-\theta_0|}\right\}^{\gamma-1}}\leqslant C_2(\ln n)^{2-\gamma}; \quad (7.67)$$

a similar expression obtains for

$$\left|\frac{1}{2\pi}\int\limits_{\sigma_3}(z_0\bar{z})^{n+1}\frac{\overline{P(z)}\,F(z)}{z-z_0}\,dz\right|\leqslant C_2(\ln n)^{2-\gamma}. \quad (7.67')$$

Now bearing in mind (7.55), (7.58), and (7.65)-(7.67), we arrive at

$$|R_n(z_0)|\leqslant\frac{C_1}{n^{k-2}}+2C_2(\ln n)^{2-\gamma}+|\gamma_n|+$$
$$+\frac{1}{\pi}\int\limits_{\sigma_1+\sigma_2}|Q_n(z)|\cdot\frac{|F(z)|\cdot|dz|}{|z-z_0|}. \quad (7.68)$$

Let us evaluate the last integral: by integrating over σ_2 we have

$$|\varepsilon_{n+1}(z_0)|,\quad |\varepsilon_{n+1}(z)|<\varepsilon_{n+1},\quad \left|\frac{1}{\pi(z)}\right|=\sqrt{p(\theta)}\leqslant\sqrt{M},$$
$$|F(z)|\leqslant M_1,$$

and therefore

$$\frac{1}{2\pi}\int_{\sigma_2}\left|\frac{Q_n(z)F(z)\,dz}{z-z_0}\right| \leqslant C_3\varepsilon_{n+1}\int_{\theta_2}\frac{d\theta}{|\theta-\theta_0|} \leqslant C_4\varepsilon_{n+1}\ln n.$$

By integrating over σ_1 we have $|z-z_0| \geqslant 2\sin\frac{\varepsilon}{2}$.

Further,

$$\|\varepsilon_{n+1}(z)\|_2^{\sigma} = \|\pi_0(\theta) - \varphi_{n+1}^*(z)\|_2^{\sigma} \leqslant$$

$$\leqslant \left\|\pi_0(\theta) - \frac{\alpha_{n+1}}{\alpha}\varphi_{n+1}^*(z)\right\|_2^{\sigma} + \left(1 - \frac{\alpha_{n+1}}{\alpha}\right)\|\varphi_{n+1}^*(z)\|_2^{\sigma},$$

and then, using (2.8) and (2.20), we obtain

$$\|\varepsilon_{n+1}(z)\|_2^{\sigma_0} \leqslant \|\varepsilon_{n+1}(z)\|_2^{\sigma} \leqslant C_5\delta_{n+1}. \tag{7.69}$$

With this result (7.56) leads to

$$\left|\frac{1}{2\pi}\int_{\sigma_1}\frac{Q_n(z)F(z)}{z-z_0}\,dz\right| \leqslant \frac{1}{2\sin\frac{\varepsilon}{2}}\left\{\varepsilon_{n+1}\left\|\frac{F(z)}{\pi(z)}\right\|_2 + \right.$$

$$\left. + |\pi(z_0)|\,\|\varepsilon_{n+1}(z)\|_2^{\sigma_0}\cdot\left\|\frac{F(z)}{\pi(z)}\right\|_2 + \varepsilon_{n+1}\|\varepsilon_{n+1}(z)\|_2^{\sigma_0}\cdot\left\|\frac{F(z)}{\pi(z)}\right\|_2\right\} \leqslant$$

$$\leqslant C_6\varepsilon_{n+1} + C_7\delta_{n+1}.$$

Finally, we arrive at the desired estimate (7.52) for the remainder.

To find the conditions for equiconvergence one must examine, therefore, conditions sufficient to guarantee that on $[\alpha, \beta]$ Eq. (7.50) holds with error

$$\varepsilon_n = o\left(\frac{1}{\ln n}\right). \tag{7.70}$$

In Table VIII we give sufficient conditions for equiconvergence on $[\alpha, \beta]$; these conditions correspond to those of Table V. Condition I is due to Szegö ([1] Section 13.3), and is sufficient for equiconvergence at θ_0.

Szegö ([1] Section 13.7) has also shown that if $F(z)$ is bounded for $|z| < 1$, uniform equiconvergence results throughout $[0, 2\pi]$ if

$$0 < m \leqslant p(\theta) \leqslant M, \quad \omega(\delta; p) \leqslant C\left(\ln\frac{1}{\delta}\right)^{-\gamma}, \quad \gamma > 2, \quad 0 \leqslant \theta \leqslant 2\pi.$$

CHAPTER VIII

PARAMETRIC DESCRIPTION OF ORTHOGONAL SETS

8.1. In all of the preceding chapters we have been examining the properties of an orthogonal set by imposing requirements of one kind or another on $\sigma(\theta)$. In this chapter we shall base our considerations on the so-called parameters of the orthogonal set, and the requirements we shall impose will be on these.

We first introduce the polynomials $\left\{ \Phi_n(z) = \frac{\varphi_n(z)}{\alpha_n} \right\}$, in terms of which (1.2) and (1.2') become

$$\left.\begin{aligned} \Phi_{n+1}(z) &= z\Phi_n(z) - \overline{a}_n \Phi_n^*(z), \\ \Phi_{n+1}^*(z) &= \Phi_n^*(z) - a_n z \Phi_n(z) \qquad (n = 0, 1, \ldots). \end{aligned}\right\} \tag{8.1}$$

We now define the parameters $\{a_n\}$ by

$$a_n = -\overline{\Phi_{n+1}(0)} = -\frac{\overline{\varphi_{n+1}(0)}}{\alpha_{n+1}} \qquad (n = 0, 1, \ldots). \tag{8.2}$$

From (8.1) we easily obtain the three-term recursion relation

$$\overline{a}_n \Phi_{n+2}(z) = (\overline{a}_n z + \overline{a}_{n+1}) \Phi_{n+1}(z) - \overline{a}_{n+1} z (1 - |a_n|^2) \Phi_n(z), \tag{8.3}$$

$$a_n \Phi_{n+2}^*(z) = (a_n + a_{n+1} z) \Phi_{n+1}^*(z) - a_{n+1} z (1 - |a_n|^2) \Phi_n^*(z)$$

$$(n = 0, 1, \ldots). \tag{8.3'}$$

We now show the relation between the parameters $\{a_n\}$ and the moments $\{c_n\}$ defined by

$$\frac{1}{2\pi} \int_0^{2\pi} e^{-ik\theta} \, d\sigma(\theta) = c_k \qquad (k = 0, 1, \ldots). \tag{8.4}$$

In terms of the so-called Toeplitz determinants

$$\Delta_k = | c_{i-j} |_0^k, \quad c_{-k} = \bar{c}_k \qquad (k = 0, 1, \ldots), \tag{8.4'}$$

it is easily seen that the $\Phi_n(z)$ can be written

$$\Phi_n(z) = \frac{1}{\Delta_{n-1}} \begin{vmatrix} c_0 & c_{-1} & c_{-2} & \ldots & c_{-n} \\ c_1 & c_0 & c_1 & \ldots & c_{-n+1} \\ \cdot & \cdot & \cdot & \cdot & \cdot \\ c_{n-1} & c_{n-2} & c_{n-3} & \ldots & c_{-1} \\ 1 & z & z^2 & \ldots & z^n \end{vmatrix} = z^n + \ldots \tag{8.5}$$

$$(n = 0, 1, \ldots), \ \Delta_{-1} = 1.$$

Multiplying (8.5) by z^{-n}, (8.3) by z^{-n-1}, setting $z \equiv e^{i\theta}$, and integrating, we obtain

$$\frac{1}{2\pi} \int_0^{2\pi} \Phi_n(e^{i\theta})\, e^{-in\theta}\, d\sigma(\theta) = \frac{\Delta_n}{\Delta_{n-1}} = \frac{1}{\alpha_n^2}, \qquad \left(\frac{\alpha_n}{\alpha_{n+1}}\right)^2 = 1 - | a_n |^2$$

$$(n = 0, 1, \ldots),$$

whence

$$\frac{1}{\alpha_n^2} = \frac{\Delta_n}{\Delta_{n-1}} = \frac{1}{\alpha_0^2} \prod_{k=0}^{n-1} \{1 - | a_k |^2\}, \quad (n = 1, 2, \ldots), \quad \frac{1}{\alpha_0^2} = c_0. \tag{8.6}$$

<u>Theorem 8.1.</u> An arbitrary choice of parameters $\{a_n\}$ subjected to the single condition

$$| a_n | < 1 \qquad (n = 0, 1, 2, \ldots) \tag{8.7}$$

determines the entire orthogonal set $\{\Phi_n(z)\}$ and the nondecreasing bounded function $\sigma(\theta)$ with a nondenumerable set of points of increase.

Indeed, since we know that $\Phi_0(z) = 1$, we can construct the entire set $\{\Phi_n(z)\}_1^\infty$ by (8.1).

Further, (8.6) implies that the condition (8.7) is equivalent to

$$\Delta_n > 0 \qquad (n = 0, 1, \ldots), \tag{8.8}$$

and the positiveness of all the Toeplitz determinants is equivalent to the existence of a bounded nondecreasing function $\sigma(\theta)$ which has a nondenumerable set of points of increase and satisfies condition

(8.4).* To find this function explicitly, we remark first that by using (8.3') and (1.13) it can be shown that the finite difference equation

$$a_n y_{n+2} - (a_n + a_{n+1} z) y_{n+1} + a_{n+1} z (1 - |a_n|^2) y_n = 0 \quad (8.9)$$

has two linearly independent polynomial solutions

$$\left.\begin{aligned} y_n &= \Phi_n^*(z) = \frac{1}{a_n} \varphi_n^*(z) \quad \text{for} \quad y_0 = 1, \ y_1 = 1 - a_0 z, \\ y_n &= \Psi_n^*(z) = \frac{1}{a_n} \psi_n^*(z) \quad \text{for} \quad y_0 = 1, \ y_1 = 1 + a_0 z. \end{aligned}\right\} \quad (8.9')$$

Thus to the polynomials of the second kind, defined in (1.13), correspond the parameters $\{-a_n\}_0^\infty$.

Making use of (1.16), we obtain

$$F(z) = \frac{1}{2\pi c_0} \int_0^{2\pi} \frac{e^{i\theta} + z}{e^{i\theta} - z} \, d\sigma(\theta) = \lim_{n \to \infty} \frac{\psi_n^*(z)}{\varphi_n^*(z)}, \qquad |z| < 1, \quad (8.10)$$

from which, with the inversion formula for $\sigma(\theta)$,** we arrive at

$$\frac{\sigma(\theta + 0) + \sigma(\theta - 0)}{2} = \text{const} + c_0 \lim_{r \to 1-0} \int_0^\theta \Re\{F(re^{i\varphi})\} \, d\varphi. \quad (8.11)$$

As an illustration, let us turn to the case $\{a_n\}_0^\infty = a$, $|a| < 1$. Solving the finite-difference equation

$$y_{n+2} - (z+1) y_{n+1} + z(1 - |a|^2) y_n = 0,$$

we arrive easily at

$$y_n = \Phi_n^*(z) = \frac{w_1^{n+1} - w_2^{n+1}}{w_1 - w_2} - (1 + a) z \frac{w_1^n - w_2^n}{w_1 - w_2}$$
$$(n = 0, 1, 2, \ldots),$$

where we have set

$$w_{1,2} = \frac{z + 1 \pm \Phi(z)}{2}, \qquad \Phi(z) = \sqrt{(z - e^{i\alpha})(z - e^{-i\alpha})},$$
$$e^{i\alpha} = 1 - 2|a|^2 + 2i|a|\sqrt{1 - |a|^2}.$$

* See N. I. Akhiezer and M. G. Krein [1], p. 44.

** See N. I. Akhiezer and M. G. Krein [1], pp. 49-50.

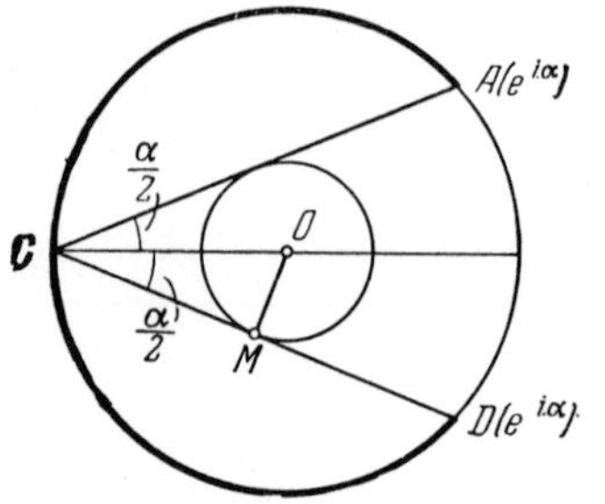

Fig. 2. $OA = 1, \ OM = |a|$.

Let B be the z plane cut along the arc ACD, i.e., along the arc $[e^{i\alpha}, e^{-i\alpha}]$ (see Fig. 2). We choose that branch of the two-valued function $\Phi(z)$ for which $\Phi(0) = 1$. It is easily seen that

$$z = w \cdot \frac{w-1}{w-(1-|a|^2)},$$

$$w^2 - (z+1)w + z(1-|a|^2) = 0$$

is a function giving a Zhukovskii-Chaplygin conformal mapping; the function $w_1(z)$ and $w_2(z)$ map B onto the regions outside and inside the circle $|w| = \sqrt{1-|a|^2}$, and therefore for $|z| < 1$ we have $|w_2/w_1| < 1$, so that $\lim_{n\to\infty}\left(\frac{w_2}{w_1}\right)^n = 0$. Using (8.10), we are led by some simple operations to

$$F(z) = \lim_{n\to\infty} \frac{w_1^{n+1} - w_2^{n+1} - (1-a)z(w_1^n - w_2^n)}{w_1^{n+1} - w_2^{n+1} - (1+a)z(w_1^n - w_2^n)} =$$

$$= \frac{az + \bar{a} + \Phi(z)}{1 + \bar{a} - z(1+a)}, \qquad |z| < 1.$$

Let us now set $a = -i|a|e^{-\frac{i\alpha}{2}}$, which corresponds to point M in Fig. 2. Then from (1.21) we have

$$F(re^{i\theta}) = i\,\mathrm{tg}\frac{\alpha}{2} +$$

$$+ \frac{1}{\cos\frac{\alpha}{2}} \sqrt{\frac{(1+r)\sin\frac{\theta+\alpha}{2} + i(1-r)\cos\frac{\theta+\alpha}{2}}{(1+r)\sin\frac{\theta-\alpha}{2} + i(1-r)\cos\frac{\theta-\alpha}{2}}}, \qquad r < 1;$$

$$p(\theta) = c_0 \sqrt{\frac{\sin\frac{\theta+\alpha}{2}}{\sin\frac{\theta-\alpha}{2}}}.$$

Setting $c_0 = 1 - |a|^2 = \cos^2(\alpha/2)$ we find normalized polynomials

$$\frac{1}{\alpha_n^2} = \left(\cos\frac{\alpha}{2}\right)^{2n+1},$$

$$\varphi_n^*(z) = \left(\cos\frac{\alpha}{2}\right)^{-n-\frac{1}{2}} \Phi_n^*(z) \qquad (n = 0, 1, 2, \ldots).$$

In the notation of (4.14), we have

$$w_{1,2}(e^{i\theta}) = \cos\frac{\alpha}{2}\, e^{i\left(\frac{\theta}{2}\pm\lambda\right)},$$

and this implies (4.14').

8.2. Some of our previous theorems can be stated in a somewhat different form by formulating the conditions not in terms of $\sigma(\theta)$, but in terms of the $\{a_n\}$.

Theorem 8.2. Conditions a)-f) of proposition 15) of Chapter I are equivalent to the convergence of the numerical series

$$\sum_{n=0}^{\infty} |a_n|^2 < \infty, \tag{8.12}$$

that is to say, they are equivalent to the assertion that

$$\left.\begin{aligned} &|\varphi_n^*(z) - \pi(z)| = o(\delta_n),\\ &\delta_n \leqslant \sqrt{\sum_{k=n}^{\infty} |a_k|^2}, \qquad |z| < 1, \end{aligned}\right\} \tag{8.13}$$

and that*

$$\frac{1}{\alpha^2} = \exp\left\{\frac{1}{2\pi}\int_0^{2\pi} \ln\sigma'(\theta)\, d\theta\right\} = c_0 \prod_{n=0}^{\infty} \{1 - |a_n|^2\}. \tag{8.14}$$

Indeed, (8.6) implies that the existence and finiteness of $\lim_{n\to\infty} \alpha_n = \alpha$ is equivalent to the convergence of the infinite product (8.14), and therefore also to the convergence of the series (8.12). From (2.8), (2.7'), and (8.2) we obtain

* See also S. Verblunsky [1].

$$\delta_n = \frac{1}{\alpha}\sqrt{\sum_{k=n+1}^{\infty} |\varphi_k(0)|^2} = \frac{1}{\alpha}\sqrt{\sum_{k=n+1}^{\infty} \alpha_k^2 |a_{k-1}|^2}, \quad (8.15)$$

which gives

$$\left.\begin{aligned} &\frac{\alpha_0}{\alpha}\sqrt{\sum_{k=n}^{\infty} |a_k|^2} \leqslant \delta_n \leqslant \sqrt{\sum_{k=n}^{\infty} |a_k|^2}, \\ &|a_n| \leqslant \frac{\alpha}{\alpha_0}\delta_n; \qquad \alpha_0 = \frac{1}{\sqrt{c_0}}. \end{aligned}\right\} \quad (8.15')$$

Hence (5.86) implies (8.13).

<u>Theorem 8.3</u>. If the $\{a_n\}$ satisfy condition (8.7), the orthonormal polynomials are bounded according to

$$|\varphi_n(z)| \leqslant \alpha_n \exp\left\{\sum_{k=0}^{n-1} |a_k|\right\}, \qquad |z| \leqslant 1. \quad (8.16)$$

If, in addition, (8.12) is satisfied, then

$$\left.\begin{aligned} &|\varphi_n(z)| \leqslant \alpha e^{\gamma\sqrt{n}}, \qquad |z| \leqslant 1, \\ &\gamma = \sqrt{\ln c_0 - \frac{1}{2\pi}\int_0^{2\pi} \ln \sigma'(\theta)\, d\theta} = \sqrt{\ln(c_0\alpha^2)}. \end{aligned}\right\} \quad (8.17)$$

If, finally, $|a_n| \leqslant \frac{\beta}{n}$, $n \geqslant n_0$ or $|a_n| \leqslant \frac{\beta}{n \ln n}$, $n \geqslant n_0$, then we obtain, respectively,*

$$|\varphi_n(z)| \leqslant C_1 n^{\beta} \text{ or } |\varphi_n(z)| \leqslant C_2 (\ln n)^{\beta}, \qquad |z| \leqslant 1. \quad (8.18)$$

To prove this we make use of the formula

$$\Phi_n^*(z) = \prod_{k=0}^{n-1}\left\{1 - a_k z \frac{\Phi_k(z)}{\Phi_k^*(z)}\right\} \qquad (n = 1, 2, \ldots), \quad (8.19)$$

* Here C, C_1, C_2 are constants independent of both n and z.

which is obtained from (8.1). Then in the closed circle $|z| \leq 1$ we have

$$\prod_{k=0}^{n-1} \{1-|a_k|\} \leqslant |\Phi_n^*(z)| \leqslant \prod_{k=0}^{n-1} \{1+|a_k|\},$$

an inequality which cannot be improved upon; equality may be attained, for instance, if

$$-1 < a_k < 0 \qquad (k=0, 1, \ldots), \qquad z=1.$$

From the above we obtain the estimate

$$\ln \left| \frac{\varphi_n^*(z)}{a_n} \right| \leqslant \sum_{k=0}^{n-1} \ln \{1+|a_k|\} < \sum_{k=0}^{n-1} |a_k|, \qquad |z| \leqslant 1.$$

If, now, (8.12) is fulfilled, the inequality

$$\frac{1}{n} \sum_{k=0}^{n-1} |a_k| \leqslant \sqrt{\frac{1}{n} \sum_{k=0}^{n-1} |a_k|^2}, \qquad \sum_{k=0}^{n-1} |a_k| \leqslant \sqrt{n} \cdot \sqrt{\sum_{k=0}^{n-1} |a_k|^2}$$

carries us to (8.17), since according to (8.14)

$$\sum_{k=0}^{n-1} |a_k|^2 \leqslant \sum_{k=0}^{\infty} |a_k|^2 < -\sum_{k=0}^{\infty} \ln (1-|a_k|^2) =$$

$$= -\ln \prod_{k=0}^{\infty} \{1-|a_k|^2\} = \ln c_0 - \frac{1}{2\pi} \int_0^{2\pi} \ln \sigma'(\theta)\, d\theta.$$

The following natural question arises: what is the accuracy of (8.17), the majorant for orthonormal polynomials subjected to the single restriction that

$$\int_0^{2\pi} \ln \sigma'(\theta)\, d\theta > -\infty.$$

We will show that these polynomials may increase at a rate very close to that given by (8.17). For this purpose we write

$$a_0 = a_1 = 0, \qquad a_k = -\frac{1}{k^{1-\lambda}}, \qquad \lambda < \frac{1}{2} \qquad (k=2, 3, \ldots).$$

Then, as is easily shown, we have

$$\ln \prod_{k=2}^{n-1} \frac{1+|a_k|}{1-|a_k|} > 2\sum_{k=2}^{n-1} |a_k| =$$

$$= 2\sum_{k=2}^{n-1} k^{\lambda-1} > 2\int_2^n x^{\lambda-1}\,dx = 2\,\frac{n^\lambda - 2^\lambda}{\lambda},$$

and therefore, using (8.6), for z = 1 we have

$$\varphi_n^*(1) = \frac{1}{\sqrt{c_0}} \sqrt{\prod_{k=2}^{n-1} \frac{1+|a_k|}{1-|a_k|}} \geqslant C \exp\left(\frac{n^\lambda}{\lambda}\right),$$

where λ is arbitrarily close to $\frac{1}{2}$. The sharper result

$$\varphi_n^*(1) \geqslant C_1 \exp\left\{\frac{2\sqrt{n}}{(\ln n)^\gamma}\right\}$$

is obtained if we set

$$a_0 = a_1 = 0, \qquad a_k = -\frac{1}{\sqrt{k}\,(\ln k)^\gamma},$$

$$\gamma > \frac{1}{2} \qquad (k = 2, 3, \ldots).$$

From (8.18) we obtain

Theorem 8.4. If the $\{a_n\}$ are such that

$$|a_n| \leqslant \frac{\beta}{n \ln n}, \qquad n \geqslant n_0, \qquad \beta < 3, \tag{8.20}$$

the existence of the radial boundary value

$$\lim_{r\to 1-0} \pi(re^{i\theta_0}) = \pi(e^{i\theta_0}) \tag{8.21}$$

is equivalent of the existence of the limit

$$\lim_{n\to\infty} \varphi_n^*(e^{i\theta_0}) \tag{8.21'}$$

and to the equality of these two:

$$\lim_{r\to 1-0} \pi(re^{i\theta_0}) = \pi(e^{i\theta_0}) = \lim_{n\to\infty} \varphi_n^*(e^{i\theta_0}). \tag{8.21''}$$

To prove this it is sufficient to note that according to (8.1)

$$\Phi_n^*(z) = 1 - z\sum_{k=0}^{n-1} a_k \Phi_k(z) \qquad (n = 1, 2, \ldots). \tag{8.22}$$

The series

$$\sum_{n=0}^{\infty} a_n \Phi_n(z) = \sum_{n=0}^{\infty} \frac{a_n}{\alpha_n} \varphi_n(z)$$

has coefficients

$$g_n = \frac{a_n}{\alpha_n}, \qquad |g_n| \leqslant \frac{|a_n|}{\alpha_0} \leqslant \frac{\beta}{\alpha_0 n \ln n}, \qquad n \geqslant n_0. \tag{8.23}$$

On the other hand, from (8.18') we may write, in the notation of Theorem 6.3,

$$M_n = C_2 (\ln n)^{\beta},$$

$$|g_n| \leqslant \frac{\beta}{\alpha_0 n (\ln n)^{\frac{\beta}{3}}} \cdot (\ln n)^{\frac{\beta}{3} - 1} = o\left\{\frac{1}{n (\ln n)^{\frac{\beta}{3}}}\right\} = o\left\{\frac{1}{n \sqrt[3]{M_n}}\right\}$$

and then the assertion follows from Theorem 6.3.

8.3. Finally, we pass on to a theorem analogous to Theorem 5.2.

Theorem 8.5. Assume that

$$\sum_{n=0}^{\infty} |a_n| < \infty. \tag{8.24}$$

Then it follows that on the entire $[0, 2\pi]$ interval the function $\sigma(\theta)$ is absolutely continuous and the weight $p(\theta)$ is bounded from below and continuous, while in the closed region $|z| \leq 1$,

$$\varepsilon_n = |\varphi_n^*(z) - \pi(z)| \leqslant C \sum_{k=n}^{\infty} |a_k| \qquad (n = 0, 1, 2, \ldots). \tag{8.25}$$

From (8.19) we obtain

$$\prod_{k=0}^{\infty} \{1 - |a_k|\} \leqslant \prod_{k=0}^{n-1} \{1 - |a_k|\} \leqslant |\Phi_n^*(z)| \leqslant$$

$$\leqslant \prod_{k=0}^{n-1} \{1 + |a_k|\} \leqslant \prod_{k=0}^{\infty} \{1 + |a_k|\}, \qquad |z| \leqslant 1.$$

In view of the convergence of both of these products, the limit

$$\lim_{n\to\infty} \Phi_n^*(z) = \lim_{n\to\infty} \frac{\varphi_n^*(z)}{\alpha_n} = \frac{\pi(z)}{\alpha}, \qquad |z| \leqslant 1, \tag{8.26}$$

exists, and the convergence is uniform throughout the closed region $|z| \leq 1$. Therefore $\pi(z)$ is continuous for $|z| \leq 1$ and satisfies the inequalities

$$\left.\begin{array}{c} 0 < \alpha \prod_{n=0}^{\infty} \{1 - |a_n|\} \leqslant |\pi(z)| \leqslant \alpha \prod_{n=0}^{\infty} \{1 + |a_n|\}, \\ |z| \leqslant 1. \end{array}\right\} \tag{8.27}$$

This implies the boundedness and continuity of

$$p(\theta) = \frac{1}{|\pi(e^{i\theta})|^2}.$$

From (8.22) we obtain

$$\frac{\pi(z)}{\alpha} - \Phi_n^*(z) = -z \sum_{k=n}^{\infty} a_k \Phi_k(z), \qquad |z| \leqslant 1,$$

which leads to

$$\left|\frac{\pi(z)}{\alpha} - \Phi_n^*(z)\right| = \left|\frac{\pi(z)}{\alpha} - \frac{\varphi_n^*(z)}{\alpha_n}\right| \leqslant \sum_{k=n}^{\infty} |a_k| \cdot |\Phi_k(z)| \leqslant$$

$$\leqslant \prod_{k=0}^{\infty} \{1 + |a_k|\} \sum_{k=n}^{\infty} |a_k|.$$

To prove the absolute continuity of $\sigma(\theta)$, we note that the polynomials $\{\psi_n^*(z)\}$ of the second kind satisfy a formula analogous to (8.25), namely

$$|\psi_n^*(z) - \omega(z)| \leqslant C \sum_{k=n}^{\infty} |a_k|, \qquad |z| \leqslant 1, \tag{8.25'}$$

where $\omega(z)$ has the same properties as $\pi(z)$. Then, using (8.25), (8.25'), and (8.10), we have

$$\lim_{n\to\infty} \frac{\psi_n^*(z)}{\varphi_n^*(z)} = F(z) = \frac{\omega(z)}{\pi(z)}, \qquad |z| < 1, \tag{8.28}$$

and we note that $\omega(z)/\pi(z)$ is a function continuous in the closed region $|z| \leq 1$. Thus $F(z)$ is identically equal to $\omega(z)/\pi(z)$. Since the family of harmonic functions

$$u_r(\theta) = \Re\{F(re^{i\theta})\} = \Re\left\{\frac{\omega(re^{i\theta})}{\pi(re^{i\theta})}\right\}, \qquad r < 1$$

is uniformly bounded for $r \leq 1$, the integrals $\int_0^\theta u_r(\varphi)\,d\varphi$ are absolutely equicontinuous on $[0, 2\pi]$, and therefore $u_r(\theta)$ can be represented by a Poisson-Lebesgue integral.* Then from (1.22) we obtain $d\sigma(\theta) = p(\theta)\,d\theta$.

<u>Theorem 8.6.</u> The assertion made in the preceding theorem is valid also if

$$\sum_{n=1}^{\infty} \frac{\delta_n}{\sqrt{n}} < \infty; \tag{8.29}$$

in this case

$$\varepsilon_n \leqslant C \sum_{k=n_0}^{\infty} \frac{\delta_k}{\sqrt{k}}, \qquad n_0 = \left[\frac{n}{4}\right].$$

Indeed, setting $2^{r-1} \leq n < 2^r$, we have, in analogy with (5.20),

$$\sum_{k=n}^{\infty} |a_k| \leqslant C \sum_{\nu=2^{r-2}}^{\infty} \frac{1}{\sqrt{\nu}} \sqrt{|a_\nu|^2 + |a_{\nu+1}|^2 + \dots} \leqslant$$

$$\leqslant C_1 \sum_{\nu=n_0}^{\infty} \frac{\delta_\nu}{\sqrt{\nu}}. \tag{8.30}$$

8.4. We have seen how important δ_n is in many of our inequalities. In particular if $\lim_{n\to\infty} \delta_n = 0$, then δ_n is, according to (2.8), the best approximation (in the metric of L_2^σ) to $\pi_0(\theta)$ by means of polynomials of degree $\leq n$. The following question then arises: *is it possible for the nonincreasing sequence $\{\delta_n\}$ to decrease in an arbitrary way; in particular, is it possible to*

---

* See I. I. Privalov [1], p. 64.

construct an orthogonal set for which this sequence will approach zero arbitrarily rapidly?

Theorem 8.7. Given an arbitrary nonincreasing sequence $\{\delta_n\}$ of positive numbers and choosing $0 < |a_0| < 1$ arbitrarily, the square moduli of all the parameters will be given by

$$|a_n|^2 = \frac{\delta_n^2 - \delta_{n+1}^2}{\delta_0^2 - \delta_1^2 + |a_0|^2 (\delta_1^2 - \delta_{n+1}^2)} \cdot |a_0|^2 \quad (n = 1, 2, \ldots). \tag{8.31}$$

To prove this we note that according to (8.15) and (8.6)

$$\alpha^2 \delta_n^2 = \sum_{k=n+1}^{\infty} \alpha_k^2 |a_{k-1}|^2, \qquad \alpha^2 (\delta_n^2 - \delta_{n+1}^2) = \alpha_{n+1}^2 |a_n|^2,$$

$$\left(\frac{\alpha_n}{\alpha_{n+1}}\right)^2 = 1 - |a_n|^2,$$

and this leads simply to

$$\frac{|a_n|^2}{1 - |a_n|^2} = \frac{\delta_n^2 - \delta_{n+1}^2}{\delta_{n-1}^2 - \delta_n^2} \cdot |a_{n-1}|^2.$$

We have thus arrived at the linear inhomogeneous finite-difference equation

$$y_{n+1} - \lambda_n y_n = 1, \quad y_n = \frac{1}{|a_n|^2}, \quad \lambda_n = \frac{\delta_n^2 - \delta_{n+1}^2}{\delta_{n+1}^2 - \delta_{n+2}^2},$$

whose solution gives (8.31).

We have gone into the parametric description of sets of orthogonal polynomials for two reasons:* First, some quantities difficult to evaluate in terms of the structural properties of $\sigma(\theta)$ are very easily expressed in terms of the parameters; an example is the δ_n, which are given in terms of the parameters by the simple expression (8.15). Second, the theory has some very important and interesting generalizations. Our $\{\Phi_n(z)\}$ polynomials and the parameters $\{a_n\}$ are functions of the integral argument n. Krein [2] has developed a general theory for analogous functions, but of an argument r varying continu-

* A detailed parametric study of the properties of orthogonal sets will be found in other work by the present author [1, 9].

ously on $[0, \infty]$; in other words, he has constructed the continuous analog of the theory of polynomials orthogonal on the unit circle. Then the analog of the $\{a_n\}$ is a function $A(r)$, and conditions (8.12) and (8.7) are replaced by $A \in L_1(0, \infty)$ and $A \in L_2(0, \infty)$.

CHAPTER IX

POLYNOMIALS ORTHOGONAL ON A FINITE INTERVAL OF THE REAL AXIS

9.1. Consider the polynomials $\{p_n(x)\}$ orthonormal with respect to the measure $d\psi(x)$ on a finite interval of the real axis, which can always be linearly transformed, without loss of generality, into the interval [-1, +1]. We have

$$\int_{-1}^{1} p_n(x)\, p_m(x)\, d\psi(x) = \begin{cases} 0, & n \neq m, \\ 1, & n = m, \end{cases} \tag{9.1}$$

$$p_n(x) = \beta_n x^n + \ldots, \quad \beta_n > 0 \quad (n = 0, 1, 2, \ldots),$$

where $\psi(x)$ is a nondecreasing bounded function with an infinite set of points of increase on [-1, +1], and for which we shall set $\psi(-1) = 0$.

We introduce the nondecreasing function

$$\sigma(\theta) = \begin{cases} -\psi(\cos\theta), & 0 \leqslant \theta \leqslant \pi, \\ \psi(\cos\theta), & \pi \leqslant \theta \leqslant 2\pi, \end{cases} \tag{9.2}$$

which is bounded on $[0, 2\pi]$. We then have

$$\sigma(2\pi) - \sigma(2\pi - 0) = \sigma(+0) - \sigma(0) = \psi(1) - \psi(1 - 0),$$
$$\sigma(\pi + 0) - \sigma(\pi) = \sigma(\pi) - \sigma(\pi - 0) = \psi(-1 + 0) - \psi(-1),$$

and may proceed to construct the set of polynomials $\{\varphi_n(z)\}$ orthonormal with respect to the measure $d\sigma(\theta)$ on the circumference $|z| = 1$; it is easy to see, further, that all the coefficients on these polynomials are real. From (9.2) we may conclude that almost everywhere on the interval [-1, +1],

$$\left.\begin{aligned} w(x) = \psi'(x) = \frac{\sigma'(\theta)}{|\sin\theta|} = \frac{p(\theta)}{|\sin\theta|}, \quad x = \cos\theta, \\ p(\theta) = w(x)\sqrt{1-x^2}. \end{aligned}\right\} \quad (9.3)$$

If $\psi(x)$ is absolutely continuous on $[-1, +1]$, we shall call $w(x)$ the *weight*, and $p(\theta)$ the *trigonometric weight** corresponding to the orthonormal set $\{p_n(x)\}$.

In all that follows we shall use the expression $x = \frac{1}{2}(z + 1/z)$ to relate the variables $\underline{x}$ and $\underline{z}$, so that $z = x \pm \sqrt{x^2 - 1}$. In this latter expression we shall always choose that branch of the two-valued function which maps the x plane cut along $[-1, +1]$ into the circle $|z| < 1$, and therefore when $|x + \sqrt{x^2-1}| > 1$ we must set $z = x - \sqrt{x^2 - 1}$, and then as $x \to \infty$, we have $z \to 0$. The relation between the $\{p_n(x)\}$ and the $\{\varphi_n(z)\}$ is given by

Theorem 9.1. The $\{p_n(x)\}$ polynomials, orthonormal on $[-1, +1]$ with respect to the measure $d\psi(x)$, are related to the $\{\varphi_k(z)\}$ polynomials, orthonormal on the circle $|z| = 1$ with respect to the measure $d\sigma(\theta)$, for which $\sigma(\theta)$ is given by (9.2), according to

$$p_n(x) = \frac{\varphi_{2n}(z) + \varphi^*_{2n}(z)}{\sqrt{2\pi\left[1 + \frac{\varphi_{2n}(0)}{\alpha_{2n}}\right]}} \cdot z^{-n} \qquad (n = 0, 1, 2, \ldots),$$
$$x = \frac{1}{2}\left(z + \frac{1}{z}\right). \qquad (9.4)$$

To prove this we note first that writing $\varphi_{2n}(z) = \sum_{k=0}^{2n} \lambda_k z^k$, we find that if $z = e^{i\theta}$, then

$$\{\varphi_{2n}(z) + \varphi^*_{2n}(z)\} z^{-n} = \sum_{k=0}^{2n} \lambda_k [e^{i(k-n)\theta} + e^{i(n-k)\theta}] =$$
$$= 2\lambda_n + 2\sum_{k=0}^{n-1} (\lambda_k + \lambda_{2n-k}) \cos(n-k)\theta,$$

* See S. N. Bernshtein [1].

which means that the right-hand side of (9.4) is a polynomial of degree n in the variable $x = \cos\theta$.

Further, for $\nu = 0, 1, \ldots, n-1$, we have

$$\int_{-1}^{1} p_n(x)\cos\nu\theta\, d\psi(x) = -\int_{\pi}^{0} p_n(\cos\theta)\cos\nu\theta\, d\sigma(\theta) =$$

$$= \frac{1}{2}\int_{0}^{2\pi} p_n(\cos\theta)\cos\nu\theta\, d\sigma(\theta) = \frac{\pi}{2\sqrt{2\pi\left[1+\frac{\varphi_{2n}(0)}{\alpha_{2n}}\right]}} \times$$

$$\times \int_{0}^{2\pi} \{\varphi_{2n}(e^{i\theta}) + \varphi_{2n}^{*}(e^{i\theta})\}\, e^{-in\theta}(e^{i\nu\theta} + e^{-i\nu\theta})\, d\sigma(\theta) = 0$$

which is obtained using the relations

$$\frac{1}{2\pi}\int_{0}^{2\pi} \varphi_{2n}(e^{i\theta})\, e^{-i(n\pm\nu)\theta}\, d\sigma(\theta) = 0,$$

$$\frac{1}{2\pi}\int_{0}^{2\pi} \varphi_{2n}^{*}(e^{i\theta})\, e^{-i(n\pm\nu)\theta}\, d\sigma(\theta) =$$

$$= \frac{1}{2\pi}\int_{0}^{2\pi} \varphi_{2n}(e^{-i\theta})\, e^{i(n\pm\nu)\theta}\, d\sigma(\theta) = 0,$$

$$\varphi_{2n}^{*}(e^{i\theta}) = e^{2in\theta}\varphi_{2n}(e^{-i\theta}).$$

For $\nu = n$ we obtain

$$\int_{-1}^{1} p_n(x)\cos n\theta\, d\psi(x) = \frac{2^{n-1}}{\beta_n}\int_{-1}^{1} p_n^2(x)\, d\psi(x) =$$

$$= \frac{2^{n-1}}{2\beta_n\left[1+\frac{\varphi_{2n}(0)}{\alpha_{2n}}\right]} \cdot \frac{1}{2\pi}\int_{0}^{2\pi} \{[\varphi_{2n}(e^{i\theta})]^2 e^{-2in\theta} + [\varphi_{2n}(e^{-i\theta})]^2 e^{2in\theta} +$$

$$+ 2\varphi_{2n}(e^{i\theta})\,\varphi_{2n}(e^{-i\theta})\}\, d\sigma(\theta),$$

from which it is easily shown that*

$$\int_{-1}^{1} p_n^2(x)\,d\psi(x) = \frac{1}{2\left[1+\frac{\varphi_{2n}(0)}{\alpha_{2n}}\right]}\left\{\frac{\varphi_{2n}(0)}{\alpha_{2n}} + \frac{\varphi_{2n}(0)}{\alpha_{2n}} + 2\right\} = 1.$$

Having obtained (9.4), we can now arrive at estimates and asymptotic formulas for the $\{p_n(x)\}$ by using the corresponding results previously arrived at for the $\{\varphi_n(z)\}$

Theorem 9.2. The following assertions are equivalent:

1) The integral

$$\int_{-1}^{1} \frac{\ln \psi'(x)\,dx}{\sqrt{1-x^2}} \tag{9.5}$$

exists.

2) There exists an infinite bounded subsequence $\{\beta_{n_\nu} 2^{-n_\nu}\}$.

3) There is at least one point x_0 in the region $|x + \sqrt{x^2 - 1}| > 1$ at which there exists an infinite bounded subsequence of the form

$$\left(x_0 + \sqrt{x_0^2 - 1}\right)^{-n_\nu} p_{n_\nu}(x_0) \qquad (\nu = 1, 2, \ldots). \tag{9.6}$$

To prove this we use (9.2) and consider the integral

$$\frac{1}{2\pi}\int_0^{2\pi} \ln \sigma'(\theta)\,d\theta = \frac{1}{\pi}\int_{-1}^{1} \ln\left\{w(x)\sqrt{1-x^2}\right\}\frac{dx}{\sqrt{1-x^2}} =$$

$$= \frac{1}{\pi}\int_{-1}^{1}\frac{\ln w(x)\,dx}{\sqrt{1-x^2}} + \frac{1}{\pi}\int_0^{\pi} \ln \sin\theta\,d\theta = \frac{1}{\pi}\int_{-1}^{1}\frac{\ln w(x)\,dx}{\sqrt{1-x^2}} - \ln 2, \tag{9.7}$$

which implies that the integrals of (7.5) and (9.5) exist simultaneously.

From (8.6) we obtain

$$\frac{1}{\sqrt{1-a_{2n-1}}} = \frac{\alpha_{2n}\sqrt{1+a_{2n-1}}}{\alpha_{2n-1}}, \quad a_{2n-1} = -\frac{\varphi_{2n}(0)}{\alpha_{2n}}. \tag{9.8}$$

* We have here reproduced Szegö's proof [1], Section 11.5; elsewhere, the present author [1] (Section 30) derives (9.4) differently.

Now dividing both sides of (9.4) by x^n, going to the limit as $x \to \infty$, and using (8.7), we arrive at

$$\left.\begin{aligned} \frac{\beta_n}{2^n} &= \frac{\alpha_{2n}}{\sqrt{2\pi}}\sqrt{1-a_{2n-1}} \leqslant \frac{\alpha_{2n}}{\sqrt{\pi}}; \\ \frac{\beta_n}{2^n} &= \frac{\alpha_{2n-1}}{\sqrt{2\pi}\sqrt{1+a_{2n-1}}} \geqslant \frac{\alpha_{2n-1}}{2\sqrt{\pi}}. \end{aligned}\right\} \tag{9.9}$$

Because of the monotonic increase of α_n, these inequalities imply that the existence of a bounded subsequence of the form $\{\beta_{n_\nu} 2^{-n_\nu}\}$ is equivalent to the existence of a bounded subsequence of the form $\{\alpha_{k_s}\}$, which, in turn, is equivalent to the existence of the integral of (7.5) and therefore also of the integral of (9.5).

From (1.2) and (1.2') one easily derives the relation

$$\alpha_{2n-1}\{\varphi_{2n}(z)+\varphi^*_{2n}(z)\} = \{z\varphi_{2n-1}(z)+\varphi^*_{2n-1}(z)\}\,\alpha_{2n}(1-a_{2n-1}).$$

Then using (9.4) and (9.8) we find that for $|z| \leq 1$,

$$|z^n p_n(x)| \leqslant \frac{|\varphi_{2n}(z)|+|\varphi^*_{2n}(z)|}{\sqrt{2\pi}} \cdot \frac{\alpha_{2n}\sqrt{1+|a_{2n-1}|}}{\alpha_{2n-1}} \leqslant \leqslant \frac{2\alpha_{2n}|\varphi^*_{2n}(z)|}{\sqrt{\pi}\,\alpha_{2n-1}},$$

$$|z^n p_n(x)| = \frac{|\varphi^*_{2n-1}(z)|}{\sqrt{2\pi}} \cdot \left|1+z\frac{\varphi_{2n-1}(z)}{\varphi^*_{2n-1}(z)}\right| \frac{\alpha_{2n}\sqrt{1-a_{2n-1}}}{\alpha_{2n-1}} \leqslant \leqslant \frac{2\alpha_{2n}|\varphi^*_{2n-1}(z)|}{\sqrt{\pi}\alpha_{2n-1}}. \tag{9.10}$$

On the other hand, for $|z| < 1$ we have

$$|z^n p_n(x)| = \frac{|\varphi^*_{2n-1}(z)|}{\sqrt{2\pi(1+a_{2n-1})}} \cdot \left|1+z\frac{\varphi_{2n-1}(z)}{\varphi^*_{2n-1}(z)}\right| \geqslant \geqslant \frac{|\varphi^*_{2n-1}(z)|}{2\sqrt{\pi}}(1-|z|). \tag{9.11}$$

These last two inequalities imply that assertion 3) is equivalent to the existence of a bounded subsequence $\{\varphi^*_{n_s}(z_0)\}$, $|z_0| < 1$, which in turn is equivalent to the existence of the integral of (7.5), and therefore of (9.5).

9.2. From (9.4) and the condition that $|a_n| \leq a < 1$ for $n \geq n_0$, we obtain the following inequality for $|z| = 1$ (i.e., for $-1 \leq x \leq 1$):

$$|p_n(x)| \leqslant \frac{|\varphi^*_{2n}(z)| + |\varphi_{2n}(z)|}{\sqrt{2\pi(1-a)}} \leqslant \sqrt{\frac{2}{\pi(1-a)}}\,|\varphi^*_{2n}(z)|.$$

In particular, if (9.5) exists, we have $\sum\limits_{k=0}^{\infty} a_k^2 < \infty$, and the condition $|a_n| \leq \epsilon$ for $n \geq n_0$ is satisfied for every $\epsilon > 0$. Therefore every estimate for the $|\varphi^*_{2n}(e^{i\theta})|$ can be used to establish a corresponding one for the $|p_n(\cos\theta)|$, so that for the orthonormal polynomials $\{p_n(x)\}$ we obtain the estimates of Tables II throughout $[-1, +1]$, where by $p(\theta)$ we now mean the trigonometric weight defined by $p(\theta) = \psi'(x)\sqrt{1-x^2}$, $x = \cos\theta$. In Table II we need only replace $\sigma(\theta)$ by $\psi(x)$, the interval $(0, 2\pi]$ by $[-1, +1]$, and the $\{\varphi_n(e^{i\theta})\}$ by the $\{p_n(x)\}$. An interval $[a, b] \subset [-1, +1]$ corresponds to an interval $[\alpha, \beta] \subset [0, 2\pi]$, where $a = \cos\beta$ and $b = \cos\alpha$, so that for the $\{p_n(x)\}$ we obtain the *local estimates* of Table III. For these, conditions IV and V are replaced by (9.5), while conditions VI and VII are replaced by

$$\int_{-1}^{1} \frac{dx}{w(x)} < \infty \text{ *)}. \tag{9.12}$$

If we have a situation in which $[a, b]$ lies *strictly in the interior* of $[-1, +1]$, we can replace the estimates and moduli of continuity for $p(\theta)$ by the corresponding estimates and moduli of continuity for $w(x) = \psi'(x)$.

9.3. Let us now go onto a discussion of limit relations. Assume first that $|x + \sqrt{x^2 - 1}| > 1$ or $|z| < 1$.

---

* One need only reproduce the proof of Theorem 4.5 as applied to the $\{p_n(x)\}$ polynomials.

Theorem 9.3. Any one of the conditions of Theorem 9.2 is necessary and sufficient for the validity of the limit relation

$$\lim_{n\to\infty}\left\{\frac{p_n(x)}{(x+\sqrt{x^2-1})^n}\right\}=\frac{\pi(z)}{\sqrt{2\pi}}=\frac{1}{\sqrt{\pi}\,\Delta(z)\sqrt{1-z^2}} \tag{9.13}$$

in the region $|x + \sqrt{x^2 - 1}| > 1$. Further, the convergence is uniform for $|x + \sqrt{x^2 - 1}| \geq 1 + \eta$, $\eta > 0$, and $\Delta(z)$ is an analytic function regular for $|z| < 1$, and such that

$$\lim_{r\to 1-0} |\Delta(re^{i\theta})|^2 = w(\cos\theta) \tag{9.14}$$

almost everywhere in $[0, \pi]$.*

To prove this theorem one need only remark that the conditions of Theorem 9.2 are equivalent to the existence of the integral (7.5), and therefore to the validity of the relation

$$\varphi_n^*(z)=\pi(z)+\varepsilon_n, \quad |z|<1, \quad \lim_{n\to\infty}\varepsilon_n=0 \tag{9.15}$$

From (9.4) we have

$$z^n p_n(x)-\frac{\pi(z)}{\sqrt{2\pi}}=\frac{\varphi_{2n}(z)+\varepsilon_{2n}}{\sqrt{2\pi(1-a_{2n-1})}}+\frac{\pi(z)}{\sqrt{2\pi}}\left(\frac{1}{\sqrt{1-a_{2n-1}}}-1\right),$$

and since $\lim_{n\to\infty}\varepsilon_{2n}=\lim_{n\to\infty}a_{2n-1}=\lim_{n\to\infty}\varphi_{2n}(z)=0$, this implies (9.13) uniformly for $|x + \sqrt{x^2 - 1}| \geq 1 + \eta$, $\eta > 0$. Then (9.14) is obtained from (9.13), (9.3), and (2.4).

Remark 9.1. To estimate the error involved in (9.13) one must know the order of magnitude of ϵ_{2n}, a_{2n-1}, and $\varphi_{2n}(z)$. Now, according to (5.86) and (8.15) we have

$$\varepsilon_{2n}=o(\delta_{2n}),\ |z|\leqslant r<1;\ |a_{2n-1}|\leqslant\sqrt{\sum_{k=2n-1}^{\infty}a_k^2}\leqslant C\delta_{2n-1}.$$

We have not succeeded, however, in finding the order of $|\varphi_n(z)|$ as $n \to \infty$.

Let us now turn to an asymptotic formula at a point of the interval [-1, +1].

---

* S. N. Bernshtein [1] and G. Szegö [6], Section 8, have proved the sufficiency of condition (9.5) if $\psi(x)$ is an absolutely continuous function.

In (9.13) we choose that branch of $\sqrt{1-z^2}$ which is positive for $z = 0$.

The relation

$$\varphi_n^*(e^{i\theta}) = \pi(e^{i\theta}) + \varepsilon_n, \quad 0 \leqslant \theta \leqslant 2\pi \tag{9.16}$$

implies

$$\varphi_n(e^{i\theta}) = e^{in\theta}\,\overline{\pi(e^{i\theta})} + e^{in\theta}\bar{\varepsilon}_n \tag{9.16'}$$

so that if $x \in [-1, +1]$ (9.4) leads to

$$p_n(\cos\theta) = \frac{e^{-in\theta}\pi(e^{i\theta}) + e^{in\theta}\overline{\pi(e^{i\theta})}}{\sqrt{2\pi(1-a_{2n-1})}} + \frac{e^{-in\theta}\varepsilon_{2n} + e^{in\theta}\bar{\varepsilon}_{2n}}{\sqrt{2\pi(1-a_{2n-1})}},$$

$$\theta \in [0, \pi].$$

Now, according to (2.6) and (9.3) we may write

$$\pi(e^{i\theta}) = |\pi(e^{i\theta})|\, e^{i\gamma(\theta)} = \frac{e^{i\gamma(\theta)}}{\sqrt{p(\theta)}} = \frac{e^{i\gamma(\theta)}}{\sqrt{w(\cos\theta)\,|\sin\theta|}},$$

so that we arrive at

$$p_n(\cos\theta) - \sqrt{\frac{2}{\pi}} \cdot \frac{\cos[n\theta - \gamma(\theta)]}{\sqrt{w(\cos\theta)\sin\theta}} = \eta_n(\theta), \; 0 \leqslant \theta \leqslant \pi, \tag{9.17}$$

$$|\eta_n| \leqslant \sqrt{\frac{2}{\pi}} \cdot \frac{|\varepsilon_{2n}|}{\sqrt{1-a_{2n-1}}} + \sqrt{\frac{2}{\pi}} \frac{1}{\sqrt{w(\cos\theta)\sin\theta}} \left\{ \frac{1}{\sqrt{1-a_{2n-1}}} - 1 \right\}.$$

For $|a_n| \leq a$, $n \geq n_0$ and $w(\cos\theta)\,|\sin\theta| \geq m > 0$, therefore, we find as a result of (8.15') that

$$|\eta_n| \leqslant C_1|\varepsilon_{2n}| + C_2|a_{2n-1}| \leqslant C_1|\varepsilon_{2n}| + C_3\delta_{2n-1} \leqslant C_4\delta_{2n}. \tag{9.17'}$$

<u>Theorem 9.4</u>. Under condition (9.5) the limit relation (9.16) for the $\{\varphi_n^*(e^{i\theta})\}$ gives the asymptotic formula (9.17) for the $\{p_n(\cos\theta)\}$ with the error given by (9.17').

Thus all the conditions of Tables IV and V guarantee an asymptotic formula for the $\{p_n(x)\}$ throughout $[-1, +1]$ or on an internal interval $[a, b]$; in these conditions we replace $\sigma(\theta)$ by $\psi(x)$, the interval $[0, 2\pi]$ by $[-1, +1]$, the interval $[\alpha, \beta]$ by $[a, b]$, and the polynomials $\{\varphi_n^*(e^{i\theta})\}$ by $\{p_n(x)\}$, and use (9.3) for $p(\theta)$.

<u>Remark 9.2</u>. The function $\gamma(\theta)$ can be obtained from (2.6) or, as has been shown by Bernshtein [1] and Szegö [1] (Section 12.2) from the relation

$$\gamma(\theta) = -\frac{1}{2\pi}\int_{-1}^{1}\frac{\ln W(\xi) - \ln W(x)}{\xi - x}\sqrt{\frac{1-x^2}{1-\xi^2}}\,d\xi,\quad x = \cos\theta, \tag{9.18}$$

where

$$W(x) = w(x)\sqrt{1-x^2}. \tag{9.18'}$$

We note also the limit relation given by

Theorem 9.5. Assume that the integral of (9.5) exists, and that on an interval [a, b] in the interior of [-1, +1] the function $\psi(x)$ is absolutely continuous, while $w(x) \geq m > 0$ is continuous. Then in [a, b] we have, uniformly,

$$\lim_{n\to\infty}\frac{1}{n+1}\sum_{k=0}^{n} p_k^2(x) = \frac{1}{\pi w(x)\sqrt{1-x^2}}. \tag{9.19}$$

Theorem 9.6. If the integral of (9.5) exists, we obtain the limit relation

$$\lim_{n\to\infty}\left\| p_n(\cos\theta)\sqrt{w(\cos\theta)\,|\sin\theta|} - \sqrt{\frac{2}{\pi}}\cos[n\theta - \gamma(\theta)]\right\|_2 = 0. \tag{9.20}$$

The proofs of these two theorems are analogous to those of theorems 5.7 and 5.8.

9.4. Let us now pass to a consideration of orthogonal series of the form

$$\sum_{k=0}\gamma_k p_k(x). \tag{9.21}$$

As in Section 6.1, we define the modulus of increase of $\psi(x)$ by

$$a(\delta) = \inf\int_{e} d\psi(x), \qquad \mathrm{Mes}\, e = \delta,\ e \in [-1, +1], \tag{9.22}$$

in terms of which we obtain the analog of Theorem 6.1.

Theorem 9.7. If

$$\lim_{\delta\to 0}\left\{\sqrt{\delta}\ln a(\delta)\right\} = 0, \tag{9.23}$$

then for $|x+\sqrt{x^2-1}|>1$ the limit

$$\lim_{n\to\infty}\sqrt[n]{|p_n(x)|}=\left|x+\sqrt{x^2-1}\right| \tag{9.24}$$

exists, and the convergence is uniform on every internal region.

To prove this, it is sufficient to reproduce the argument of Theorem 6.1, replacing the inequality of Szasz stated in (3.42) by the inequality

$$\max|G_n'(x)|\leqslant n^2\max|G_n(x)|,\quad -1\leqslant x\leqslant 1 \tag{9.25}$$

due to A. A. Markov, and using the theorem of Walsh ([1], Section 7.4).

For unnormalized polynomials $P_n(x)=p_n(x)/\beta_n$ we have the following assertion:* if $\psi'(x)>0$ almost everywhere on $[-1,+1]$, then for $|x+\sqrt{x^2-1}|>1$ the limit

$$\lim_{n\to\infty}\sqrt[n]{|P_n(x)|}=\frac{|x+\sqrt{x^2-1}|}{2} \tag{9.26}$$

exists.

From the limit relations proved, we obtain

Theorem 9.8. Assume (9.23) to be satisfied. Then 1) if the orthogonal series (9.21) converges at a point x_0 outside of $[-1,+1]$, it converges absolutely in the ellipse with foci at the points ± 1 and passing through x_0, and uniformly in every internal region; 2) if

$$\overline{\lim_{n\to\infty}}\sqrt[n]{|\gamma_n|}=\frac{1}{R}<1, \tag{9.27}$$

the ellipse whose foci are at the points ± 1 and the sum of whose semi-axes is R is the ellipse of convergence for the series (9.21) (the analog of the domain of convergence for a power series).

The proof is similar to the proof of the theorems of Abel and Cauchy-Hadamard for power series.

We may remark that the theorem for orthogonal series of the form of (9.21), a generalization of Luzin's theorem, is proved in Section 6.3.

* See Ya. L. Geronimus [7].

9.5. Let us now turn to the Fourier-Chebyshev expansion of a function $f(x)$ defined on $[-1, +1]$,

$$s_n(f;\, x) = \sum_{k=0}^{n} c_k p_k(x), \qquad c_k = \int_{-1}^{1} f(x)\, p_k(x)\, d\psi(x). \quad (9.28)$$

In distinction from the situation we had when dealing with orthogonality on the unit circle, the finiteness of the interval of orthogonality in the present case causes the set of polynomials (or, equivalently, the set of powers $\{x^n\}_{0}^{\infty}$,) to be always closed in the space L_2^{ψ} of functions $f(x)$ with norm*

$$\| f \|_2^{\psi} = \left\{ \int_{-1}^{1} f^2(x)\, d\psi(x) \right\}^{\frac{1}{2}} < \infty.$$

Thus the expansion (9.28) of a function $f(x) \in L_2^{\psi}$ always converges in the metric of L_2^{ψ} to the function $f(x)$. Furthermore, in Chapter VII, when we were dealing with the convergence of the expansion in the metric of the space C, we were forced to restrict our considerations to functions equivalent to the boundary values of certain analytic functions regular in the region $|z| < 1$; now, however, we can deal with arbitrary measurable functions.

Before passing to this general case, let us turn to a most simple theorem analogous to Theorem 7.8.

Theorem 9.9. Let $f(x)$ be an analytic function regular in some region G of the x plane whose interior contains the interval $[-1, +1]$, and assume condition (9.23) fulfilled. We then have

$$\lim_{n \to \infty} s_n(f;\, x) = \sum_{k=0}^{\infty} c_k p_k(x) = f(x) \quad (9.29)$$

if x lies in the smallest ellipse Γ whose foci are at the points ± 1 and which passes through a singular point x_0 of $f(x)$; outside this ellipse the series diverges.**

* See, for instance, G. Szegö [1], Section 1.5.

** This theorem was first proved by Szegö [6] under the more restrictive conditions that $\psi(x)$ be absolutely continuous and that the integral of (9.5) exist.

The proof is similar to that of Theorem 7.8; in it we use the known theorem that one may make the approximation

$$|f(x)-G_{n-1}(x)|\leqslant\frac{C}{R_1^n}, \qquad 1<R_1<R$$

when

$$|x+\sqrt{x^2-1}|<|x_0+\sqrt{x_0^2-1}|=R.$$

9.6. We now pass to a discussion of the Fourier-Chebyshev expansion of a function $f(x)$ defined on [-1, +1]. For $f(x)$ continuous throughout [-1, +1], Table VI gives sufficient conditions for convergence on this interval; one need only replace $\sigma(\theta)$ by $\psi(x)$, the interval $[0, 2\pi]$ by [-1, +1], and $f(e^{i\theta})$ by $f(x)$.

If, on the other hand, $f(x)$ is summable on [-1, +1] and discontinuous only on an internal interval [a, b], then in accordance with arguments presented in Sections 7.5, 7.7, and 7.8, we arrive at conditions II-XIII of Table IX, the analogs of conditions II-XIII of Table VII.

A different condition is treated in

Theorem 9.10. Let $f(x)\in L_2^{\psi}$ be of bounded variation on an internal interval $[a,b]\subset[-1,+1]$, and on this same interval let $\psi(x)$ be absolutely continuous, $w(x)$ satisfy the inequality $w(x)\leq M$, and the entire orthonormal system be uniformly bounded* according to

$$|p_n(x)|\leqslant C, \qquad a\leqslant x\leqslant b \qquad (n=0, 1, 2, \ldots). \quad (9.30)$$

We then have

$$\lim_{n\to\infty} s_n(f;\, x_0)=f(x_0), \qquad a+\eta\leqslant x_0\leqslant b-\eta, \qquad \eta>0,$$

at each point of continuity of $f(x)$ within [a, b].

To prove the theorem we choose an arbitrary small $\epsilon > 0$ and a $\lambda > 0$ such that the variation of $f(x)$ on $|x_0, x_0 \pm \lambda|$ be less than ϵ:

$$\int_{x_0}^{x_0+\lambda}|df(x)|<\varepsilon, \quad \int_{x_0-\lambda}^{x_0}|df(x)|<\varepsilon, \qquad (9.31)$$

$$-1<a<x_0-2\lambda<x_0+2\lambda<b<1.$$

* A sufficient condition for this is that on the interval $[a-\epsilon, b+\epsilon]$, $\epsilon > 0$, one of the conditions V-VII of Table III be fulfilled.

That this is always possible follows from the fact that the function $F(x) = f(x) - f(x_0)$ is of bounded variation, continuous at x_0 and $F(x_0) = 0$.*

Using the Christoffel-Darboux formula

$$k_n(x, y) = \sum_{k=0}^{n} p_k(x) p_k(y) = \frac{\beta_n}{\beta_{n+1}} \cdot \frac{p_{n+1}(x) p_n(y) - p_n(x) p_{n+1}(y)}{x - y}, \tag{9.32}$$

we may write

$$s_n(f; x_0) - f(x_0) = \int_{-1}^{1} \{f(x) - f(x_0)\} k_n(x, x_0) \, d\psi(x). \tag{9.33}$$

We now choose an $n > 1/\lambda$ and introduce the points

$$-1 < x_0 - \lambda < x_0 - \frac{1}{n} < x_0 + \frac{1}{n} < x_0 + \lambda < 1,$$

in terms of which we break up the integral into the five integrals i_1, . . . , i_5, each of which we evaluate separately.

First, by assumption we have

$$|i_3| = \left| \int_{x_0 - \frac{1}{n}}^{x_0 + \frac{1}{n}} \right| \leqslant (n+1) C^2 M \cdot \frac{2}{n} \cdot \max_{|x - x_0| \leqslant \frac{1}{n}} |f(x) - f(x_0)|, \tag{9.34}$$

so that $i_3 = o(1)$.

In evaluating the remaining integrals we shall make use of the function

$$f_1(x) = \frac{f(x) - f(x_0)}{x - x_0}.$$

From (9.32) and (9.33) we obtain

$$i_1 = \int_{-1}^{x - \lambda} \{f(x) - f(x_0)\} k_n(x, x_0) \, d\psi(x) = \frac{\beta_n}{\beta_{n+1}} \cdot \{p_n(x_0) d_{n+1} - p_{n+1}(x_0) d_n\},$$

---

* See, for instance, A. Zygmund [1], Section 26.

where we have written

$$d_k = \int_{-1}^{x_0-\lambda} f_1(x)\, p_k(x)\, d\psi(x), \quad k=n, \ n+1 \ (n=0, 1, 2, \ldots);$$

analogous results are obtained for i_2, i_4, i_5. Now according to (9.9)

$$\frac{\beta_n}{\beta_{n+1}} = \frac{1}{2} \cdot \frac{a_{2n}}{a_{2n+2}} \sqrt{\frac{1-a_{2n-1}}{1-a_{2n+1}}} =$$

$$= \frac{1}{2} \sqrt{(1-a_{2n-1})(1-a_{2n}^2)(1+a_{2n+1})} < 1,$$

so that in view of (9.30) it is sufficient to show that $\lim\limits_{n\to\infty} d_n = 0$.

Consider the function

$$f_2(x) = \begin{cases} f_1(x), & x \in [-1, x_0-\lambda], \\ 0, & x \overline{\in} [-1, x_0-\lambda]; \end{cases} \qquad d_k = \int_{-1}^{1} f_2(x)\, p_k(x)\, d\psi(x).$$

Since $|x - x_0| \geq \lambda$ for $1 \leq x \leq x_0 - \lambda$, it follows that

$$|f_2(x)| = |f_1(x)| = \left|\frac{f(x)-f(x_0)}{x-x_0}\right| \leqslant \frac{|f(x)|+|f(x_0)|}{\lambda}$$

so that $f_2(x) \in L_2^\psi$. The Bessel's inequality implies that $\lim\limits_{n\to\infty} d_n = 0$, so that $i_1 = o(1)$; an analogous result is obtained for i_5. Further, we have

$$i_2 = \int_{x_0-\lambda}^{x+\frac{1}{n}} = \frac{\beta_n}{\beta_{n+1}} \{p_n(x_0)\, b_{n+1} - p_{n+1}(x_0)\, b_n\}, \tag{9.35}$$

where we have written

$$b_k = \int_{x_0-\lambda}^{x_0-\frac{1}{n}} f_1(x)\, p_k(x)\, d\psi(x) =$$

$$= \int_{x_0-\lambda}^{x_0-\frac{1}{n}} \frac{f(x)-f(x_0)}{x-x_0} p_k(x)\, w(x)\, dx.$$

Since $1/(x_0 - x)$ is a monotonically increasing function on

$[x_0-\lambda,\ x_0-1/n]$, the second mean value theorem implies that

$$b_n = -n \int_{a'_n}^{x_0-\frac{1}{n}} \{f(x)-f(x_0)\}\, p_n(x)\, w(x)\, dx,$$

$$x_0-\lambda < a'_n < x_0-\frac{1}{n}.$$

Now we introduce the function

$$\varphi(x)=\begin{cases} f(x)-f(x_0), & x\in\left[a'_n,\ x_0-\frac{1}{n}\right],\\ 0, & x\bar{\in}\left[a'_n,\ x_0-\frac{1}{n}\right],\end{cases}$$

whose Fourier-Chebyshev coefficients are $-b_n/n$; then the orthogonality of the $\{p_n(x)\}$ means that

$$-\frac{b_n}{n}=\int_{-1}^{1}\varphi(x)\,p_n(x)\,d\psi(x)= \int_{-1}^{1}\{\varphi(x)-G_{n-1}(x)\}\,p_n(x)\,d\psi(x), \tag{9.36}$$

from which we obtain

$$\frac{|b_n|}{n}\leqslant \int_{x_0-2\lambda}^{x_0+2\lambda} |\varphi(x)-G_{n-1}(x)|\,|p(x)|\,w(x)\,dx + \int_{e}|G_{n-1}(x)|\,|p_n(x)|\,d\psi(x)=I_1+I_2, \tag{9.37}$$

where $e=[-1,\ x_0-2\lambda]+[x_0+2\lambda,\ 1]$.

We shall take the polynomial $G_{n-1}(\cos\theta)$ to be the Jackson sum (3.1) of order $2\nu-2\leq n-1$ associated with the function $\varphi(\cos\theta)$,

$0 \leq \theta \leq 2\pi$ (in our case this sum is a polynomial of degree $2\nu - 2$ in $\cos\theta$, i.e., of degree no higher than $n-1$ in $\underline{x}$). We introduce the notation

$$\left.\begin{array}{ll} \cos\alpha = x_0 + 2\lambda, & \cos\beta = x_0 - 2\lambda, \\ \cos\alpha' = x_0, & \cos\beta' = x_0 - \lambda, \\ \multicolumn{2}{c}{0 < \alpha < \alpha' < \beta' < \beta < \pi.} \end{array}\right\} \tag{9.38}$$

Since $\varphi(x) \equiv 0$ for $x \overline{\in} [x_0 - \lambda, x_0]$, it follows that $\varphi(\cos\theta) \equiv 0$ for $\beta' \leq \theta \leq 2\pi - \beta'$ and $2\pi - \alpha' \leq \theta \leq \alpha'$. Then, as a consequence of Lemma 5.3, we have $G_{n-1}(\cos\theta) = O\left(\frac{1}{n^3}\right)$ in these intervals, or

$$G_{n-1}(x) = G_{n-1}(x) - \varphi(x) = O\left(\frac{1}{n^3}\right), \qquad x \in \mathrm{e}.$$

Then for I_2 we have

$$I_2 = \int_{\mathrm{e}} G_{n-1}(x)\, p_n(x) \,|\, d\psi(x) = O\left(\frac{1}{n^3}\right) \cdot \|p_n(x)\|_2^{\psi} = O\left(\frac{1}{n^3}\right).$$

Finally, let us obtain an estimate for I_1. We have

$$I_1 \leqslant MC \int_{x_0 - 2\lambda}^{x_0 + 2\lambda} |\, \varphi(x) - G_{n-1}(x)\,|\, dx \leqslant$$

$$\leqslant C' \frac{1}{2\pi} \int_0^{2\pi} \varphi(\cos\theta) - G_{n-1}(\cos\theta)\,|\, d\tau(\theta),$$

where we have written

$$\tau(\theta) = \begin{cases} \text{const}, & \theta \overline{\in} \mathrm{e}', \\ \theta, & \theta \in \mathrm{e}', \end{cases} \quad \mathrm{e}' = [\alpha, \beta] + [2\pi - \beta,\ 2\pi - \alpha]. \tag{9.39}$$

We now apply Lemma 3.1 with $r = 1$; then (3.6) gives

$$I_1 \leqslant C_1 \omega_1^{\tau}\left[\frac{1}{\nu};\ \varphi(\cos\theta)\right] \leqslant$$

$$\leqslant C_2 \sup_{|h| \leqslant \frac{1}{\nu}} \frac{1}{2\pi}\int_0^{2\pi} |\varphi[\cos(\theta+h)] - \varphi(\cos\theta)|\, d\tau(\theta) =$$

$$= \frac{C_2}{\pi} \sup_{|h'| \leqslant \frac{1}{\nu}} \int_{x_0-2\lambda}^{x_0+2\lambda} |\varphi(x+h') - \varphi(x)| \frac{dx}{\sqrt{1-x^2}} \leqslant$$

$$\leqslant C_3 \sup_{|h'| \leqslant \frac{1}{\nu}} \int_{x_0-2\lambda}^{x_0+2\lambda} |\varphi(x+h') - \varphi(x)|\, dx. \qquad (9.40)$$

Reproducing the arguments of Hardy and Littlewood [1], we arrive at

$$\int_{x_0-2\lambda}^{x_0+2\lambda} |\varphi(x+h') - \varphi(x)|\, dx = \int_{x_0-2\lambda}^{x_0+2\lambda} dx \left| \int_x^{x+h} d\varphi(t) \right| \leqslant$$

$$\leqslant \int_{x_0-2\lambda}^{x_0+2\lambda} dx \int_x^{x+h'} |d\varphi(t)| \leqslant \int_{x_0-2\lambda}^{x_0+2\lambda+h'} |d\varphi(t)| \int_{t-h'}^{t} dx =$$

$$= h' \int_{x_0-2\lambda}^{x_0+2\lambda+h'} |d\varphi(t)|, \qquad (9.41)$$

whence, using (9.31), we obtain

$$I_1 \leqslant \frac{C_3}{\nu} \int_{x_0-2\lambda}^{x_0+2\lambda+\frac{1}{\nu}} |d\varphi(t)| = \frac{C_3}{\nu} \int_{x_0-\lambda}^{x_0} |d\varphi(t)| < \frac{C_3}{\nu}\varepsilon, \qquad (9.42)$$

since $\varphi(x) \equiv 0$ outside of $[a_n', x_0 - 1/n]$. From (9.40), (9.41), (9.37), and (9.34) we now have

$$\lim_{n\to\infty} b_n = 0, \quad i_2 = o(1),$$

since ϵ is an arbitrary small quantity; in just the same way $i_4 = o(1)$. We thus arrive at Table IX. It may be remarked that under conditions XI-XIII we have quasi-uniform convergence, and under conditions XIV-XVI we have convergence at every internal point over [a, b].

9.7. From the conditions of Table IX we obtain the *localization principle*, i.e., the necessary conditions for two functions $f_1(x)$ and $f_2(x)$ of a given class, coinciding on [a, b], to satisfy in this interval the relation

$$\lim_{n\to\infty} \{s_n(f_1;\ x) - s_n(f_2;\ x)\} = 0. \tag{9.43}$$

To obtain this principle, obviously, one must find the conditions under which $f(x) \equiv 0$, $a \le x \le b$ implies $\lim_{n\to\infty} s_n(f;\ x) = 0$ in [a, b]. If $f(x) \equiv$ $\equiv 0$ on [a, b], we may consider any one of the conditions in the last column of Table IX to be fulfilled. We therefore arrive at the following *localization theorem*:

Theorem 9.11. If $f(x)$ is summable on [-1, +1] and satisfies the conditions of Table IX on this interval,* then with given conditions on $\psi(x)$ the convergence of the Fourier-Chebyshev expansion for $f(x)$ on $[a, b] \subset [-1, +1]$ depends exclusively on its behavior on this interval.

We may recall the conditions for the localization theorem as given by Freud [2] and Jackson [3], who assumed that $\psi(x)$ is absolutely continuous throughout [-1, +1].

Freud gives two conditions, each of which is sufficient: 1) $w(x) \le$ $\le M$ in the interior of [-1, +1], the entire orthogonal set is uniformly bounded, $w(x) f(x) \in L_1$ on [-1, +1], and at the ends of the interval $w(x) f^2(x) \in L_2$; 2) $|p_n(x)| \le K(x)$, $(n = 0, 1, \ldots)$ throughout [-1, +1], where $w(x) K(x) \in L_1$ and $w(x) K(x) f(x) \in L_1$ throughout [-1, +1].

Jackson gives the following condition: $|p_n(x)| \leqslant A$, $x \in E \subset [-1, +1]$, $w(x) f(x) \in L_1$ on [-1, +1], and $w(x) f^2(x)$ is summable on CE. These conditions involve the uniform boundedness of the orthonormal set, but the conditions sufficient for this are not given.

* The continuity of $f(x)$ on [a, b] and the conditions in the last column of Table IX may be dropped.

9.8. In conclusion we turn to the equiconvergence theorem which compares the convergence of the Fourier-Chebyshev expansion (9.28) of a given function with the expansion in Chebyshev polynomials $\{T_k(x)\}$ of the same function:

$$s_n^{(0)}(f;\, x) = \sum_{k=0}^{n} \gamma_k T_k(x), \quad \gamma_k = \int_{-1}^{1} f(x)\, T_k(x) \frac{dx}{\sqrt{1-x^2}}, \tag{9.44}$$

$$T_k(x) = \sqrt{\frac{2}{\pi}} \cos k\theta \quad (k = 1, 2, \ldots), \quad x = \cos\theta, \qquad T_0 = \frac{1}{\sqrt{\pi}}, \tag{9.45}$$

which is the same as the expansion of $f(\cos\theta)$ in a Fourier cosine series.

Theorem 9.12. Let $f(\cos\theta)$ be in both L_1 and L_2^σ, and assume that on an internal interval $[a, b]$ we have $|f(x)| \leq M_0$; let the integral of (9.5) exist, and assume that on $[a, b]$ the function $\psi(x)$ is absolutely continuous while $w(x) \geq m > 0$ is continuous and such that

$$\omega(\delta;\, w) \leqslant C\left(\ln\frac{1}{\delta}\right)^{-\gamma}, \quad \gamma > 2. \tag{9.46}$$

Then on $a + \eta \leq x_0 \leq b - \eta$, $\eta > 0$, we obtain*

$$|s_n(f;\, x_0) - s_n^{(0)}(f;\, x_0)| \leqslant \gamma_n + \ln n\,(C_1|\varepsilon_{2n}| + C_2|\varepsilon_{2n+2}|), \tag{9.47}$$

where γ_n tends to zero as $n \to \infty$.

We again consider the function defined by $f_0(x) \equiv f(x)$ on the set of points of $[-1, +1]$ on which $\psi'(x) > 0$ exists, and $f_0(x) \equiv 0$ outside this set; then

$$s_n(f_0;\, x_0) = \int_{-1}^{1} f_0(x)\, k_n(x, x_0)\, d\psi(x) = \int_{-1}^{1} f_0(x)\, k_n(x, x_0)\, w(x)\, dx, \tag{9.48}$$

* We are using the notation of (7.50) and (7.50'). As usual, C, C_1, C_2, . . . are constants independent of both n and x_0.

and in this Lebesgue integral we can replace $f_0(x)$ by the equivalent function $f(x)$.

We thus have

$$s_n(f;\, x_0) - s_n^{(0)}(f;\, x_0) = \int_{-1}^{1} f(x)\,\Delta_n(x,\, x_0)\frac{dx}{\sqrt{1-x^2}}, \quad (9.49)$$

where we have written [recalling (9.32)]

$$\Delta_n(x,\, x_0) = \frac{\beta_n}{\beta_{n+1}} \cdot \frac{p_{n+1}(x)\,p_n(x_0) - p_n(x)\,p_{n+1}(x_0)}{x - x_0} \cdot p(\theta) -$$

$$-\frac{1}{2\pi}\left\{\frac{\sin\,(2n+1)\dfrac{\theta+\theta_0}{2}}{\sin\dfrac{\theta+\theta_0}{2}} + \frac{\sin\,(2n+1)\dfrac{\theta-\theta_0}{2}}{\sin\dfrac{\theta-\theta_0}{2}}\right\}, \quad (9.50)$$

$$x = \cos\theta, \quad x_0 = \cos\theta_0.$$

First, using (9.9) and (8.6) we have

$$\frac{\beta_n}{\beta_{n+1}} = \frac{1}{2}\cdot\frac{\alpha_{2n}}{\alpha_{2n+2}}\sqrt{\frac{1-a_{2n-1}}{1+a_{2n+1}}} =$$

$$= \frac{1}{2}\cdot\sqrt{(1-a_{2n-1})(1-a_{2n}^2)(1+a_{2n+1})},$$

which, with (8.15), gives

$$\frac{\beta_n}{\beta_{n+1}} = \frac{1}{2} + o(\delta_{2n-1}) = \frac{1}{2} + o(1). \quad (9.51)$$

further, according to (9.17), we have

$$p_{n+1}(\cos\theta)\,p_n(\cos\theta_0) - p_n(\cos\theta)\,p_{n+1}(\cos\theta_0) =$$

$$= \frac{2}{\pi\sqrt{p(\theta)\,p(\theta_0)}}\{\cos[(n+1)\,\theta - \gamma(\theta)]\cdot\cos[n\theta_0 - \gamma(\theta_0)] -$$

$$-\cos[n\theta - \gamma(\theta)]\cos[(n+1)\,\theta_0 - \gamma(\theta_0)]\} + \lambda_n(x,\, x_0),$$

where, in view of Theorem 9.4,

$$|\lambda_n(x,\, x_0)| \leqslant |\eta_n(\theta)\,\eta_{n+1}(\theta_0)| + |\eta_{n+1}(\theta)\,\eta_n(\theta_0)| +$$

$$+\sqrt{\frac{2}{\pi}}\left\{\frac{|\eta_n(\theta)| + |\eta_{n+1}(\theta)|}{\sqrt{p(\theta_0)}} + \frac{|\eta_n(\theta_0)| + |\eta_{n+1}(\theta_0)|}{\sqrt{p(\theta)}}\right\} \leqslant$$

$$\leqslant C_1|\eta_n(\theta)| + C_2|\eta_{n+1}(\theta)| + \frac{C_3|\varepsilon_{2n}| + C_4|\varepsilon_{2n+2}|}{\sqrt{p(\theta)}}. \quad (9.52)$$

We transform the cosine product into a sum, and after some simple calculations arrive at

$$\Delta_n(x, x_0) = a_n(\theta, \theta_0) + a_n(\theta, -\theta_0) + c_n(\theta, \theta_0), \tag{9.53}$$

where we have written

$$a_n(\theta, \theta_0) = \frac{1}{2\pi}\left\{\sqrt{\frac{p(\theta)}{p(\theta_0)}} \cdot \frac{\sin\left[(2n+1)\frac{\theta-\theta_0}{2} - \gamma(\theta) + \gamma(\theta_0)\right]}{\sin\frac{\theta-\theta_0}{2}} - \right.$$

$$\left. - \frac{\sin(2n+1)\frac{\theta-\theta_0}{2}}{\sin\frac{\theta-\theta_0}{2}}\right\}, \quad |c_n(\theta, \theta_0)| \leqslant \frac{C\,|\lambda_n(x, x_0)|\,p(\theta)}{|\cos\theta - \cos\theta_0|}, \tag{9.54}$$

$$a < x_0 = \cos\theta_0 < b.$$

We have now to prove the validity of the limit relation

$$\lim_{n\to\infty}\int_0^{2\pi} f(\cos\theta)\, a_n(\theta, \pm\theta_0)\, d\theta = 0$$

for $\alpha + 2\epsilon \leq \theta_0 \leq \beta - 2\epsilon$, where $b = \cos\alpha$ and $a = \cos\beta$. Setting $z = e^{i\theta}$, $z_0 = e^{i\theta_0}$, it is easily shown that

$$2\pi a_n(\theta, \theta_0) = \frac{1}{\sin\frac{\theta-\theta_0}{2}}\, \mathfrak{I}\left\{e^{i\left(n+\frac{1}{2}\right)(\theta-\theta_0)}\left[\frac{\pi(z_0)}{\pi(z)} - 1\right]\right\} =$$

$$= -2\mathfrak{R}\left\{F(z)\, z^{n+1}\right\}, \quad F(z) = \frac{\pi(z_0) - \pi(z)}{\pi(z)\,(z - z_0)\, z_0^n}. \tag{9.55}$$

We now show that $f(\cos\theta)\, F(e^{i\theta}) \in L_1$. Indeed, according to (7.60) if $\alpha + \epsilon \leq \theta \leq \beta - \epsilon$, then

$$\int_{\alpha+\epsilon}^{\beta-\epsilon} |f(\cos\theta)|\,|F(e^{i\theta})|\, d\theta \leqslant$$

$$\leqslant C\int_{\alpha+\epsilon}^{\beta-\epsilon} \frac{d\theta}{|\theta-\theta_0|\left\{\ln\frac{1}{|\theta-\theta_0|}\right\}^{\gamma-1}} < \infty. \tag{9.56}$$

Further, if $\theta \in e$, where $e = [0, \pi] - [\alpha + \epsilon, \beta - \epsilon]$, then $|\theta - \theta_0| \geq \epsilon$ and

$$\int_e |f(\cos\theta)| \cdot |F(e^{i\theta})|\, d\theta \leqslant C_1 \int_e \left| \frac{f(\cos\theta)}{\pi(e^{i\theta})} \right| d\theta + C_2 \int_e |f(\cos\theta)|\, d\theta \leqslant$$

$$\leqslant C_3 \| f(\cos\theta) \|_2^\sigma + C_4 \| f(\cos\theta) \|_1 < \infty. \tag{9.57}$$

This proves the desired result, namely $f(\cos\theta)\, F(e^{i\theta}) \in L_1$. According to the Riemann-Lebesgue theorem we have

$$\lim_{n \to \infty} \int_0^\pi f(\cos\theta)\, F(e^{i\theta})\, e^{i(n+1)\theta}\, d\theta = 0,$$

and this, together with (9.55), leads simply to the desired limit relation

$$\lim_{n \to \infty} \int_0^{2\pi} f(\cos\theta) \{a_n(\theta, \theta_0) + a_n(\theta, -\theta_0)\}\, d\theta = 0, \qquad \alpha + 2\varepsilon \leqslant \theta_0 \leqslant \beta - 2\varepsilon. \tag{9.58}$$

It remains to prove the analogous assertion for

$$\lim_{n \to \infty} \int_0^{2\pi} f(\cos\theta)\, c_n(\theta, \theta_0)\, d\theta, \tag{9.59}$$

where, according to (9.54) and (9.55),

$$c_n(\theta, \theta_0) = \Delta_n(x, x_0) - a_n(\theta, \theta_0) - a_n(\theta, -\theta_0) =$$

$$= \left\{ p(\theta) \sum_{l=0}^{n} p_k(x)\, p_k(x_0) - \frac{1}{2\pi} \left[\frac{\sin(2n+1)\frac{\theta - \theta_0}{2}}{\sin\frac{\theta - \theta_0}{2}} + \right.\right.$$

$$\left.\left. + \frac{\sin(2n+1)\frac{\theta + \theta_0}{2}}{\sin\frac{\theta + \theta_0}{2}} \right] \right\} - a_n(\theta, \theta_0) - a_n(\theta, -\theta_0). \tag{9.60}$$

Let us break up $[-1, +1]$ into the three sets e_1, e_2, e_3, where

$$e_1 = \left[x_0 - \frac{1}{n^k},\ x_0 + \frac{1}{n^k} \right], \quad k > 1;$$

$$e_2 = \left[a + \eta,\ x_0 - \frac{1}{n^k} \right] + \left[x_0 + \frac{1}{n^k},\ b - \eta \right];$$

we will denote the corresponding sets of $[0, 2\pi]$ by E_1, E_2, E_3. It is evident from the fact that $x = \cos\theta$ that to every point $\underline{x}$ of $[-1, +1]$ correspond the two points θ and $2\pi - \theta$ of $[0, 2\pi]$.

Let us break up the integral of (9.59) into the three integrals over the sets E_1, E_2, E_3, and let us evaluate each separately.

Since on E_1 and E_2 the orthonormal set is uniformly bounded, the expression in curly brackets in (9.60) is $O(n)$; in addition, on these sets we have, according to (9.56) and (7.60)

$$|a_n(\theta, \theta_0)| \leqslant \frac{1}{\pi}\left|\frac{\pi(e^{i\theta}) - \pi(e^{i\theta_0})}{\pi(e^{i\theta})(e^{i\theta} - e^{i\theta})}\right| \leqslant \frac{C\sqrt{p(\theta)}}{|\theta - \theta_0|\left\{\ln\frac{1}{|\theta - \theta_0|}\right\}^{\gamma-1}}.$$

Therefore

$$|i_1| = \left|\int\limits_{E_1}\right| \leqslant \frac{C_1}{n^{k-1}} + \frac{C_2}{(\ln n)^{\gamma-2}}. \tag{9.61}$$

Proceeding, according to (9.54) and (9.52),

$$\begin{aligned} |i_2| = \left|\int\limits_{E_2}\right| &\leqslant C\int\limits_{E_2}\frac{p(\theta)\,|\lambda_n(x, x_0)|}{|\cos\theta - \cos\theta_0|}\,d\theta \leqslant \\ &\leqslant \ln n\,\{C_3'\,|\varepsilon_{2n}| + C_4'\,|\varepsilon_{2n+2}|\}, \end{aligned} \tag{9.62}$$

since on E_1 and E_2 we have $|\eta_n(\theta)| \leq C\,|\epsilon_{2n}|$. On E_3, so long as $a + 2\eta \leq x_0 \leq b - 2\eta$ we have $|x - x_0| \geq \eta$; and then from (9.52) we obtain

$$|i_3| = \left|\int\limits_{E_3}\right| \leqslant \frac{C}{\eta}\int\limits_{E_3}|f(\cos\theta)|\,p(\theta)\,|\lambda_n(x, x_0)|\,d\theta \leqslant$$

$$\leqslant \{C_5\,|\varepsilon_{2n}| + C_6\,|\varepsilon_{2n+2}|\}\cdot\int\limits_{E_3}\sqrt{p(\theta)}\cdot|f(\cos\theta)|\,d\theta +$$

$$+ C_7\int\limits_{E_3}p(\theta)\,|f(\cos\theta)|\,|\eta_n(\theta)|\,d\theta +$$

$$+ C_8\int\limits_{E_3}p(\theta)\,|f(\cos\theta)|\,|\eta_{n+1}(\theta)|\,d\theta.$$

In view of the fact that $f(\cos\theta) \in L_2^{\sigma}$

$$\frac{1}{2\pi}\int_{E_3} \sqrt{p(\theta)}\,|f(\cos\theta)|\,d\theta \leqslant \|f\|_2^{\sigma_0}\sqrt{c_0} < \infty.$$

Further, (7.69) and Theorem 9.4 lead to the inequality

$$\frac{1}{2\pi}\int_{E_3} p(\theta)\,|f(\cos\theta)\,\eta_k(\theta)|\,d\theta \leqslant \|f\|_2^{\sigma_0}\cdot\|\eta_k\|_2^{\sigma_0} \leqslant C_9\,\delta_{2k-1},$$

$$k = n,\quad n+1,$$

and hence

$$|i_3| \leqslant C_5\,|\varepsilon_{2n}| + C_6\,|\varepsilon_{2n+2}|. \tag{9.63}$$

The conditions under which (7.70) is fulfilled and which are therefore sufficient for the equiconvergence of expansions (9.28) and (9.44) on an internal interval $[a, b] \subset [-1, +1]$ are given in Table VIII, where one should replace $\sigma(\theta)$ by $\psi(x)$, the interval $[0, 2\pi]$ by $[-1, +1]$ the interval $[\alpha, \beta]$ by $[a, b]$, and $f(z)$ by $f(x) \in L_2^{\psi}$, $f(\cos\theta) \in L_1$.

Szegö ([1], Section 13.8) treats, instead of condition VII the following conditions: $\psi(x)$ is absolutely continuous, the trigonometric weight $p(\theta)$ satisfies condition I of Table IV (with $\gamma > 2$) throughout $[0, 2\pi]$ (i.e., the asymptotic formula (9.16) with $\lim_{n\to\infty} \varepsilon_n = 0$ holds throughout $[-1, +1]$), and $f(x)$ is measurable and bounded throughout $[-1, +1]$. Under these conditions uniform equiconvergence obtains in the interior of $[-1, +1]$. In proving Theorem 9.12 we have used Szegö's method, generalizing it appropriately.

Let us compare Theorems 9.10 and 9.12. In the first of these $f(x)$ was subjected to more restrictive requirements on $[a, b]$ than it was in the second, but $\psi(x)$ was subjected to much weaker conditions; even the existence of the integral of (9.5) is not required.

From Theorem 9.12 we obtain

<u>Theorem 9.13</u>. Let the function $f(\cos\theta) \in L_2^{\sigma}$ and $f(\cos\theta) \in L_1$, and assume that on an internal interval $[a, b]$ it is of bounded variation; let the integral of (9.5) exist and assume that on $[a, b]$ the function $\psi(x)$ is absolutely continuous, $w(x) \geq m > 0$ is continu-

ous with modulus of continuity given by (9.46), and (7.50) and (7.50′) are valid, together with (7.70).* Then at every internal point $a + \epsilon \leq x_0 \leq b - \epsilon$ we have

$$\lim_{n \to \infty} s_n(f;\ x_0) = \frac{f(x_0+0)+f(x_0-0)}{2}. \qquad (9.64)$$

Jackson ([3], Chapter II, Section 14) has investigated the special case of this theorem for Legendre polynomials (i.e., for $d\psi(x) \equiv dx$).

We note in conclusion that combining Theorems 9.11 and 9.12 gives the following theorem:

Theorem 9.4. Let $f_1(x)$ and $f_2(x)$ be two functions satisfying the conditions of Theorems 9.11 and 9.12, and let them be expanded in two sets of orthonormal polynomials $\{p_n^{(1)}(x)\}$, $\{p_n^{(2)}(x)\}$, satisfying the conditions of these theorems. Then

$$\lim_{n \to \infty} \{s_n^{(1)}(f_1;\ x) - s_n^{(2)}(f_2;\ x)\} = 0 \qquad (9.65)$$

in the interior of [a, b].

Indeed, according to Theorem 9.12

$$\lim_{n \to \infty} \{s_n^{(1)}(f_1;\ x) - s_n^{(0)}(f_1;\ x)\} =$$

$$= \lim \{s_n^{(2)}(f_2;\ x) - s_n^{(0)}(f_2;\ x)\} = 0,$$

and according to Theorem 9.11,

$$\lim_{n \to \infty} \{s_n^{(0)}(f_1;\ x) - s_n^{(0)}(f_2;\ x)\} = 0,$$

which gives the desired result (9.65).

* Conditions sufficient for this are given in Table VIII.

NOTATION IN THE TABLES

I. Orthonormal polynomials.

The polynomials $\{\varphi_n(z)\}$ are orthonormal on the circle $z = e^{i\theta}$ with respect to the measure $d\sigma(\theta)$, and $\sigma'(\theta) = p(\theta)$ is the weight.

$\pi(z)$ is a function analytic for $|z| < 1$, defined by

$$\pi(z) = \exp\left\{-\frac{1}{4\pi}\int^{2\pi} \frac{e^{i\theta}+z}{e^{i\theta}-z} \ln \sigma'(\theta)\, d\theta\right\}, \quad |z| < 1.$$

$\varphi_n^*(z)$ are polynomials defined by

$$\varphi_n^*(z) = z^n \bar{\varphi}_n\left(\frac{1}{z}\right).$$

The polynomials $\{p_n(x)\}$ are orthonormal on $[-1, +1]$ with respect to the measure $d\psi(x)$, and $\psi'(x) = w(x)$ is the weight, while $p(\theta) = w(\cos\theta)|\sin\theta|$ is the trigonometric weight.

II. Sets.

E is the set of points on which the derivative $\sigma'(\theta) > 0$ exists.

CE is the complement of E.

E_h is the set of points displaced with respect to CE through a distance h.

$\gamma_E(\theta)$ is the characteristic function of E.

$$\pi_0(\theta) = \pi(e^{i\theta})\gamma_E(\theta), \quad \frac{1}{p_0(\theta)} = \frac{1}{p(\theta)}\gamma_E(\theta) = |\pi_0(\theta)|^2,$$

$$f_0(\theta) = f(e^{i\theta})\gamma_E(\theta).$$

III. Function classes.

C is the class of continuous functions.

AC is the class of absolutely continuous functions.

V is the class functions of bounded variation.

L_p^σ is the class of functions Lebesgue-Stieltjes integrable with exponent p:

$$\|f\|_p^\sigma = \left\{ \frac{1}{2\pi} \int_0^{2\pi} |f(\theta)|^p \, d\sigma(\theta) \right\}^{\frac{1}{p}} < \infty.$$

L_p is the class of functions Lebesgue integrable with exponent p, i.e., with $d\sigma(\theta) = d\theta$.

A_h is the class of functions with the following properties: for every $N > 0$ there exists a number h such that if $p(\theta) > N$, then $|f(\theta + h)| < A$, where $|h| < h_0$, and A is independent of h.

L_p^ψ is the class of functions such that

$$\|f\| = \left\{ \int_{-1}^{1} |f(x)|^p \, d\psi(x) \right\}^{\frac{1}{p}} < \infty.$$

$\mathrm{Lip}(\alpha, p)$ is the class of functions such that $\omega_p(\delta, f) \leq C\delta^\alpha$, $0 < \alpha \leq 1$.

IV. Moduli of continuity.

$$\omega(\delta; f) = \sup_{|h| \leqslant \delta} |f(\theta + h) - f(\theta)|, \quad \theta, \theta + h \in [0, 2\pi];$$

$$\omega'(\delta; f) = \sup_{|h| \leqslant \delta} |f(\theta + h) - f(\theta), \quad \theta, 0 + h \in [\alpha, \beta];$$

$$\omega_p^\sigma(\delta; f) = \sup_{|h| \leqslant \delta} \|f(\theta + h) - f(\theta)\|_p^\sigma;$$

$$\omega_p(\delta; f) = \sup_{|h| \leqslant \delta} \|f(\theta + h) - f(\theta)\|_p;$$

$$\omega_p'(\delta; f) = \sup_{|h| \leqslant \delta < \varepsilon} \left\{ \frac{1}{2\pi} \int_{\alpha+}^{\beta - \varepsilon} |f(\theta + h) - f(\theta)|^p \, d\theta \right\}^{\frac{1}{p}};$$

$$I(\delta) = \sup_{|h| \leqslant \delta} \left\| \frac{p(\theta + h) - p(\theta)}{p(\theta)} \right\|_1;$$

$$\delta_n' = \omega_2^{\sigma_0}\left(\frac{1}{n}; \pi\right) \leqslant \sqrt{I\left(\frac{1}{n}\right)};$$

$$\delta_n = \min_k \left\| \pi_0(\theta) - \sum_{k=0}^{n} \alpha_k e^{ik\theta} \right\|_2^\sigma.$$

TABLE I

Estimates of $\delta'_n = \omega_2^{\sigma_0}\left(\frac{1}{n};\ \pi\right) \leqslant \sqrt{I\left(\frac{1}{n}\right)}$ for $d\sigma_0(\theta) = p(\theta)\,d\theta$

№	Conditions on $p(\theta)$ on $[0, 2\pi]$	Majorant for δ'_n
I	$0 < m \leqslant p(\theta) \leqslant M$	$C_1\omega_2\left(\frac{1}{n};\ p\right)$, or $C_2\sqrt{\omega_1\left(\frac{1}{n};\ p\right)}$
II	$0 < m \leqslant p(\theta)$	$C_1\omega_4\left(\frac{1}{n};\ \ln p\right) + C_2\omega_2\left(\frac{1}{n};\ \sqrt{p}\right)$ or $C_3\sqrt{\omega_1\left(\frac{1}{n};\ p\right)}$
III	$p(\theta) \in L_r,\ \frac{1}{p(\theta)} \in L_{r'},$ $\frac{1}{r} + \frac{1}{r'} = 1,\ r > 1$	$C_1\omega_4\left(\frac{1}{n};\ \ln p\right) + C_2\omega_{2r}\left(\frac{1}{n};\ \sqrt{p}\right)$, or $C_3\sqrt{\omega_r\left(\frac{1}{n};\ p\right)}$, or $C_4\sqrt{\omega_{r'}\left(\frac{1}{n};\frac{1}{p}\right)}$
IV	$p(\theta) \leqslant M,\ \frac{1}{p(\theta)} \in L_1$	$C_1\omega_4\left(\frac{1}{n};\ \ln p\right) + C_2\omega_2\left(\frac{1}{n};\ \frac{1}{\sqrt{p}}\right)$ or $C_3\sqrt{\omega_1\left(\frac{1}{n};\ \frac{1}{p}\right)}$
V	$\lim\limits_{\delta\to 0} I(\delta) = 0$	$C_1\sqrt{I\left(\frac{1}{n}\right)}$

TABLE II

Estimates for the Orthonormal Polynomials $\varphi_n(z)$ on the Entire Circumference $z=e^{i\theta}$, $0\leqslant\theta\leqslant 2\pi$

№	Conditions on $\sigma(\theta)$ on $[0, 2\pi]$	Estimates for $\lvert\varphi_n(e^{i\theta})\rvert$
I	$0<m\leqslant p(\theta)$	$o(\sqrt{n})$
	$\sigma(\theta)\in AC$, $I(\delta)\leqslant C\left(\ln\frac{1}{\delta}\right)^{-\gamma}$, $\gamma>1$	$C\sqrt{n}$ almost everywhere on $[0, 2\pi]$
III	$\sigma(\theta)\in AC$, $0<m\leqslant p(\theta)$	$C\sqrt{n}$
IV	$0<m\leqslant p(\theta)$; $\frac{1}{p_0(\theta)}\in C$, $\theta\in E_h$	$C_1+C_2\sqrt{n}\left\{\sqrt{\omega'\left(\frac{1}{n};\frac{1}{p_0}\right)}+\delta'_n\right\}$
V	$\sigma(\theta)\in AC$, $0<m\leqslant p(\theta)\leqslant M$	$C_1+C_2\sqrt{n}\left\{\omega_r\left(\frac{1}{n};p\right)\right\}^{\frac{r}{2}}$, $r=1$ or $r=2$
VI	$0<m\leqslant p(\theta)$; $\frac{1}{p_0(\theta)}\in L_1$ $\theta\in E_h$	$C+C_1\sqrt{n}\,\omega_4\left(\frac{1}{n};\ln p\right)+$ $+C_2\sqrt{n}\,\omega_2\left(\frac{1}{n};\sqrt{p}\right)+$ $+C_3\sqrt{n}\sqrt{\omega'\left(\frac{1}{n};\frac{1}{p_0}\right)}$ or $C+C_4\sqrt{n}\sqrt{\omega_1\left(\frac{1}{n};p\right)}+$ $+C_5\sqrt{n}\sqrt{\omega'\left(\frac{1}{n};\frac{1}{p_0}\right)}$
VII	$\sigma(\theta)\in AC$, $0<m\leqslant p(\theta)\leqslant M$, $p(\theta)\in \mathrm{Lip}\left(\frac{1}{2},2\right)$	C
VIII	$\sigma(\theta)\in AC$, $0<m\leqslant p(\theta)$, $p(\theta)\in \mathrm{Lip}(1,1)$ or $p(\theta)\in V$	C

TABLE II (continued)

№	Conditions on $\sigma(\theta)$ on $[0, 2\pi]$	Estimates for $\lvert\varphi_n(e^{i\theta})\rvert$
IX	$\sigma(\theta) \in AC,\ 0 < m \leqslant p(\theta),$ $p(\theta) \in C,\quad p(\theta) \in \mathrm{Lip}\,1$	C
X	$\sigma(\theta) \in AC,\ 0 < m \leqslant p(\theta),$ $p(\theta) \in C$ $\omega(\delta;\ p) \leqslant A\left(\ln\frac{1}{\delta}\right)^{-\gamma},$ $\gamma > 1$	C
XI	$\frac{1}{p(\theta)} \in L_{r'},\quad r' > 0$	$o\left(n^{\frac{1}{2}+\frac{1}{2r'}}\right)$
XII	$\sigma(\theta) \in AC,\ p(\theta) \in L_r,$ $\frac{1}{p(\theta)} \in L_{r'},\ \frac{1}{r}+\frac{1}{r'}=1,$ $r > 1$	$C_1 + C_2 n^{1-\frac{1}{2r}}\sqrt{\omega_r\left(\frac{1}{n};\ p\right)}$ or $C_1 + C_3 n^{1-\frac{1}{2r}}\sqrt{\omega_{r'}\left(\frac{1}{n};\frac{1}{p}\right)}$
XIII	$\sigma(\theta) \in AC,\ p(\theta) \leqslant M,$ $\frac{1}{p(\theta)} \in L_1$	$C_1 + C_2 n\sqrt{\omega_1\left(\frac{1}{n};\ \frac{1}{p}\right)}$
XIV	$\ln p(\theta) \in L_1$	$\alpha e^{\gamma\sqrt{n}}$ $\alpha = \exp\left\{-\frac{1}{4\pi}\int_0^{2\pi}\ln p(\theta)\,d\theta\right\},$ $\gamma = \sqrt{\ln(c_0\alpha^2)},\ c_0 = \frac{1}{2\pi}\int_0^{2\pi} d\sigma(\theta)$

TABLE III

Local Estimates for the Orthonormal Polynomials $[e^{i\alpha}, e^{i\beta}]$ in the Interior of an Arc $[e^{i\alpha}, e^{i\beta}]$

In all cases $\sigma(\theta)$ is absolutely continuous on $[\alpha, \beta]$, and $p(\theta)$ is bounded from below on the same interval: $p(\theta) \geq m > 0$.

№	Conditions on $\sigma(\theta)$		Estimate for $\lvert\varphi_n(e^{i\theta})\rvert$, $\alpha+\varepsilon<\theta<\beta-\varepsilon$, $\varepsilon>0$
	on the interval $[0, 2\pi]$	on the interval $[\alpha, \beta]$	
I	$\sigma(\theta) \in AC$, $0 < m \leqslant p(\theta)$	$p(\theta) < M$	$o(\sqrt{n})$
II	$\sigma(\theta) \in AC$, $p(\theta) = p_1(\theta)\, p_2(\theta)$ $p_1(\theta) = \prod_{k=1}^{l} \lvert e^{i\theta} - e^{i\theta_k} \rvert^{\alpha_k}$, $\alpha_k > 0$, even integer; $0 < m_2 \leqslant p_2(\theta) \leqslant M_2$		$C\sqrt{n}$
III			$C\sqrt{n}$
IV	$\ln p(\theta) \in L_1$		$O(\sqrt{n} \cdot \delta_n) = o(\sqrt{n})$
V	$\ln p(\theta) \in L_1$	$p(\theta) \in C$; $\omega(\delta; p) \leqslant C_1 \sqrt{\delta}\left(\ln \frac{1}{\delta}\right)^{-\gamma}$ $\gamma > 1$	C
VI	$\frac{1}{p(\theta)} \in L_1$	$p(\theta) \in V$	C
VII	$\frac{1}{p(\theta)} \in L_1$	$p(\theta) \in C$; $\omega(\delta; p) \leqslant C_1\left(\ln \frac{1}{\delta}\right)^{-\gamma}$, $\gamma > 1$	C
VIII	$\frac{1}{p(\theta)} \in L_1$	$p(\theta) \leqslant M$ for $\theta \in [\alpha, \alpha+2\varepsilon]$, $[\beta-2\varepsilon, \beta]$	$C_1 + C_2\sqrt{n\omega_1'\left(\frac{1}{n}; p\right)}$
IX	$\frac{1}{p(\theta)} \in L_1$	$p(\theta) \leqslant M$	$C_1 + C_2\sqrt{n} \times \left\{\omega_r'\left(\frac{1}{n}; p\right)\right\}^{\frac{r}{2}}$, $r=1$ or $r=2$

TABLE IV

The Limit Relation $\varphi_n^*(e^{i\theta}) - \pi(e^{i\theta}) = \varepsilon_n = o(1)$ on the Entire Circumference

In all cases $\sigma(\theta)$ is absolutely continuous, and $p(\theta)$ is bounded from below and from above throughout $[0, 2\pi]$.

№	Conditions on $p(\theta)$ on $[0, 2\pi]$	Estimate for $\lvert\epsilon_n\rvert$
I	$p(\theta) \in C,\ \omega(\delta; p) \leqslant C\left(\ln\frac{1}{\delta}\right)^{-\gamma},\ \gamma > 1$	$C_1(\ln n)^{1-\gamma}$
II	$\omega_2(\delta; p) = o(\sqrt{\delta})$	$C_1\lvert\pi(e^{i\theta}) - \pi(re^{i\theta})\rvert + C_2\left\{n\omega_2^2\left(\frac{1}{n}; p\right)\right\}^{\frac{1}{3}}$, $r = 1 - \left\{\frac{1}{n}\,\omega_2\left(\frac{1}{n}; p\right)\right\}^{\frac{2}{3}}$
III	$\int_0^a x^{-\frac{3}{2}}\omega_2(x; p)\,dx < \infty$	$C_1\int_0^{\frac{1}{n}} x^{-\frac{3}{2}}\omega_2(x; p)\,dx$
IV	$\pi(z) \in C,\ \pi(z) \neq 0,\ \lvert z\rvert \leqslant 1;\ \pi(z) \in AC,\ \lvert z\rvert = 1$	

TABLE V

The Local Limit Relation in the Interior of the Arc $[e^{i\alpha}, e^{i\beta}]$

$$\varphi_n^*(e^{i\theta}) - \pi(e^{i\theta}) = \varepsilon_n = o(1),\ \alpha + \varepsilon \leqslant \theta \leqslant \beta - \varepsilon$$

On $[\alpha, \beta]$ in all cases $\sigma(\theta)$ is absolutely continuous, and $p(\theta) \geq m > 0$ is continuous.

№	Conditions on $\sigma(\theta)$		Estimate for $\lvert\epsilon_n\rvert$
	on the interval $[0, 2\pi]$	on the interval $[\alpha, \beta]$	
I	$\ln p(\theta) \in L_1$	$\omega(\delta; p) \leqslant C\sqrt{\delta}\left(\ln\frac{1}{\delta}\right)^{-\gamma},\ \gamma > 1$	

TABLE V (continued)

№	Conditions on $\sigma(\theta)$ on the interval $[0, 2\pi]$	Conditions on $\sigma(\theta)$ on the interval $[\alpha, \beta]$	Estimate for $\|\epsilon_n\|$
II	$\ln p(\theta) \in L_1$	$\omega(\delta; p'') \leqslant \leqslant C\left(\ln\frac{1}{\delta}\right)^{-\gamma}$, $\gamma > 1$	
III	$p(\theta) = p_1(\theta)\, p_2(\theta)$ $p_1(\theta) = = \prod_{k=1}^{s} \|e^{i\theta} - e^{i\theta_k}\|^{\alpha_k}$, $\alpha_k > 0$, $0 < m_2 \leqslant \leqslant p_2(\theta) \leqslant M_2$	$\frac{1}{(\theta-\theta_0)^2}\|p(\theta) - - p(\theta_0) - - p'(\theta_0)(\theta-\theta_0)\| \leqslant C$	
IV	$p(\theta) \leqslant M$, $\frac{1}{p(\theta)} \in L_2$ $\frac{1}{p_0(\theta)} \leqslant M$, $\theta \in E_h$	$\omega(\delta; p) \leqslant C\left(\ln\frac{1}{\delta}\right)^{-\gamma}$, $\gamma > 1$	$C_1\delta_{n-1} + + C_2\omega_2\left(\frac{1}{n}; \frac{1}{p}\right) + + C_3(\ln n)^{1-\gamma}$
V	$p(\theta) \in L_r$, $\frac{1}{p(\theta)} \in L_{r'}$ $\frac{1}{r} + \frac{1}{r'} = 1$, $r > 1$, $\frac{1}{p_0(\theta)} \leqslant M_1$, $\theta \in E_h$	$\omega(\delta; p) \leqslant C\left(\ln\frac{1}{\delta}\right)^{-\gamma}$, $\gamma > 2$	$C_1\delta_n + + C_2\omega_{2r}\left(\frac{1}{n}; \sqrt{p}\right) + + C_3\omega_4\left(\frac{1}{n}; \ln p\right) + + C_4(\ln n)^{2-\gamma}$ or $C_1\delta_n + + C_5\sqrt{\omega_r\left(\frac{1}{n}; p\right)} + + C_4(\ln n)^{2-\gamma}$

TABLE V (continued)

№	Conditions on $\sigma(\theta)$		Estimate for $\mid \epsilon_n \mid$
	on the interval $[0, 2\pi]$	on the interval $[\alpha, \beta]$	
VI	$0 < m \leqslant p(\theta)$	$\omega(\delta; p) \leqslant C\left(\ln \frac{1}{\delta}\right)^{-\gamma}$, $\gamma > 2$	$C_1\delta_n + C_2\omega_4\left(\frac{1}{n}; \ln p\right) + C_3\omega_2\left(\frac{1}{n}; \sqrt{p}\right) + C_4(\ln n)^{2-\gamma}$ or $C_1\delta_n + C_5\sqrt{\omega_1\left(\frac{1}{n}; p\right)} + C_4(\ln n)^{2-\gamma}$
VII	$p(\theta) \leqslant M$, $\frac{1}{p(\theta)} \in L_1$, $\frac{1}{p_0(\theta)} \leqslant M_1, \theta \in E_h$	$\omega(\delta; p) \leqslant C\left(\ln \frac{1}{\delta}\right)^{-\gamma}$, $\gamma > 2$	$C_1\delta_n + C_2\omega_4\left(\frac{1}{n}; \ln p\right) + C_3\omega_2\left(\frac{1}{n}; \frac{1}{\sqrt{p}}\right) + C_4(\ln n)^{2-\gamma}$ or $C_1\delta_n + C_5\sqrt{\omega_1\left(\frac{1}{n}; \frac{1}{p}\right)} + C_4(\ln n)^{2-\gamma}$
VIII	$\lim\limits_{\delta \to 0} I(\delta) = 0$, $\frac{1}{p_0(\theta)} \leqslant M_1, \theta \in E_h$	$\omega(\delta; p) \leqslant C\left(\ln \frac{1}{\delta}\right)^{-\gamma}$, $\gamma > 2$	$C_1\delta_n + C_2\sqrt{I\left(\frac{1}{n}\right)} + C_3(\ln n)^{2-\gamma}$
IX	$0 < m \leqslant p(\theta) \leqslant M$, $\frac{1}{p_0(\theta)} \leqslant M_1, \theta \in E_h$	$\omega(\delta; p) \leqslant C\left(\ln \frac{1}{\delta}\right)^{-\gamma}$, $\gamma > 2$	$C_1\delta_n + C_2(\ln n)^{2-\gamma} + C_3\left\{\omega_r\left(\frac{1}{n}; p\right)\right\}^{\frac{r}{2}}$, $r = 1$ or $r = 2$
X	$0 < m \leqslant p(\theta) \leqslant M$, $p(\theta) \in \mathrm{Lip}\left(\frac{1}{2}, 2\right)$	$\omega(\delta; p) \leqslant C\left(\ln \frac{1}{\delta}\right)^{-\gamma}$, $\gamma > 1$	$C_1\delta_n + C_2(\ln n)^{1-\gamma}$

TABLE VI

Convergence of the Fourier-Chebyshev Expansion on $|z|=1$ for a Function $f(z)$ Continuous for $|z|\leqslant 1$

№	Conditions on the interval $[0, 2\pi]$	
	on $\sigma(\theta)$	on the boundary function $f(e^{i\theta})$
I	$0<m<p(\theta)$	$\omega(\delta; f)=o(\sqrt{\delta})$
II	$\sigma(\theta)\in AC$ $0<m\leqslant p(\theta)\leqslant M,$ $p(\theta)\in \text{Lip}\left(\frac{1}{r}; r\right)$ $r=1$ or $r=2$	$\omega(\delta; f)=o\left(\frac{1}{\ln\frac{1}{\delta}}\right)$
III	$\sigma(\theta)\in AC$ $0<m\leqslant p(\theta)\leqslant M$	$\omega(\delta; f)\,\omega_{r}^{r}(\delta; p)=o\left(\frac{\delta}{\ln\frac{1}{\delta}}\right),$ $r=1$ or $r=2$
IV	$\sigma(\theta)\in AC,\ p(\theta)\in L_{r},$ $\frac{1}{p(\theta)}\in L_{r'}\ \frac{1}{r}+\frac{1}{r'}=1,$ $r>1$	$\omega(\delta; f)\,\omega_{r}(\delta; p)=o\left(\frac{\delta^{2-\frac{1}{r}}}{\ln\frac{1}{\delta}}\right)$
V	$\sigma(\theta)\in AC,\ p(\theta)\in L_{r}$ $\frac{1}{p(\theta)}\in L_{r'}\ \frac{1}{r}+\frac{1}{r'}=1,$ $1<r<2$ $p(\theta)\in \text{Lip}\left(\frac{1}{r}, r\right)$	$\omega(\delta; f)=o\left(\frac{\delta^{\frac{2}{r'}}}{\ln\frac{1}{\delta}}\right)$

TABLE VII

Convergence of the Fourier–Chebyshev Expansion on an Arc $[e^{i\alpha}, e^{i\beta}]$ for a Function $f(z)$ of Class H_1

In all cases the boundary function $f(e^{i\theta})$ is continuous on $[e^{i\alpha}, e^{i\beta}]$; on $[\alpha, \beta]$ the function $\sigma(\theta)$ is absolutely continuous and $p(\theta)$ is bounded from below: $p(\theta) \geq m > 0$.

№	Conditions on the interval $[0, 2\pi]$		Conditions on the interval $[\alpha, \beta]$	
	on $\sigma(\theta)$	on $f(e^{i\theta})$	on $\sigma(\theta)$	on $f(e^{i\theta})$
I	$\sigma(\theta) \in AC$ $p(\theta) \leqslant M$	$f \in L_2$ $\sum_{n=1}^{\infty} \frac{\omega_2\left(\frac{1}{n}; f\right)}{\sqrt{n}} < \infty$		
II	$\sigma(\theta) \in AC$ $0 < m \leqslant p(\theta) \leqslant M$ $p(\theta) \in \mathrm{Lip}\left(\frac{1}{2}, 2\right)$			$\omega(\delta; f) = o\left(\frac{1}{\ln \frac{1}{\delta}}\right)$
III	$\ln p(\theta) \in L_1$	$f \in L_2,\ f \in A_h$ $f_0(\theta + h) \in L_2^{\sigma}$ $\|h\| \leqslant h_0$	$p(\theta) \in C$ $\omega(\delta; p) \leqslant$ $\leqslant C_1 \sqrt{\delta} \left(\ln \frac{1}{\delta}\right)^{-\gamma},$ $\gamma > 1$	$\omega(\delta; f) = o\left(\frac{1}{\ln \frac{1}{\delta}}\right)$
IV	$\frac{1}{p(\theta)} \in L_1$	$f \in L_2,\ f \in A_h$ $f_0(\theta + h) \in L_2^{\sigma},\ \|h\| \leqslant h_0$	$p(\theta) \in V$	$\omega(\delta; f) = o\left(\frac{1}{\ln \frac{1}{\delta}}\right)$

TABLE VII (continued)

№	Conditions on the interval $[0, 2\pi]$		Conditions on the interval $[\alpha, \beta]$	
	on $\sigma(\theta)$	on $f(e^{i\theta})$	on $\sigma(\theta)$	on $f(e^{i\theta})$
V	$\frac{1}{p(\theta)} \in L_1$	$f \in L_2,\ f \in A_h$ $f_0(\theta + h) \in L_2^\sigma$ $\|h\| \leqslant h_0$	$p(\theta) \in C$ $\omega(\delta; p) \leqslant C_1\left(\ln\frac{1}{\delta}\right)^{-\gamma}$ $\gamma > 1$	$\omega(\delta; f) = o\left(\frac{1}{\ln\frac{1}{\delta}}\right)$
VI	$\sigma(\theta) \in AC$ $p(\theta) \leqslant M$	$f \in L_2$ $\omega_2(\delta; f) = o(\sqrt{\delta})$		$\omega(\delta; p) = o(\sqrt{\delta})$
VII	$0 < m \leqslant p(\theta)$ $\omega_1(\delta; p) = o(\sqrt{\delta})$ $\omega'\left(\delta; \frac{1}{p_0}\right) = o(\sqrt{\delta})$	$f \in L_2,\ f \in A_h$ $\omega_2(\delta; f) = O\left(\sqrt[4]{\delta}\right)$ $f_0(\theta + h) \in L_2^\sigma,\ \|h\| \leqslant h_0$	$p(\theta) \leqslant M$	$\omega(\delta; f) = O\left(\frac{\sqrt{\delta}}{\ln\frac{1}{\delta}}\right)$
VIII	$p(\theta) \in L_r,\ \frac{1}{p(\theta)} \in L_{r'}$ $\frac{1}{r} + \frac{1}{r'} = 1,\ r > 1$ $\omega_r(\delta; p) = o(\sqrt{\delta})$ $\omega'\left(\delta; \frac{1}{p_0}\right) = o(\sqrt{\delta})$	$f \in L_2,\ f \in A_h$ $\omega_2(\delta; f) = O\left(\sqrt[4]{\delta}\right)$ $f_0(\theta + h) \in L_2^\sigma,\ \|h\| \leqslant h_0$	$p(\theta) \leqslant M$	$\omega(\delta; f) = O\left(\frac{\sqrt{\delta}}{\ln\frac{1}{\delta}}\right)$

IX	$\sigma(\theta) \in AC$ $0 < m \leqslant p(\theta) \leqslant M$ $\omega_2(\delta; p) = o(\sqrt[4]{\delta})$	$f \in L_2$ $\omega_2(\delta; f) = O(\sqrt[4]{\delta})$		$\omega(\delta; f) = O\left(\dfrac{\sqrt{\delta}}{\ln \frac{1}{\delta}}\right)$
X	$\sigma(\theta) \in AC$ $p(\theta) \leqslant M, \ \dfrac{1}{p(\theta)} \in L_1$ $\omega_1\left(\delta; \dfrac{1}{p}\right) = o(\sqrt{\delta})$	$f \in L_2$ $\omega_2(\delta; f) = O(\sqrt[4]{\delta})$		$\omega(\delta; f) = O\left(\dfrac{\sqrt{\delta}}{\ln \frac{1}{\delta}}\right)$
XI	$\ln p(\theta) \in L_1$	$\dfrac{f(e^{i\theta})}{\pi(e^{i\theta})} \in L_2$	$p(\theta) \in C$ $\omega(\delta; p) \leqslant C\sqrt{\delta}\left(\ln \frac{1}{\delta}\right)^{-\gamma},$ $\gamma > 1$	$\omega(\delta; f) \leqslant C_2\left(\ln \frac{1}{\delta}\right)^{-\lambda},$ $\lambda > 1$
XII	$\dfrac{1}{p(\theta)} \in L_1$	$\dfrac{f(e^{i\theta})}{\pi(e^{i\theta})} \in L_2$	$p(\theta) \in V$	$\omega(\delta; f) \leqslant C_2\left(\ln \frac{1}{\delta}\right)^{-\lambda},$ $\lambda > 1$
XIII	$\dfrac{1}{p(\theta)} \in L_1$	$\dfrac{f(e^{i\theta})}{\pi(e^{i\theta})} \in L_2$	$p(\theta) \in C$ $\omega(\delta\ p) \leqslant C_1\left(\ln \frac{1}{\delta}\right)^{-\gamma},$ $\gamma > 1$	$\omega(\delta; f) \leqslant C_2\left(\ln \frac{1}{\delta}\right)^{-\lambda},$ $\lambda > 1$

TABLE VIII

Conditions for Uniform Equiconvergence in the Interior of $[e^{i\alpha}, e^{i\beta}]$ of the Fourier-Chebyshev and Maclaurin Expansions of a Function $f(z) \in H_2$ such that $\frac{f(z)}{\pi(z)} \in H_2$ and Which Is Bounded on This Arc

In all cases, on $[\alpha, \beta]$ the function $\sigma(\theta)$ is absolutely continuous, and $p(\theta) \geq m > 0$ is continuous.

No.	Conditions on $\sigma(\theta)$		
	on the interval $[0, 2\pi]$	on E_h	on the interval $[\alpha, \beta]$
I	$\sigma(\theta) \in AC,\ p(\theta) = p_1(\theta)\,p_2(\theta)$ $p_1(\theta) = \prod_{k=1}^{s} \lvert e^{i\theta} - e^{i\theta_k} \rvert^{\alpha_k};\ \alpha_k > 0$ $0 < m_2 \leqslant p_2(\theta) \leqslant M_2$		$\frac{1}{(\theta - \theta_0)^2} \cdot \lvert p(\theta) - p(\theta_0) - p'(\theta_0)(\theta - \theta_0)^2 \rvert \leqslant C$
II	$\sigma(\theta) \in AC, p(\theta) \leqslant M, \frac{1}{p(\theta)} \in L_2$ $\omega_2\left(\delta; \frac{1}{p}\right) = o\left(\frac{1}{\ln \frac{1}{\delta}}\right)$		$\omega(\delta; p) \leqslant C\left(\ln \frac{1}{\delta}\right)^{-\gamma}$, $\gamma > 2$
III	$\in L_r, \frac{1}{p(\theta)} \in L_{r'}, \frac{1}{r} + \frac{1}{r'} = 1, r > 1$ $\omega_4(\delta; \ln p)$ & $\omega_{2r}(\delta; \sqrt{p}) = o\left(\frac{1}{\ln \frac{1}{\delta}}\right)$ or $\omega_r(\delta; p) = o\left\{\frac{1}{\left(\ln \frac{1}{\delta}\right)^2}\right\}$	$\frac{1}{p_0(\theta)} \in C$ $\omega'\left(\delta; \frac{1}{p_0}\right) = o\left\{\frac{1}{\left(\ln \frac{1}{\delta}\right)^2}\right\}$	$\omega(\delta; p) \leqslant C\left(\ln \frac{1}{\delta}\right)^{-\gamma}$, $\gamma > 3$

IV	$0 < m \leqslant p(\theta)$ $\omega_4(\delta;\ \ln p)\ \&\ \omega_2(\delta;\ \sqrt{p}) = o\left(\frac{1}{\ln\frac{1}{\delta}}\right)$ or $\omega_1(\delta;\ p) = o\left\{\frac{1}{\left(\ln\frac{1}{\delta}\right)^2}\right\}$	$\frac{1}{p_0(\theta)} \in C$ $\omega'\left(\delta;\ \frac{1}{p_0}\right) = o\left\{\frac{1}{\left(\ln\frac{1}{\delta}\right)^2}\right\}$	$\omega(\delta;\ p) \leqslant C\left(\ln\frac{1}{\delta}\right)^{-\gamma}$, $\gamma > 3$
V	$\sigma(\theta) \in AC,\ p(\theta) \leqslant M,\ \frac{1}{p(\theta)} \in L_1$ $\omega_4(\delta;\ln p)\ \&\ \omega_2\left(\delta;\ \frac{1}{\sqrt{p}}\right) = o\left(\frac{1}{\ln\frac{1}{\delta}}\right)$ or $\omega_1(\delta;\ p) = o\left\{\frac{1}{\left(\ln\frac{1}{\delta}\right)^2}\right\}$		$\omega(\delta;\ p) \leqslant C'\left(\ln\frac{1}{\delta}\right)^{-\gamma}$, $\gamma > 3$

TABLE VIII (continued)

№	Conditions on $\sigma(\theta)$		
	on the interval $[0, 2\pi]$	on E_h	on the interval $[\alpha, \beta]$
VI	$I(\delta) = o\left\{\frac{1}{\ln\left(\frac{1}{\delta}\right)^2}\right\}$	$\frac{1}{p_0(\theta)} \in C$ $\omega'\left(\delta; \frac{1}{p_0}\right) = o\left\{\frac{1}{\ln\left(\frac{1}{\delta}\right)^2}\right\}$	$\omega(\delta; p) \leqslant C\left(\ln\frac{1}{\delta}\right)^{-\gamma}$, $\gamma > 3$
VII	$\sigma(\theta) \in AC$, $0 < m \leqslant p(\theta) \leqslant M$ $\{\omega_r(\delta; p)\}^r = o\left\{\frac{1}{\ln\left(\frac{1}{\delta}\right)^2}\right\}$, $r = 1$ or $r = 2$		$\omega(\delta; p) \leqslant C\left(\ln\frac{1}{\delta}\right)^{-\gamma}$, $\gamma > 3$
VIII	$\sigma(\theta) \in AC$, $0 < m \leqslant p(\theta) \leqslant M$ $p(\theta) \in \mathrm{Lip}\left(\frac{1}{2}, 2\right)$		$\omega(\delta; p) \leqslant C\left(\ln\frac{1}{\delta}\right)^{-\gamma}$, $\gamma > 2$

TABLE IX

Convergence on $[a, b]$ of the Fourier-Chebyshev Expansion of a Function $f(x)$ Summable on $[-1, +1]$

In all cases, on [a, b] the function $f(x)$ is continuous, $\psi(x)$ is absolutely continuous, and $w(x)$ is bounded below $w(x) \geq m > 0$.

№	Conditions on the interval [-1, +1]		Conditions on the interval [a, b]	
	on $\psi(x)$	on $f(x)$	on $\psi(x)$	on $f(x)$
I	$\psi(x) \in AC$ $p(\theta) \leqslant M$	$f \in L_2$ $\sum_{n=1}^{\infty} \frac{1}{\sqrt{n}} \omega_2\left(\frac{1}{n}, f\right) < \infty$		
II	$\psi(x) \in AC$ $0 < m \leqslant p(\theta) \leqslant M$ $p(\theta) \in \mathrm{Lip}\left(\frac{1}{2}, 2\right)$			$\omega(\delta; f) = o\left(\frac{1}{\ln \frac{1}{\delta}}\right)$
III	$\int_{-1}^{1} \frac{\ln w(x)\, dx}{\sqrt{1 - x^2}} > -\infty$	$f \in L_2,\ f \in A_h$ $f_0(x+h) \in L_2^{\psi},\ \lvert h \rvert \leqslant h_0$	$w(x) \in C$ $\omega(\delta; w) \leqslant$ $\leqslant C_1 \sqrt{\delta}\left(\ln \frac{1}{\delta}\right)^{-\gamma}$, $\gamma > 1$	$\omega(\delta; f) = o\left(\frac{1}{\ln \frac{1}{\delta}}\right)$
IV	$\frac{1}{p(\theta)} \in L_1$	$f \in L_2,\ f \in A_h$ $f_0(x+h) \in L_2^{\psi},\ \lvert h \rvert \leqslant h_0$	$w(x) \in V$	$\omega(\delta; f) = o\left(\frac{1}{\ln \frac{1}{\delta}}\right)$

TABLE IX (continued)

№	Conditions on the interval [-1, +1]		Conditions on the interval [a, b]	
	on $\psi(x)$	on $f(x)$	on $\psi(x)$	on $f(x)$
V	$\frac{1}{p(\theta)} \in L_1$	$f \in L_2,\ f \in A_h$ $f_0(x+h) \in L_2^{\psi},\ \lvert h \rvert \leqslant h_0$	$w(x) \in C$ $\omega(\delta;\ w) \leqslant C_1\left(\ln\frac{1}{\delta}\right)^{-\gamma}$, $\gamma > 1$	$\omega(\delta; f) = o\left(\frac{1}{\ln\frac{1}{\delta}}\right)$
VI	$\psi(x) \in AC$ $p(\theta) \leqslant M$	$f \in L_2$ $\omega_2(\delta; f) = o(\sqrt{\delta})$		$\omega(\delta; f) = o(\sqrt{\delta})$
VII	$0 < m \leqslant p(\theta)$ $\omega_1(\delta;\ p) = o(\sqrt{\delta})$ $\omega'\left(\delta;\ \frac{1}{p_0}\right) = o(\sqrt{\delta})$	$f \in L_2,\ f \in A_h$ $f_0(x+h) \in L_2^{\psi},\ \lvert h \rvert \leqslant h_0$ $\omega_2(\delta; f) = O\left(\sqrt[4]{\delta}\right)$	$w(x) \leqslant M$	$\omega(\delta; f) = O\left(\frac{\sqrt{\delta}}{\ln\frac{1}{\delta}}\right)$
VIII	$p(\theta) \in L_r,\ \frac{1}{p(\theta)} \in L_{r'}$ $\frac{1}{r} + \frac{1}{r'} = 1,\ r > 1$ $\omega_r(\delta;\ p) = o(\sqrt{\delta})$ $\omega'\left(\delta;\ \frac{1}{p_0}\right) = o(\sqrt{\delta})$	$f \in L_2,\ f \in A_h$ $f_0(x+h) \in L_2^{\psi},\ \lvert h \rvert \leqslant h_0$ $\omega_2(\delta; f) = o\left(\sqrt[4]{\delta}\right)$	$w(x) \leqslant M$	$\omega(\delta; f) = O\left(\frac{\sqrt{\delta}}{\ln\frac{1}{\delta}}\right)$

IX	$\psi(x) \in AC$ $0 < m \leqslant p(\theta) \leqslant M$ $\omega_2(\delta; p) = o(\sqrt[4]{\delta})$	$f \in L_2$ $\omega_2(\delta; f) = O(\sqrt[4]{\delta})$		$\omega(\delta; f) = O\left(\frac{\sqrt{\delta}}{\ln \frac{1}{\delta}}\right)$
X	$\psi(x) \in AC$ $p(\theta) \leqslant M,\ \frac{1}{p(\theta)} \in L_1$ $\omega_1\left(\delta; \frac{1}{p}\right) = o(\sqrt{\delta})$	$f \in L_2$ $\omega_2(\delta; f) = O(\sqrt[4]{\delta})$		$\omega(\delta; f) = O\left(\frac{\sqrt{\delta}}{\ln \frac{1}{\delta}}\right)$
XI	$\int_{-1}^{1} \frac{\ln w(x)\, dx}{\sqrt{1-x^2}} > -\infty$	$f \cdot \in L_2^{\psi}$	$w(x) \in C$ $\omega(\delta; w) \leqslant C_1 \sqrt{\delta} \left(\ln \frac{1}{\delta}\right)^{-\gamma}$, $\gamma > 1$	$\omega(\delta; f) \leqslant C_2 \left(\ln \frac{1}{\delta}\right)^{-\lambda}$, $\lambda > 1$
XII	$\frac{1}{p(\theta)} \in L_1$	$f \in L_2^{\psi}$	$w(x) \in V$	$\omega(\delta; f) \leqslant C_2 \left(\ln \frac{1}{\delta}\right)^{-\lambda}$, $\lambda > 1$

TABLE IX (continued)

№	Conditions on the interval [-1, +1]		Conditions on the interval [a, b]	
	on $\psi(x)$	on $f(x)$	on $\psi(x)$	on $f(x)$
XIII	$\frac{1}{p(\theta)} \in L_1$	$f \in L_2^{\psi}$	$w(x) \in C$ $\omega(\delta; w) \leqslant C_1\left(\ln \frac{1}{\delta}\right)^{-\gamma}$, $\gamma > 1$	$\omega(\delta; f) \leqslant C_2\left(\ln \frac{1}{\delta}\right)^{-\lambda}$, $\lambda > 1$
XIV	$\int_{-1}^{1} \frac{\ln w(x)\, dx}{\sqrt{1-x^2}} > -\infty$	$f \in L_2^{\psi}$	$w(x) \in C$ $\omega(\delta; w) \leqslant$ $\leqslant C_1 \sqrt{\delta}\left(\ln \frac{1}{\delta}\right)^{-\gamma}$, $\gamma > 1$	$f \in V$
XV	$\frac{1}{p(\theta)} \in L_1$	$f \in L_2^{\psi}$	$w(x) \in V$	$f \in V$
XVI	$\frac{1}{p(\theta)} \in L_1$	$f \in L_2^{\psi}$	$w(x) \in C$ $\omega(\delta; w) \leqslant C_1\left(\ln \frac{1}{\delta}\right)^{-\gamma}$, $\gamma > 1$	$f \in V$

NOTES

CHAPTER I

The integral in (1.1) and the later integrals are Lebesgue-Stieltjes integrals.

If $\sigma(\theta)$ has a finite number of points of increase $\{\theta_k\}^m$, then $\Phi_m(z) = \prod_{k=1}^{m}\left(z - e^{i\theta_k}\right)$ is a polynomial orthogonal to all the $\{\varphi_\nu(z)\}^{m-1}$; but since for this polynomial we have

$$\frac{1}{2\pi}\int_0^{2\pi} |\Phi_m(e^{i\theta})|^2 d\sigma(\theta) = 0,$$

it follows that $\alpha_m = \infty$; and therefore in this case one can construct only the finite set $\{\varphi_\nu(z)\}_0^{m-1}$.

1.1. Concentrated mass. If $z_0 = e^{i\theta_0}$ in (1.10), then the greatest mass $\mu_{max}^{(n)}(\theta_0)$ that can be concentrated at θ_0, assuming that for $d\sigma_n(\theta)$ we know only the first n moments $\{c_k\}_0^n$ of Eq. (1.20), is given by $\mu_{max}^{(n)}(\theta_0) = 1/K_0(z_0, z_0)$; a result which can be obtained from the obvious inequality *

$$\frac{1}{2\pi}\int_0^{2\pi} \left|\frac{G_n(e^{i\theta})}{G_n(e^{i\theta_0})}\right|^2 d\sigma(\theta) \geqslant \frac{\sigma(\theta_0+0) - \sigma(\theta_0-0)}{2\pi}. \qquad (1)$$

In the notation of (8.4') and (8.5) we have $\varphi_n(z) = \dfrac{\Phi_n(z)}{\sqrt{\Delta_n\Delta_{n-1}}}$, from which it is clear that the $\{\varphi_k(z)\}_0^n$, and therefore also the $K_n(z,z)$, depend only on the $\{c_k\}_0^n$. Applying Stieltjes' considerations, one can show that if all the moments $\{c_k\}_0^\infty$ are given, then**

---

* See, for instance, N. I. Akhiezer and M. G. Krein [2].

** See Ya. L. Geronimus [1], Section 20.

$$\frac{\sigma(\theta_0+0)-\sigma(\theta_0-0)}{2\pi}=\frac{1}{\sum_{k=0}^{\infty}|\varphi_k(e^{i\theta_0})|^2}, \tag{2}$$

from which it is clear that the series $\sum_{k=0}^{\infty}|\varphi_k(e^{i\theta_0})|^2$ converges at points of mass concentration.

The class $H\delta$. A function $f(z)$ regular in the region $|z| < 1$ belongs to the class $H\delta$ ($\delta > 0$) if

$$I_r(f)=\frac{1}{2\pi}\int_0^{2\pi}|f(re^{i\theta})|^{\delta}\,d\theta\leqslant C,\quad r<1, \tag{3}$$

where C is independent of r.

Since the integral does not decrease as r is allowed to increase,* the limit $\lim_{r\to 1-0} I_r(f)$ always exists. For a function of class $H\delta$ this limit is finite, and we write

$$\left.\begin{aligned}\lim_{r\to 1-0} I_r(f)&=\frac{1}{2\pi}\int_0^{2\pi}|f(e^{i\theta})|^{\delta}\,d\theta,\\ |f(re^{i\theta})|&\leqslant\left\{\frac{2I(f)}{1-r}\right\}^{\frac{1}{\delta}},\qquad r<1.\end{aligned}\right\} \tag{4}$$

A function $f(z)\in H_\delta$ has, on the circumference $|z|= 1$, radial boundary values $f(e^{i\theta})=\lim_{r\to 1-0} f(re^{i\theta})$ almost everywhere, and these are such that $|f(e^{i\theta})|^{\delta}$ and $|f(e^{i\theta})|$ are in L_1. If $\delta > \nu$, then $H_\delta\subset H_\nu$,

Theorem of V. I. Smirnov. If $f(z)$ is regular for $|z| < 1$, and pseudopositive (i.e., has positive real part), then $f(z)\in H_\delta$, where $0 < \delta < 1$.

* See, for instance, G. Pólya and G. Szegö [1], Vol. I, Part III, Problem 310.

Summation by Abel's (or Poisson's) method. If

$$c_n = \frac{1}{2\pi} \int_0^{2\pi} e^{-in\theta}\, d\sigma(\theta) = a_n + ib_n, \qquad (n = 0, 1, 2, \ldots), \tag{5}$$

then $\frac{a_0}{2} + \sum_{n=1}^{\infty} (a_n \cos n\theta - b_n \sin n\theta)$ is a Fourier-Stieltjes series which is if formally identical with that obtained from term-by-term differentiation of the Fourier series for $\sigma(\theta)$. We apply Fatou's theorem, which states if at θ_0 the generalized symmetric first derivative $\sigma_{(1)}(\theta_0)$, exists, then the differentiated Fourier series of $\sigma(\theta)$ sums at the point θ_0 by Abel's (or Poisson's) method to the value $\sigma_{(1)}(\theta_0)$. This means that according to (1.22) the limit

$$\frac{a_0}{2} + \lim_{r \to 1-0} \sum_{k=1}^{\infty} r^k (a_k \cos k\theta_0 - b_k \sin k\theta_0) = \\ = \lim_{r \to 1-0} c_0 \Re \left\{ F(re^{i\theta_0}) \right\} = \sigma_{(1)}(\theta_0). \tag{6}$$

exists. The generalized derivative $\sigma_1(\theta_0)$ exists almost everywhere in $[0, 2\pi]$.

1.2. Integral of the Cauchy-Stieltjes type. Let $\tau(\theta)$ be any complex-valued function of bounded variation defined on $[0, 2\pi]$. Then

$$F(z) = \frac{1}{2\pi} \int_0^{2\pi} \frac{e^{i\theta}\, d\tau(\theta)}{e^{i\theta} - z} \tag{7}$$

is called an integral of the Cauchy-Stieltjes type, and according to the theorem of Smirnov $F(z) \in H_\delta$ $(0 < \delta < 1)$ for $|z| < 1$.

The fundamental theorem of I. I. Privalov on the boundary values of such an integral (as applied to radial boundary values) states that almost everywhere on the circumference $|z| = 1$ we have

$$\lim_{r \to 1 \mp 0} \frac{1}{2\pi} \int_0^{2\pi} \frac{e^{i\theta}\, d\tau(\theta)}{e^{i\theta} - re^{i\theta_0}} = \frac{1}{2\pi} \int_0^{2\pi} \frac{e^{i\theta}\, d\tau(\theta)}{e^{i\theta} - e^{i\theta_0}} \pm \frac{1}{2} \tau'(\theta_0), \tag{8}$$

where the integral on the right-hand side is defined as singular.

An integral of the Cauchy-Stieltjes type is called a Cauchy-Stieltjes integral if its boundary values from the interior of the unit circle taken along all nontangent paths are equal to $\tau'(\theta_0)$ almost everywhere. A necessary and sufficient condition for this is that $F(z) \equiv 0$ for $|z| > 1$, which, in turn, is equivalent to

$$\int_0^{2\pi} e^{in\theta}\, d\tau(\theta) = 0, \qquad (n = 1, 2, \ldots). \tag{9}$$

We may then apply the theorem of G. M. Fichtenholz which states that if a function F(z) is regular in the region $|z| < 1$, and can be represented in this region by a Cauchy-Stieltjes integral, then $F(z) \in H_1$ and it can therefore be represented in terms of its boundary values through the Cauchy integral formula.

The theorem of Montel. Given a family $\{f(z)\}$ of functions regular in a region B and satisfying the inequality $|f(z) - a| \geq m > 0$, in this region, from every infinite sequence of these functions one can choose a subsequence converging uniformly in B to a function which may be identically infinite.

Theorem of Hurwitz. Let the sequence of analytic functions $\{f_n(z)\}$, regular in a region B, converge uniformly in the interior of B to some function $f(z) \not\equiv 0$. If $z = a$ is a zero of order k of $f(z)$, there exists a neighborhood $e = |z-a| < \delta$ and a number $N > 0$ such that if $n > N$, each $f_n(z)$ has k zeros in e.

CHAPTER II

Properties of the class H_2. By definition of $H\delta$, if

$f(z) = \sum_{k=0}^{\infty} a_k z^k \in H_2$ then

$$I_2(f) = \sum_{k=0}^{\infty} |a_k|^2 r^{2k} \leq C, \qquad r < 1, \tag{10}$$

which means that $\sum_{k=0}^{\infty} a_k z^k \in H_2$ if and only if $\sum_{k=0}^{\infty} |a_k|^2 < \infty$.

An inequality for weighted means. The inequality

$$\exp\left\{\frac{\int_a^b p(x)\ln f(x)\,dx}{\int_a^b p(x)\,dx}\right\} \leqslant \frac{\int_a^b p(x) f(x)\,dx}{\int_a^b p(x)\,dx} \tag{11}$$

is in general true,* where p(x) and f (x) are nonnegative and finite almost everywhere on [a, b], and p(x) is a summable function. In our particular case the role of p(x) is played by P(r; $\theta - \varphi$).

Parametric representation of the class $H\delta$. Every $f(z) \in H_\delta$ can be represented parametrically according to

$$f(z) = z^m e^{i\lambda} \prod_{n=1}^{\infty} \frac{|\alpha_n|}{\alpha_n} \frac{\alpha_n - z}{1 - \bar{\alpha}_n z} \cdot \exp\left\{\frac{1}{2\pi}\int_0^{2\pi} \ln q(\theta) \frac{e^{i\theta}+z}{e^{i\theta}-z}\,d\theta\right\} \times$$

$$\times \exp\left\{\frac{1}{2\pi}\int_0^{2\pi} \frac{e^{i\theta}+z}{e^{i\theta}-z}\,d\psi(\theta)\right\}, \qquad |z| < 1, \tag{12}$$

where m ≥ 0 is an integer, $0 \leqslant \lambda < 2\pi$, $\{|\alpha_n|\}_1^{\infty} < 1$, and $\sum_{n=1}^{\infty}\{1 - |\alpha_n|\} < \infty$. Here q($\theta$) is a nonnegative function such that $\ln q(\theta), \{q(\theta)\}^{\delta} \in L_1$, and $\psi(\theta)$ is a nonincreasing function whose derivative vanishes almost everywhere.

Conjugate functions. If $f(\theta) \in L\ (0, 2\pi)$ is a function such that the trigonometric series $\frac{a_0}{2} + \sum_{k=1}^{\infty}(a_k \cos k\theta + b_k \sin k\theta)$ is its Fourier series, the conjugate trigonometric series $\sum_{k=1}^{\infty}(a_k \sin k\theta - b_k \cos k\theta)$ is not in general the Fourier series of a class L_1 function. It is summable by Abel's (or Poisson's) method almost everywhere on [0, 2π], which means that

* See Hardy, Littlewood, and Pólya [1], Section 6.7.

$$\lim_{r \to 1-0} \sum_{k=1}^{\infty} (a_k \sin k\theta_0 - b_k \cos k\theta_0) r^k =$$

$$= \frac{1}{2\pi} \int_0^{2\pi} \operatorname{ctg} \frac{\theta_0 - \theta}{2} f(\theta)\, d\theta = \bar{f}(\theta_0) \tag{13}$$

exists. This integral, understood in the sense of the Cauchy principal value, exists almost everywhere in $[0, 2\pi]$, and $\bar{f}(\theta)$ is the function conjugate to $f(\theta)$.

Boundary values of $\pi(z)$. According to (2.16) and (2.4) we have, in our case,

$$f(\theta) = \ln \frac{1}{\sqrt{p(\theta)}} \in L_1, \quad \bar{f}(\theta) = \arg \pi (e^{i\theta}). \tag{14}$$

Since the Poisson-Lebesgue integral of (2.16') may be considered a special case of a Poisson-Stieltjes integral, we may use Fatou's theorem as we did in 1.1, and we then find that the limit of the real part of (2.16) exists at all points θ_0 for which

$$\lim_{h \to 0} \left\{ \frac{1}{2h} \int_{\theta_0 - h}^{\theta_0 + h} \ln p(\theta)\, d\theta \right\} \tag{15}$$

exists, and then

$$\lim_{r \to 1-0} \ln |\pi(re^{i\theta_0})| = -\frac{1}{2} \lim_{h \to 0} \left\{ \frac{1}{2h} \int_{\theta_0 - h}^{\theta_0 + h} \ln p(\theta)\, d\theta \right\}. \tag{15'}$$

The theorem of F. and M. Riesz. If $f(z) \in H_1$, and if its boundary value $f(e^{i\theta})$ is of bounded variation on $[0, 2\pi]$, then it is also absolutely continuous on $[0, 2\pi]$.

From this we obtain the following theorem: if Eq. (9) is fulfilled with a function $\tau(\theta)$ of bounded variation on $[0, 2\pi]$, then this function is absolutely continuous on $[0, 2\pi]$.

CHAPTER III

3.2. Hölder's inequality. If p > 1 and 1/p + 1/p'= 1, then

$$\left|\int_a^b u(x)\,v(x)\,d\varphi(x)\right| \leqslant \left\{\int_a^b |u(x)|^p\,d\varphi(x)\right\}^{\frac{1}{p}} \cdot \left\{\int_a^b |v(x)|^{p'}\,dx\right\}^{\frac{1}{p'}}, \tag{16}$$

where $\varphi(x)$ is a nondecreasing bounded function.* By setting p = p' = 2 we obtain the Bunyakovskii-Schwarz inequality.

Theorem of M. Riesz. If $f(\theta)\in L^p$, $p>1$, then $\bar{f}(\theta)\in L^p$.

Inequalities for logarithms. From Lagrange's mean value theorem we easily obtain the inequalities

$$|e^x - e^y| \leqslant e^M|x-y|,\quad x,\ y\leqslant M;\quad |\ln x - \ln y| \geqslant \frac{1}{M}|x-y|,$$
$$x,\ y\leqslant M;\quad |\ln x - \ln y| \leqslant \frac{1}{m}|x-y|,\quad x,\ y\geqslant m>0. \tag{17}$$

In (3.15) we have written $x=\sqrt[k]{p(\theta+\delta)},\ y=\sqrt[k]{p(\theta)},\ \ p(\theta)\geqslant m>0.$

Derivation of Szasz's inequality from Bernshtein's inequality. Consider the polynomial $P_n(z)=\sum_{k=0}^{\infty}(a_k+ib_k)z^k$

Assume that in the closed region $|z|\le 1$ the modulus of the derivative of this polynomial takes on its maximum value at z = 1, or**

$$|P'_n(z)|\leqslant P'_n(1)=M,\quad |P_n(z)|\leqslant L,\quad |z|\leqslant 1.$$

From this we obtain the inequality

$$|\operatorname{Im}\{P_n(e^{i\theta})\}| = \left|\sum_{k=1}^{n}(a_k\sin k\theta + b_k\cos k\theta)\right| \leqslant L,$$

which leads to
$$\left|\sum_{k=1}^{n} k\,(a_k\cos k\theta - b_k\sin k\theta)\right| \leqslant nL,$$

since, according to Bernshtein's theorem the inequality $|T_n(\theta)|\le L$, $0\le \theta\le 2\pi$ for a trigonometric polynomial of degree n implies the inequality $|T'_n(\theta)|\le nL$, $0\le\theta\le 2\pi$ for its derivative.

---

* The integrals on the right hand side are assumed to exist.

** This can always be done by rotating the axes and multiplying by an appropriate factor.

Therefore

$$P'_n(1) = \sum_{k=1}^{n} ka_k = M \leqslant nL.$$

3.7. Theorems of Hardy and Littlewood. 1) If a function is of bounded variation in $[0, 2\pi]$, it is equivalent to a class Lip (1, 1) function. 2) Conversely, if

$$f(\theta) \in \text{Lip}\left(\frac{1}{r}, r\right), \ r \geqslant 1, \quad \text{then} \quad f(\theta) \in \text{Lip}\left(\frac{1}{q}, q\right)$$

for $q > r$; 3) If the Fourier coefficients (a_n, b_n) of $f(\theta)$ are $O\left(\frac{1}{n}\right)$, then $f(\theta) \in \text{Lip}\left(\frac{1}{p}, p\right)$, $p \geqslant 2$.

3.8. The compactness principle. A family of functions $\{f(z)\}$ regular in a region B is called compact if from any sequence of these functions one can choose a subsequence which converges uniformly in the interior of B. A necessary and sufficient condition for compactness is that the family be uniformly bounded in the interior of B; i.e., that for every closed set F in the interior of B there exist a number $M(F) < \infty$, such that $|f(z)| \leq M(F)$ for $z \in F$.

Helly's theorems. 1) Assume that on [a, b] we are given a family $\{f(x)\}$ of functions which, together with their total variations, are uniformly bounded on [a, b]. Then from this family one can choose an infinite sequence $\{f_n(x)\}$ which converges essentially* on [a, b] to some function $\varphi(x)$ of bounded variation. 2) Assume that on [a, b] we are given a continuous function F(x) and a sequence of functions $\{f_n(x)\}$ whose total variations are uniformly bounded, and that on [a, b] this sequence converges essentially to some finite function $f(x)$. Then

$$\lim_{n \to \infty} \int_a^b F(x)\, df_n(x) = \int_a^b F(x)\, df(x). \tag{18}$$

* This means that it converges on an everywhere dense set, in particular on the points of continuity.

Uniqueness of the solution of the trigonometric
moment problem. Given a sequence of complex numbers $\{c_n\}_0^\infty$,
it can be represented in the form

$$\frac{1}{2\pi} \int_0^{2\pi} e^{-in\theta} d\sigma(\theta) = c_n, \qquad (n = 0, 1, 2, \ldots), \qquad (19)$$

where $\sigma(\theta)$ is a bounded nondecreasing function, if and only if

$$\Delta_n = |c_{i-j}| > 0, \quad c_{-n} = \bar{c}_n, \qquad (n = 0, 1, 2, \ldots). \qquad (20)$$

Further, $\sigma(\theta)$ is determined from the given moments $\{c_n\}_0^\infty$ up to an
additive constant, since it can be found by (8.11), where*

$$F(z) = 1 + \frac{2}{c_0} \sum_{k=1}^\infty c_k z^k, \qquad |z| < 1. \qquad (21)$$

A conjecture of V. A. Steklov. "Unfortunately we are
unable to write down the general set of necessary and sufficient conditions to which the weight must be subjected in order that the entire set
of orthonormal polynomials corresponding to this weight be bounded.
I believe that the entire orthonormal set is in general bounded when-
ever the weight fails to vanish in the interior of the given interval. I
have not, however, been able to obtain a rigorous proof of this assertion
or to give a counterexample in which the orthonormal set is not bounded
at every point within the interval."

CHAPTER IV

4.1. Properties of Fejèr and Jackson sums. Let

$$U_n(f; \theta_0) = \frac{1}{2\pi} \int_0^{2\pi} f(\theta) K_n(\theta, \theta_0) d\theta, \qquad (22)$$

where $f(\theta) \in L_1$, and the kernel $K_n(\theta, \theta_0)$ has the following properties:

1) $\displaystyle\int_{\theta_0-\varepsilon}^{\theta_0+\varepsilon} |K_n(\theta, \theta_0)| d\theta \leqslant C$, where C is independent of both $\underline{n}$ and θ_0;

---

* See, for instance, N. I. Akhiezer and M. G. Krein [1], pp. 43-59.

2) $\max |K_n(\theta, \theta_0| \to 0$ as $n \to \infty$ for $|\theta - \theta_0| \geq \epsilon > 0$. Then from the boundedness of $f(\theta)$, namely from

$$|f(\theta)| \leqslant M, \quad \alpha \leqslant \theta \leqslant \beta,$$

we may deduce that the $U_n(f; \theta_0)$ sums are also bounded:

$$|U_n(f; \theta_0)| \leqslant M_1, \quad \alpha + \varepsilon \leqslant \theta_0 \leqslant \beta - \varepsilon.$$

Actually, we have

$$|U_n(f; \theta)| \leqslant \frac{1}{2\pi} \int\limits_{|\theta - \theta_0| \leqslant \varepsilon} |f(\theta)| \cdot |K_n(\theta, \theta_0)|\, d\theta +$$

$$+ \frac{1}{2\pi} \int\limits_{|\theta - \theta_0| > \varepsilon} |f(\theta)| \cdot |K_n(\theta, \theta_0)|\, d\theta \leqslant$$

$$\leqslant MC + \max_{|\theta - \theta_0| \geqslant \varepsilon} |K_n(\theta, \theta_0)| \cdot \frac{1}{2\pi} \int\limits_0^{2\pi} |f(\theta)|\, d\theta.$$

$$K_n(\theta, \theta_0) = \frac{1}{2\nu} \left\{ \frac{\sin \nu (\theta - \theta_0)}{\sin \frac{1}{2} (\theta - \theta_0)} \right\}^2,$$

$$K_n(\theta, \theta_0) = \frac{3}{\pi\nu (2\nu^2 + 1)} \left\{ \frac{\sin \frac{\nu}{2} (\theta - \theta_0)}{\sin \frac{1}{2} (\theta - \theta_0)} \right\}^4, \tag{23}$$

[where in the first equation $\nu = (n+1)/2$, and in the second equation $\nu = (n+2)/2$], associated with the Fejèr and Jackson sums, have properties 1) and 2). The Poisson kernel has the same properties when one replaces the limit $n \to \infty$ by $r \to 1 - 0$, for it is clear that

$$P(r, \theta - \theta_0) \leqslant \frac{1 - r^2}{1 - 2r \cos \varepsilon + r^2}, \qquad |\theta - \theta_0| \geqslant \varepsilon. \tag{24}$$

4.2. An inequality for sin x. For $0 \leq x \leq \pi/2$, we have $(2/\pi)\, x \leq \sin x \leq 1$.

Relative magnitudes of means of different orders.

Let

$$M_r(f) = \left\{ \frac{\int_a^b |f(x)|^r\, d\varphi(x)}{\int_a^b d\varphi(x)} \right\}^{\frac{1}{r}}, \qquad r \neq 0;$$

$$G(f) = \exp\left\{ \frac{\int_a^b \ln f(x)\, d\varphi(x)}{\int_a^b d\varphi(x)} \right\}, \tag{25}$$

where $\varphi(x)$ is a bounded nondecreasing function. Then

$$\begin{aligned} &1)\ M_r(f) \leqslant M_q(f), \quad \text{if} \quad r < q; \\ &2)\ \text{if} \quad p < 0 < r, \text{ then } M_p(f) < G(f) < M_r(f).^* \end{aligned} \tag{26}$$

In particular, $\frac{1}{p(\theta)} \in L_r$, $r > 0$, implies that $\ln p(\theta) \in L_1$ for $p(\theta) \in L_1$.

4.3. Theorem of Privalov. If $f(\theta)$ is continuous in $[0, 2\pi]$ and if $f(\theta) \in \mathrm{Lip}\,\alpha$, $0 < \alpha < 1$, then $\overline{f}(\theta) \in \mathrm{Lip}\,\alpha$; if, on the other hand, $\alpha = 1$, then $\omega(\delta, \overline{f}) = O\left(\delta \ln \frac{1}{\delta}\right)$.

4.4 Bessel's inequality. Let H be separable Hilbert space and let $\{\varphi_k(x)\}_1^\infty$ be an orthonormal set of functions in it; that is, let $(\varphi_k, \varphi_s) = \delta_{ks}$. Let $f \in H$, and denote by $f_k = (f, \varphi_k)$ the Fourier-Chebyshev coefficients of this function with respect to the set $\{\varphi_k(x)\}$. Then

$$\min_\alpha \left\| f - \sum_{k=1}^n \alpha_k \varphi_k \right\| = \left\| f - \sum_{k=1}^n f_k \varphi_k \right\| = \sqrt{\|f\|^2 - \sum_{k=1}^n |f_k|^2} \geqslant 0; \tag{27}$$

and from this we obtain Bessel's inequality $\sum_{k=1}^n |f_k|^2 \leqslant \sum_{k=1}^\infty |f_k|^2 \leqslant \|f\|^2$ and, therefore, convergence of the series $\sum_{k=1}^\infty |f_k|^2$.

Denseness of one class of functions in another. If $p > q > 0$, then $L_p \subset L_q$, and the class L_p is dense in L_q. This means that every class L_q function can be approximated with arbitrary accuracy, in the metric of L_q, by a class L_p function.

---

* See Hardy, Littlewood, and Pólya [1], Section 6.18.

4.5. A property of the class H_δ for $\delta \geq 1$. If $f(z) \in H_\delta$, then $\delta \geq 1$

$$\frac{1}{2\pi i} \int_{|\zeta|=1} \frac{f(\zeta) - f(z_0)}{\zeta - z_0} d\zeta = 0, \qquad |z_0| = 1. \tag{28}$$

Indeed, for the special case in which the function $\tau(\theta)$ of (7) is absolutely continuous, we have the integral of the Cauchy type

$$F(z) = \frac{1}{2\pi i} \int_{|\zeta|-1} \frac{f(\zeta)\, d\zeta}{\zeta - z}, \qquad f(\zeta) \in L_1, \quad \zeta = e^{i\theta}, \tag{29}$$

which will be a Cauchy integral if its boundary values along every nontangent path in the interior of the unit circle coincide with $f(\zeta)$ almost everywhere on the circle. Applying (8) to the integral of the Cauchy type, we have

$$\lim_{r \to 1 \mp 0} \frac{1}{2\pi i} \int_{|\zeta|=1} \frac{f(\zeta)\, d\zeta}{\zeta - r z_0} = \frac{1}{2\pi i} \int_{|\zeta|=1} \frac{f(\zeta)\, d\zeta}{\zeta - z_0} \pm \frac{1}{2} f(z_0), \tag{30}$$

which leads to

$$\lim_{r \to 1-0} \frac{1}{2\pi i} \int_{|\zeta|=1} \frac{f(\zeta)\, d\zeta}{\zeta - r z_0} = \frac{1}{2\pi i} \int_{|\zeta|=1} \frac{f(\zeta) - f(z_0)}{\zeta - z_0} d\zeta + f(z_0). \tag{31}$$

For a Cauchy integral we obtain Eq. (28). This also implies

$$\frac{1}{2}\left\{ \lim_{r \to 1-0} \frac{1}{2\pi i} \int_{|\zeta|=1} \frac{f(\zeta)\, d\zeta}{\zeta - r z_0} + \lim_{r \to 1+0} \frac{1}{2\pi i} \int_{|\zeta|-1} \frac{f(\zeta)\, d\zeta}{\zeta - r z_0} \right\} = \tag{32}$$

$$= \frac{1}{2\pi i} \int_{|\zeta|=1} \frac{f(\zeta)\, d\zeta}{\zeta - z_0},$$

an equation which we used in proving Theorem 4.9.

4.6. Summation of Fourier-Stieltjes series. We make use of the theorem that states that at every point θ_0 at which (4.76) holds, the Fourier-Stieltjes series

$$\frac{a_0}{2} + \sum_{k=1}^{\infty} (a_k \cos k\theta_0 - b_k \sin k\theta_0), \qquad c_k = a_k + i b_k = \frac{1}{2\pi} \int_0^{2\pi} e^{-ik\theta}\, d\sigma(\theta) \tag{33}$$

is Cesàro summable to the function $\sigma'(\theta)$. The fact that the Fejèr sum of order $2\nu - 1$ can be represented by

$$\sigma_\nu(\theta_0) = \frac{1}{4\pi\nu}\int_0^{2\pi}\left\{\frac{\sin\nu(\theta-\theta_0)}{\sin\frac{1}{2}(\theta-\theta_0)}\right\}^2 d\sigma(\theta) \qquad (34)$$

implies the result (4.78).

CHAPTER V

5.1. Tauber's problem. Let $f(z) = \sum_{k=0}^{\infty} a_k z^k$ be a power series with unit radius of convergence, and consider its partial sums $s_n(z) = \sum_{k=0}^{n} a_k z^k$; one may then ask for the sufficient conditions under which the existence of one of the limits

$$\lim_{r\to 1-0}\lim_{n\to\infty} s_n(re^{i\theta}), \quad \lim_{n\to\infty}\lim_{r\to 1-0} s_n(re^{i\theta}) \qquad (35)$$

implies the existence of the other and the two limits are equal. The existence of the second is implied by the existence of the first according to Abel's theorem, but the convergence is not true without additional restrictions, as is shown by the example $\frac{1}{1-z} = \sum_{k=0}^{\infty} z^k$. Tauber's theorem states that if $a_n = o\left(\frac{1}{n}\right)$, then at every point θ_0 where the radial boundary $\lim_{r\to 1-0} f(re^{i\theta_0})$ exists, the series $\sum_{k=0}^{\infty} a_k e^{ik\theta_0}$ converges to this boundary value.*

---

* Tauber's theorem for power series has been generalized in several directions. In particular, it has been shown that the condition $a_n = o\left(\frac{1}{n}\right)$ can be replaced by the more general condition $a_n = O\left(\frac{1}{n}\right)$ or even by $a > C/n$, $C > 0$.

In our case we are dealing not with a power series, but with a more general Fourier-Chebyshev series of the form $\sum_{k=0}^{\infty} \overline{\varphi_k(0)}\, \varphi_k(z)$, and under condition (3.28) it always converges for $|z| < 1$ to $\alpha\pi(z)$. The problem is then to find sufficient conditions under which the existence of the radial boundary value $\pi(e^{i\theta_0})$ implies the limit relation

$$\lim_{n \to \infty} \varphi_n^*(e^{i\theta}) = \pi(e^{i\theta_0}).$$

5.2. Copson's inequality. If $0 < p < 1$, then

$$\sum_{n=1}^{\infty} b_n^p < p^{-p} \sum_{n=1}^{\infty} \left(\frac{b_n + b_{n+1} + \dots}{n}\right)^p, \qquad b_n \geqslant 0. \tag{36}$$

Then (5.17) is obtained by setting $p = 1/2$, $b_n = |a_n|^2$. To derive (5.18) and (5.20) we use Jensen's inequality which states that if $\varphi(u)$ is convex from above and increases for $u \geq 0$, and if $\varphi(0) = 0$, then

$$\frac{1}{n}\sum_{k=1}^{n} \varphi(t_k) < \varphi\left\{\frac{1}{n}\sum_{k=1}^{n} t_k\right\}, \qquad t_k \geqslant 0.$$

Thus

$$\frac{1}{2^m}\sum_{s=2^m}^{2^{m+1}-1} \varphi(t_s) < \varphi\left\{\frac{1}{2^m}\sum_{s=2^m}^{2^{m+1}-1} t_s\right\} < \varphi\left\{\frac{1}{2^m}\sum_{s=2^m}^{\infty} t_s\right\}.$$

Writing $a_k = \varphi\left(\frac{1}{k}\sum_{s=k}^{\infty} t_s\right)$, we see that the sequence $\{a_k\}$ is nonincreasing, and simple geometric considerations show further that $2^{m-1}a_{2^m} < \sum_{s=2^{m-1}}^{2^m-1} a_s$ so that*

$$\sum_{k=2^r}^{\infty} \varphi(t_k) < 2\sum_{m=r}^{\infty} 2^{m-1}a_{2^m} < 2\sum_{\nu=2^r-1}^{\infty} a_\nu = 2\sum_{\nu=2^r-1}^{\infty} \varphi\left\{\frac{1}{\nu}\sum_{i=\nu}^{\infty} t_i\right\}.$$

* This method is due to S. B. Stechkin [1].

Setting $2^{r-1} \leq n+1 < 2^r$, $\varphi(u) = \sqrt{u}$, $t_k = |\varphi_k(0)|^2$, we obtain

$$\sum_{k=n+1}^{\infty} |\varphi_k(0)| \leqslant \sum_{k=2^r-1}^{\infty} |\varphi_k(0)| < 2 \sum_{\nu=2^r-2}^{\infty} \frac{1}{\sqrt{\nu}} \left\{ \sum_{s=\nu}^{\infty} |\varphi_s(0)|^2 \right\}^{\frac{1}{2}} < \tag{37}$$

$$< C \sum_{\nu=2^r-2}^{\infty} \frac{1}{\sqrt{\nu}} \omega_2\left(\frac{1}{\nu-1};\ p\right) < C \sum_{\nu=2^{r-2}-1}^{\infty} \frac{1}{\sqrt{\nu}} \omega_2\left(\frac{1}{\nu};\ p\right) <$$

$$< C_1 \int_{\frac{n+1}{4}-2}^{\infty} \frac{1}{\sqrt{z}} \omega_2\left(\frac{1}{z};\ p\right) dz.$$

For sufficiently large n we have $\frac{n+1}{4} - 2 > \frac{n}{5}$; and setting $z = 1/5\, y$, we arrive at

$$\sum_{k=n+1}^{\infty} |\varphi_k(0)| < C_2 \int_{n}^{\infty} \frac{1}{\sqrt{y}} \omega_2\left(\frac{1}{y};\ p\right) dy.$$

Theorem of Hardy and Littlewood. If $f(\theta) \in \text{Lip}(\alpha, p)$, $\alpha \leqslant 1$, $p \geqslant 1$ and if $\alpha > 1/p$, then $f(\theta)$ is equivalent to a function of class $\text{Lip}(\alpha - 1/p)$.

Kuz'mina's condition. Kuz'mina's condition implies that $\pi(z)$ is a continuous function in the closed region $|z| \leq 1$, and is absolutely continuous and nonzero on the circumference $|z| = 1$. Therefore its real and imaginary parts both have the same properties, and its coefficients are therefore $o\left(\frac{1}{n}\right)$. Now (2.8) states that

$$\delta_n \leqslant M \| \pi(e^{i\theta}) - G_n(e^{i\theta}) \|_2,$$

and then, by choosing $G_n(z)$ to be the partial sum of the Maclaurin series $\pi(z)$, we obtain $\delta_n = o\left(\frac{1}{\sqrt{n}}\right)$; we may then use Theorem 5.1.

5.4. Quasi-uniform convergence. A sequence of functions $\{f_n(x)\}$ converging on $[a, b]$ to a function $f(x)$ is said to converge quasi-uniformly if for every $\epsilon > 0$ and every integer N_1 there exists an interger $N_2 > N_1$ such that if $x \in [a, b]$, then $|f_n(x) - f(x)| < \epsilon$, where the index $n = n(x)$ may depend on x, but always satisfies the inequality

$N_1 < n < N_2$. If all the $\{f_n(x)\}$, $f(x)$ are continuous, the convergence is quasi-uniform.

Mean value theorem on the circumference. If $f(z)$ and its first two derivatives are continuous on an arc Γ of the circumference $|z| = 1$, then

$$f(z_2) = f(z_1) + \mu f'(z_0)(z_2 - z_1), \quad |\mu| \leqslant \frac{\pi}{2},$$
$$f(z_2) = f(z_1) + f'(z_0)(z_2 - z_1) + \nu f''(z_0)(z_2 - z_1)^2, \quad |\nu| \leqslant \left(\frac{\pi}{2}\right)^2, \tag{38}$$

where $z_1, z_2 \in \Gamma$, and z_0 lies on Γ between z_1 and z_2.

Equicontinuity. The functions of a family $\{f(z)\}$ are said to be equicontinuous in a region B if for every $\epsilon > 0$ there exists a $\delta > 0$ such that

$$|f(z_2) - f(z_1)| < \varepsilon, \quad z_1, z_2 \in B, \tag{39}$$

for every function of the family so long as $|z_2 - z_1| < \delta$.

5.5. Cauchy-Bunyakovskii inequality. If $p > 1$ and $1/p + 1/p' = 1$, then

$$\left|\sum_{k=1}^{n} a_k b_k\right| \leqslant \left\{\sum_{k=1}^{n} |a_k|^p\right\}^{\frac{1}{p}} \cdot \left\{\sum_{k=1}^{n} |b_k|^{p'}\right\}^{\frac{1}{p'}}. \tag{40}$$

The Cauchy-Bunyakovskii inequality is obtained by setting $p = p' = 2$.

Szegö's inequality. If $P_n(z)$ is a polynomial of degree n and if $|P_n(z)| \leqslant M$, $z \in \Gamma$, where Γ is the interval $[-1, +1]$, then the derivative satisfies A. A. Markov's inequality

$$|P'_n(z)| \leqslant n^2 M, \quad z \in \Gamma. \tag{41}$$

At internal points $-1 + \epsilon \leq z \leq 1 - \epsilon$, $\epsilon > 0$ we obtain Bernshtein's inequality

$$|P'_n(z)| \leqslant CnM, \tag{41'}$$

where C is independent of both n and z.

Szegö has generalized these inequalities to the case of an arbitrary analytic curve in place of the line interval. In particular, if Γ is an arc of a circle, then (41') holds within Γ.

5.7. Convergence of a subsequence. If a sequence of functions $\{f_n(\theta)\} \in L_p^\sigma$ converges in the metric of this space, there exists a subsequence converging almost everywhere in $[0, 2\pi]$ to the same limit.

5.8. Convergence in measure. If on a measurable set E we are given a sequence of functions $\{f_n(x)\}$ and a function $f(x)$, and if all the functions are measurable and finite almost everywhere on E, we say the sequence converges in measure to $f(x)$ if

$$\lim_{n \to \infty} \text{Mes Ens}\{|f_n - f| \geqslant \varepsilon\} = 0. \tag{42}$$

If the sequence converges almost everywhere on E or if it converges in the metric of L_p^σ, then it also converges in measure to the same function. If a sequence converges in measure, it contains a subsequence converging almost everywhere to the same function.

Generalized theorem of Khinchin and Ostrovskii. Let the sequence $\{f_n(z)\}$ of functions regular in the region $|z| < 1$ satisfies the two conditions

1) $\int_0^{2\pi} \ln^+ |f_n(re^{i\theta})|\, d\theta \leqslant C,$ where C is independent of both n and r < 1,

2) there exists a set of points E of positive measure on the circumference $|z| = 1$ on which the sequence of boundary values* $\{f_n(e^{i\theta})\}$ of the given functions $\{f_n(z)\}$ converges in measure. Then the sequence $\{f_n(z)\}$ converges uniformly in the region $|z| < 1$ to some function $f(z)$, and on E the sequence $\{f_n(e^{i\theta})\}$ converges in measure to $f(e^{i\theta})$, the boundary value of $f(z)$.

CHAPTER VI

6.1. Theorem of Walsh. Let C be a bounded closed set of points of the plane whose complement G contains $z = \infty$ and is connected in regular (which means that it is possible to construct a Green's function $g(z;\infty)$ for it with a pole at infinity. Then

$$g(z;\infty)=\ln|z|+\gamma+O\left(\frac{1}{z}\right),\quad d=d(C)=e^{-\gamma}, \tag{43}$$

where γ is called Robin's constant, and d the transfinite diameter of C. The function $w=\varphi(z)=e^{g+ih}$ maps $\bar{G}$ onto $|z|>1$, where $h(z;\infty)$ is a harmonic function conjugate to $g(z;\infty)$. Now if the set F of all the zeros of the polynomials $\{P_n(z)=z^n+\dots\}^{\infty}$ has no limit points outside C, and if $|P_n(z)|\leqslant M_n,\ z\in C$, then $\lim\limits_{n\to\infty}\sqrt[n]{M_n}=d$ if and only if in G we have, uniformly, $\lim\limits_{n\to\infty}\sqrt[n]{|P_n(z)|}=d|\varphi(z)|$.

Theorem on the limit of a sequence. Let there be given a sequence $\{f_n(z)\}$ of functions such that in the region $|z|<1$ they are regular, uniformly bounded, and nonzero, and such that the limit $\lim\limits_{n\to\infty} f_n(0)=0$ exists. Then uniformly in $|z|<1$ we have

$$\lim_{n\to\infty} f_n(z)\equiv 0.$$

The inverse of an increasing function. We have made use of the following two theorems of M. G. Zaretskii: 1) A continuous strictly increasing function $f(x)$ is absolutely continuous if and only if the image $f(E)$ of the set of points on which $f'(x)=+\infty$ is of measure zero. 2) The inverse of a continuous and strictly increasing function $f(x)$ is absolutely continuous if and only if $f'(x)>0$ almost everywhere.

Fejèr's generalization of Tauber's theorem. Fejèr replaces the condition $a_n=o\left(\frac{1}{n}\right)$ in Tauber's theorem by

$$\sum_{n=1}^{\infty} n|a_n|^2<\infty.$$

---

* These boundary values are understood to be taken along any path not tangent to the circle.

6.2. Theorem of Cesàro. We have used a simple special case of the general theorem which states that if $\lim_{n\to\infty} \frac{a_n}{b_n} = s$, then

$$\lim_{n\to\infty} \frac{a_1 + a_2 + \ldots + a_n}{b_1 + b_2 + \ldots + b_n} = s.$$

Theorem of Hardy and Littlewood. If the series $f(z) = \sum_{k=0}^{\infty} a_k z^k$ has unit radius of convergence, if $a_n \geq 0$, and if $z \to 1$ as $f(z) \sim \frac{1}{1-z}$, then $\sum_{k=0}^{n} a_k \sim n$.

Theorem of Landau. If the series $f(z) = \sum_{k=0}^{n} a_k z^k$ has unit radius of convergence, if $a_n = O\left(\frac{1}{n}\right)$, and if $|f(z)| < M$ for $|z| < 1$, then $\left| \sum_{k=0}^{n} a_k e^{ik\varphi} \right| < N$, where N is independent of both n and φ.

6.3. Theorems of Luzin. 1) If the trigonometric series with coefficients (a_n, b_n) converges on a set $E \subset [0, 2\pi]$ of positive measure, then $\lim_{n\to\infty} a_n = \lim_{n\to\infty} b_n = 0$.

2) If the above convergence is absolute, then the numerical series $\sum_{n=0}^{\infty} \{|a_n| + |b_n|\}$ converges.

Privalov's theorem. Let the functions $\{\varphi_k(x)\}_1^{\infty}$, form an orthonormal set on [0, 1], and let them converge uniformly on this interval. 1) Then the convergence of $\sum_{k=1}^{\infty} g_k \varphi_k(x)$ everywhere on [0, 1] implies that $\lim_{n\to\infty} g_n = 0$. 2) If the above convergence is absolute, the numerical series $\sum_{n=1}^{\infty} |g_n|$ converges.

Egorov's theorem. Let the sequence of measurable functions $\{f_n(x)\}$ converge on a set E of positive measure. Then given any $\epsilon > 0$, there always exists a set $E' \subset E$, such that Mes E' > Mes E − ϵ, on which the sequence converges uniformly.

CHAPTER VII

7.1. Theorem of F. Riesz and Fischer. Given a separable Hilbert space H and in it an orthonormal set of functions $\{\varphi_k\}_1^\infty$, to any sequence $\{g_n\}_1^\infty$ of complex numbers such that $\sum_{n=1}^{\infty} |g_n|^2 < \infty$ there corresponds a unique function $f \in H$ such that the $\{g_n\}$ are its Fourier-Chebyshev coefficients with respect to the given set $\{\varphi_k\}_1^\infty$, and for this function the closure condition is fulfilled:

$$\lim_{n\to\infty} \left\| f - \sum_{k=1}^{n} g_k \varphi_k \right\| = \sqrt{\|f\|^2 - \sum_{k=0}^{\infty} |g_k|^2} = 0. \tag{44}$$

Theorem of Nikolaev. V. F. Nikolaev has shown for a special case, and S. M. Lozinskii and F. I. Kharshiladze have shown in in general, that if $U_n(f; x)$ is a linear operator which carries any arbitrary function $f(x)$ belonging to the class $C(a, b)$ into a polynomial $G_n(x)$, such that $U_n(G_n; x) \equiv G_n(x)$, then $\|U_n\| \geq (\ln n)/8\sqrt{\pi}$, where the norm of the operator $U_n(f; x)$ is the lower bound of the numbers M_n such that $\max|U_n(f; x)| \leq M_n \cdot \max|f(x)|$. Thus for the operator $U_n(f; x) = s_n(f; x)$ we obtain the inequality

$$\|U_n\| = \max\left\{\frac{1}{2\pi}\int_0^{2\pi} |K_n(e^{i\theta_0}, e^{i\theta})|\, d\sigma(\theta)\right\} \geqslant \frac{\ln n}{8\sqrt{\pi}}, \qquad 0 \leqslant \theta_0 \leqslant 2\pi. \tag{45}$$

Estimate for a partial sum. Expression (7.38") is a generalization of a well known result due to Lebesgue which states that if a function $f(\theta)$ is bounded according to $|f(\theta)| \leq M$, $0 \leq \theta \leq 2\pi$, then the partial sums of its Fourier series satisfy $|s_n(f; \theta)| \leq CM \ln n$, $0 \leq \theta \leq 2\pi$.

7.8. Theorem of Fatou and M. Riesz. If the series $f(z) = \sum_{k=0}^{\infty} a_k z^k$ has unit radius of convergence and if $\lim_{n\to\infty} a_n = 0$, then it converges at every point of the circumference $|z| = 1$ at which $f(z)$ is regular, and this convergence is uniform on every arc all of whose points (including the end points) are points of regularity of the function.

CHAPTER VIII

8.1. Construction of F(z) from its parameters. The function F(z) of (8.10) can be constructed from the moments $\{c_n\}_0^\infty$, which are its Maclaurin coefficients. It can also be constructed directly from the parameters $\{a_n\}_0^\infty$, which are related to its continued fraction expansion according to

$$F(z) \sim 1 + \frac{2a_0 z\,|}{|\,1 - a_0 z} - \frac{a_1(1 - |a_0|^2)\,z\,|}{|\,a_1 + a_2 z} - \frac{a_0 a_2(1 - |a_1|^2)\,z\,|}{|\,a_1 + a_2 z} - \frac{a_1 a_3(1 - |a_2|^2)\,z\,|}{|\,a_2 + a_3 z} \cdots, \tag{46}$$

an expression which converges uniformly in a circle $\{|a_n|\}_0^\infty < 1$ if $|z| < 1$. Indeed, (8.9) and (8.9') imply that

$$\frac{\psi_n^*(z)}{\varphi_n^*(z)}$$

is its convergent of order n, and this together with (1.16') implies the desired convergence.

Transformation of Zhukovskii and Chaplygin. This transformation is treated in detail in N. E. Zhukovskii's Theoretical Basis of Aeronautics [in Russian] Part I, Chapter VII (Collected Works [in Russian], Vol. VI, 1950).*

8.2. Comparison of means of different orders. If

$$m_r = \left\{ \frac{1}{n} \sum_{k=1}^{n} |a_k|^r \right\}^{\frac{1}{r}},$$ then $m_r \le m_q$ for $0 < r < q$.

8.3. Absolute equicontinuity. Consider a set E on which is defined a family of summable functions $\{f(x)\}$. These functions have absolutely equicontinuous integrals if for every $\epsilon > 0$ there exists

* Also available in French translation: N. Joukowski, Bases Théoriques de l'Aéronautique (Gauthiers-Villars, Paris, 1916).

a $\delta > 0$ such that on every subset $e \subset E$, Mes $e < \delta$ the inequality $\left| \int_e f(x)\,dx \right| < \varepsilon$ holds for arbitrary function in the family.

Representation of a harmonic function by a Poisson-Lebesgue integral. The function u(z), harmonic in the circle $|z| < 1$ can be represented in terms of its boundary values $(e^{i\theta})$ by the Poisson-Lebesgue integral

$$u(re^{i\alpha}) = \frac{1}{2\pi} \int_0^{2\pi} \frac{1-r^2}{1-2r\cos(\theta-\alpha)+r^2} u(e^{i\theta})\,d\theta, \qquad r<1, \tag{47}$$

if and only if the functions of the family $\{u(re^{i\alpha})\}$, $r < 1$ have absolutely equicontinuous integrals on $[0, 2\pi]$.

CHAPTER IX

9.6. A property of functions of bounded variation. If $f(x)$ is of bounded variation on an interval $0 < a \le x \le b$, then as $b \to 0$ this variation tends to zero. If the contrary were true there would exist a sequence of nonintersecting intervals $[a_n, b_n]$ tending to zero, on which the variation of $f(x)$ would be greater than $\delta > 0$, and then the variation on [a, b] would not be bounded.

9.8. Riemann-Lebesgue theorem. If $f(\theta) \in L_1$, then

$$\lim_{\lambda \to \infty} \int_0^{2\pi} f(\theta)\, e^{i\lambda\theta}\, d\theta = 0. \tag{48}$$

Theorem of Jordan. If $f(\theta)$ is of bounded variation on $[0, 2\pi]$, then at every point θ_0 its Fourier series converges to the value $\frac{1}{2}\{f(\theta_0+0) + f(\theta_0-0)\}$.

BIBLIOGRAPHY

N. I. AKHIEZER (Achyeser, Ahiezer, Achieser)

1. "On a proposition of A. N. Kolmogorov and a proposition of M. G. Krein," Doklady Akad. Nauk SSSR 40, 35 (1945).
2. Lectures on the Theory of Approximations [in Russian] (Gostekhizdat, Moscow, 1947). [English translation: Theory of Approximation (Ungar, New York, 1956).]
3. "On a theorem of Academician S. N. Bernshtein concerning a quadrature formula of Chebyshev," Zhurnal In-tu matemateki AN URSR 3, 75 (1937).
4. "On constructing the flow around a thin profile," Zb. prats' In-tu matemateki AN URSR 4, 151 (1940).

N. I. AKHIEZER and M. G. KREIN

1. Some Questions in the Theory of Moments [in Russian] (Khar'kov, 1938).
2. "Some observations relating to coefficients of quadrature of Gaussian-type formulas," Proceedings of Odessa State University, Mathematics, Vol. II, (1938), pp. 29-38.

S. N. BERNSHTEIN (Bernstein)

1. "On polynomials orthogonal on a finite interval," Coll. Work [in Russian] (1954), Vol. II, p. 7.

P. ERDOS and P. TURAN

1. On interpolation, III, Annals of Math. 41, (1940), 510-553.

G. FREUD

1. Über orthogonale Polynome, Acta Math. Acad. Sci. Hung. 5, Vol. III, 3-4 (1954), 291-298.
2. Über die Konvergenz orthogonaler Polynomreihen, Ibid. 3, Vol. II, 1-2 (1952), 89-98.
3. Über die absolute Konvergenz von orthogonalen Polynomreihen, Ibid. 4, Vol. II 1-2 (1953), 127-135.

YA. L. GERONIMUS (Gueronimus)

1. "Polynomials orthogonal on a circle and their application," Zapiski Nauchno-issledovatel'skogo in-ta matematiki i mekhaniki i KhMO 19, 35 (1948).
2. "On the closure of some function sets in L^p_σ," Ibid., 21, 24-45 (1949).
3. "On some properties of generalized orthogonal polynomials," Matem. sbornik 9 (51): 1, 121 (1941).
4. "On some properties of analytic functions continuous in a closed circle or circular sector," Ibid., 38 (80): 3, 319 (1956).
5. "On means and uniform approximations," Doklady Akad. Nauk SSSR 88, 597 (1953).
6. "On differential properties of some functions representable by singular integrals," Izv. AN SSSR, seriya matem. 20, 775 (1956).
7. "On some asymptotic properties of polynomials," Matem. sbornik 23 (65): 1, 77 (1948).
8. "On some distribution functions related to sets of polynomials," Doklady Akad. Nauk SSSR 44, 355 (1944).
9. "On the asymptotic properties of polynomials orthogonal on the unit circle, and some properties of positive harmonic functions," Izv. AN SSSR, seriya matem. 14; 123 (1950).
10. The Theory of Orthogonal Polynomials (Gostekhizdat, Moscow, Leningrad, 1950).

U. GRENANDER and M. ROSENBLATT

1. An extension of a theorem of G. Szegö and its application to the study of stochastic processes, Trans. Amer. Math. Soc. 76, No. 1 (1954), 112-126.

G. H. HARDY and J. E. LITTLEWOOD

1. A convergence criterion for Fourier series, Math. Zeitschr. 28 (1928), 612-634.
2. On the zeros of certain classes of integral Taylor series, Proc. Lond. Math. Soc. 2 (1905), 332-339, 401-431.

G. H. HARDY, J. E. LITTLEWOOD, and G. POLYA

1. Inequalities [Russian translation] (IL, Moscow, 1948). [English original: Cambridge, 1934.]

D. JACKSON

1. Theory of approximation, N. Y. (1930).
2. On certain problems of approximation in the complex domain, Bull. Am. Math. Soc. 36, (1930), 851-857.
3. Fourier Series and Orthogonal Polynomials [Russian trans.] (IL, Moscow, 1948). [English original: Oberlin, Ohio, 1941; Carus mathematical monographs, No. 8.]

S. YA. KHAVINSON

1. "On the problem of the uniqueness of the best-approximation polynomial in the metric of L_1," Doklady Akad. Nauk SSSR 105, 1159 (1955).

A. N. KOLMOGOROV

1. "Stationary sequences in Hilbert space," Byulleten' GMU, Matematika, Vol. II, No. 6 (1941).
2. "Interpolation and extrapolation of stationary random sequences," Matem. sbornik 5, 3 (1941).

J. KOROUS

1. O rozvoji funkcí jedné realné promenné vradu jistých ortogonál-nich polynomu. Rozpr. Ceské Acad. 48 (1938), 1–12.

M. G. KREIN

1. "On a generalization of some investigations of G. Szegö, V. I. Smirnov, and A. N. Kolmogorov," Doklady Akad. Nauk SSSR 46, 95 (1945).
2. "Continuous analogs of propositions concerning polynomials orthogonal on the unit circle," Doklady Akad. Nauk SSSR 105, 637 (1956).

A. L. KUZ'MINA

1. "On the asymptotic representation of polynomials orthogonal on the unit circle," Doklady Akad. Nauk SSSR 107, 793 (1956).

E. LANDAU

1. Principles and Background of a New Discovery in the Theory of Functions.

N. N. LUZIN (Lusin)

1. "On the absolute convergence of trigonometric series," Coll. Works, Vol. I, (1953), p. 31.

P. MONTEL

1. Normal Families of Analytic Functions [Russian translation] (GTTI, Moscow-Leningrad, 1936). [French original: Leçons sur les Familles Normales de Fonctions Analytiques et leurs Applications (Gauthier, Paris, 1927).]

I. P. NATANSON

1. Constructive Function Theory [in Russian] (Gostekhizdat, Moscow-Leningrad, 1949). (English translation: Unger, N. Y., 1959).
2. "On the order of approximation of a continuous 2π-periodic function by means of its Poisson integral," Doklady Akad. Nauk SSSR 72, 11 (1950).

V. F. NIKOLAEV

1. "On the question of approximation of continuous functions by polynomials," Doklady Akad. Nauk SSSR 61, 201 (1948).

G. PÓLYA and G. SZEGÖ

1. Problems and Theorems From Analysis [Russian translation] (Gostekhizdat, Moscow, 1956), Part I. [German original: Aufgaben und Lehrsätze aus der Analysis (Berlin, 1925).]

I. I. PRIVALOV (Privalow)

1. Boundary Properties of Analytic Functions [in Russian] (Gostekhizdat, Moscow-Leningrad, 1950).
2. "Properties of series of orthogonal functions," Matem. sbornik 29, 182 (1912-1915).

M. RIESZ

1. Sur les fonctions conjuguees, Math. Zeitschr. 27, (1927), 218-244.

W. E. SEWELL

1. Degree of approximation by polynomials in the complex domain, Princeton, 1952.

G. TS. TUMARKIN

1. "Approximation in the mean of complex-valued functions," Doklady Akad. Nauk SSSR 84, 21 (1952).

J. L. WALSH

1. Interpolation and approximation by rational functions in the complex domain, N. Y., 1935.

J. SHOHAT

1. Application of orthogonal Tchebycheff polynomials to Lagrangean interpolation and to the general theory of polynomials, Annali di Mat. 18, (1939), 201-238.
2. On continued fraction associated with, and corresponding to, the integral $\int_a^b p(y)\,dy:(x-y)$, Amer. Journ. of Math. 55, (1933), 218-230.
3. "On the development of functions in series of orthogonal polynomials, Bull. Amer. Math. Soc. 41, (1935), 49-82.
4. "On the development of continuous functions in series of Tchebycheff polynomials, Trans. Amer. Math. Soc. 27, No. 4 (1925) 537-550.

V. I. SMIRNOV (Smirnoff)

1. Sur la theorie des polynomes orthogonaux a une variable complexe, Zhurnal Leningradskogo fiz. matem. ob-va 2, 1, 155 (1928).
2. Sur les formules de Cauchy et de Green et quelques problemes qui s'y rattachent, Izv. AN SSSR, seriya matem., 337 (1932).
3. Sur les valeurs limites des fonctions regulières a l'intérieur d'un cercle, Zhurnal Leningradskogo fiz. matem. ob-va 2, 22 (1928).

S. B. STECHKIN

1. "On the absolute convergence of orthogonal series," Matem. sbornik 29 (71): 1, 225 (1951).

V. A. STEKLOV (Stekloff)

1. Une contribution nouvelle au probleme du développement des fonctions arbitraires en séries de polynomes de Tchebycheff, Izv. Ros. AN 267 (1921).
2. Une méthode de la solution du problème de développement des fonctions en séries de polynomes de Tchebycheff independante de la theorie de fermeture. Izv. Ros. AN 281, 303 (1921).

O. SZASZ

1. Ungleichungen für die Koeffizienten einer Potenzreihe, Math. Zeitschr. 1, (1918), 163-183.

G. SZEGÖ

1. Orthogonal polynomials, N. Y., 1939.
2. Über die Randwerte analytischer Funktionen, Math. Ann. 84, (1921), 232-244.
3. Über die Entwicklung einer willkürlichen Funktion nach den Polynomen eines Orthogonalsystems. Math. Zeitschr. 12, (1922), 61-94.
4. Über einen Satz von A. Markoff, Math. Zeitschr. 23, (1925), 45-61.
5. Beiträge zur Theorie der Toeplitzscher Formen, Math. Zeitschr. 6 (1920), 167-202; 9, (1921), 167-190.
6. Über die Entwicklung einer analytischer Funktion nach den Polynomen eines Orthogonalsystems, Math. Ann. 82, (1921), 188-212.

S. VERBLUNSKY

1. On positive harmonic functions. II, Proc. Lond. Math. Soc. 40, (1935), 290-320.

A. ZYGMUND

1. Trigonometric Series [Russian translation from Polish] (GONTI, Moscow, 1939). [English translation: Cambridge University Press, Cambridge, 1959 (2nd. edition).]